Frank J. Ambrosio
Monroe Community College

Student Study Guide

to accompany

DIGITAL SYTEMS:
Principles and Applications

Eighth Edition

Ronald J. Tocci
Neal S. Widmer

Prentice
Hall

Upper Saddle River, New Jersey   Columbus, Ohio

Vice President and Publisher: Dave Garza
Editor in Chief: Stephen Helba
Acquisitions Editor: Scott J. Sambucci
Associate Editor: Katie E. Bradford
Production Editor: Stephen C. Robb
Design Coordinator: Karrie M. Converse-Jones
Cover Designer: Thomas Mack
Cover Image: Kathy Hanley
Production Manager: Pat Tonneman
Marketing Manager: Ben Leonard

This book was set by Frank J. Ambrosio. It was printed and bound by Courier Stoughton, Inc. The cover was printed by Phoenix Color Corp.

10 9 8 7 6 5 4 3 2 1
ISBN 0-13-085639-8

CONTENTS

PROBLEMS

SOLUTIONS

HOW TO USE THE STUDENT STUDY GUIDE

The *Student Study Guide* should be used in conjunction with the 8th edition of the **DIGITAL SYSTEMS Principles and Applications** text book by **Ronald J. Tocci/Neal S. Widmer.** The user of the *Student Study Guide* should attempt to acquire a reasonable understanding of the material by first reading the textbook. Should the student find that he/she has difficulties in comprehending certain parts of a chapter, then consultation of the *Student Study Guide* might be all that is needed to bring a full and clear understanding of the topic in question. Some students may find that a full understanding of the text material is achieved just by reading the text and doing the problems at the end of each chapter. For those students, the *Student Study Guide* will provide additional problems for greater proficiency and mastery of the subject matter. In addition, the *Student Study Guide* will provide a valuable source of detailed information for review purposes and for examination preparation.

The glossary at the beginning of each chapter contains all of the new terms and their definition introduced in that particular chapter. In brackets, at the end of each definition, the textbook chapter and corresponding section reference is provided in case that a more in-depth explanation of the new term is needed.

The exercises, and the end-of-chapter-test, will thoroughly review the material covered in each chapter of the textbook. New circuit diagrams, as well as existing ones from the textbook will be used throughout. Wherever appropriate, troubleshooting case studies will be used to review and supplement the exercises. In any case, the step-by-step solution for each individual problem is given in the second half of the *Student Study Guide* (starting on page *242*).

Individual problems throughout the Student Study Guide are uniquely identified as follows:

⊕   Troubleshooting case studies.

☼   More difficult and challenging problems.

⧖   Problems whose answer requires a timing diagram.

🖙   Problems that require a written response.

☝   Reminders and/or hints.

The student should work out each solution in the space provided after each problem. Some problems require only a written answer, while others require diagrams, calculations, timing diagrams, etc. The Figures used in the *Solutions* part of this Study Guide, have a *'P'* preceding their number as to reference them to their respective **Problem** number (i.e. Figure P10.14, means that, this figure is part of the solution of problem 10.14). Figure numbers without a preceding 'P' are used only in the *Problems'* section of the *Student Study Guide.*

ACKNOWLEDGMENTS

My sincere thanks and appreciation go to my friend and colleague **Professor Ronald J. Tocci**, for without his support this Study Guide would have not been possible.

I am also grateful to all of those who evaluated and provided helpful comments of the seventh edition of the *Student Study Guide*: Armond Badkerhanian, ITT Technical Institute, Skidmore, CA; Karen Hershey ITT Technical Institute, Mechnaicsburg, PA; Nick Karimi, ITT Technical Institute, Youngstown, OH; Osama Maarouf, ITT Technical Institute, Houston-West; and Edward Stage, ITT Technical Institute, Henderson, NV. Many of their comments and suggestions have been incorporated into this edition. I hope that this updated edition and all of its improvements will provide students, instructors, and all other users with a more effective tool for learning about Digital Systems.

Frank J. Ambrosio

Monroe Community College

*To my parents **José** and **Georgina Ambrósio**, whose efforts and unselfish sacrifices made my education possible.*

*And, to my wife **Ana** and son **Filip**, for their patience and understanding during the writing of this Study Guide.*

1   INTRODUCTORY CONCEPTS

Objectives

Upon completion of this chapter, you will be able to:

- Distinguish between analog and digital representations.

- Name the advantages, disadvantages, and major differences among analog, digital, and hybrid systems.

- Understand the need for analog-to-digital converters (ADCs) and digital-to-analog converters (DACs).

- Recognize the basic characteristics of the binary number system.

- Convert a binary number to its decimal equivalent.

- Identify typical digital signals.

- Identify a timing diagram.

- State the differences between parallel and serial transmission.

- Describe the property of memory.

- Describe the major parts of a digital computer and understand their   functions.

- Distinguish between microcomputers, microprocessors and microcontrollers.

Glossary of key terms covered in this chapter:

- *Analog Representation* - Representation of a quantity that varies over a continuous range of values. *[sec.1.1]*

- *Analog System* - Combination of devices designed to manipulate physical quantities that are represented in analog form. *[sec.1.2]*

- *Analog-to-Digital converter* - Circuit that converts an Analog quantity to a corresponding Digital quantity. *[sec.1.2]*

- *Arithmetic/Logic Unit* - Part of the Computer dedicated to all of the arithmetic and logical operations. *[sec.1.8]*

- *Binary Digit* - Bit. *[sec.1.3]*

- *Binary Point* - A mark which separates the integer from the fractional portion of a binary quantity. *[sec.1.3]*

- *Binary System* - Number system in which there are only two possible digit values, 0 and 1. *[sec.1.3]*

- *Bit* - A digit in the Binary System. *[sec.1.3]*

- *Central Processing Unit (CPU)* - The combination of the control and the arithmetic/logic units are often considered as one unit called the Central Processing Unit (CPU). *[sec.1.8]*

- *CMOS (Complementary Metal Oxide Semiconductor)* - Integrated circuit technology which uses MOSFETS as the principal circuit element. *[sec.1.5]*

- *Control Unit* - This unit provides decoding of program instructions and the necessary timing and control signals for the execution of such instructions. *[sec.1.8]*

- *Decimal System* - Number system which uses ten different digits or symbols to represent a quantity. *[sec.1.3]*

- *Digital Computer* - A system of hardware that performs arithmetic and logic operations, manipulates data and makes decisions. *[sec.1.8]*

- *Digital Integrated Circuits* - Self-containing circuits which have been made by using one of several integrated-circuit fabrication technologies. *[sec.1.5]*

- *Digital Representation* - Representation of a quantity that varies in discreet steps over a range of values. *[sec.1.1]*

- *Digital Signals* - See timing diagrams. *[sec.1.5]*

- *Digital System* - Combination of devices designed to manipulate physical quantities that are represented in digital form. *[sec.1.2]*

- *Digital-to-Analog converter* - Circuit that converts a Digital quantity to a corresponding Analog quantity. *[sec.1.2]*

- *Embedded Controller* - See Microcontroller. *[sec.1.8]*

- *Flip-Flop* - A memory device capable of storing a logic level. *[sec.1.7]*

- *Hybrid System* - A system that employs both analog and digital techniques. *[sec.1.2]*

- *Input Unit* - This unit facilitates the feeding of information into the computer's memory unit. *[sec.1.8]*

- *Least Significant Bit (LSB)* - The rightmost bit (smallest weight) of a binary expressed quantity. *[sec.1.3]*

- *Least Significant Digit (LSD)* - The digit that carries the least weight in a particular number. *[sec.1.3]*

- *Logic Circuits* - Any circuit that behaves according to a set of logic rules. *[sec.1.5]*

- *Memory* - The ability of a circuit's output to remain at one state even after the input condition which caused that state is removed. *[sec.1.7]*

- *Memory Unit* - This unit stores instructions and data received from the Input unit, as well as results from the Arithmetic Logic Unit. *[sec.1.8]*

- *Microcomputer* - A Microcomputer is the smallest type of a computer. It generally consists of a microprocessor chip, memory chips and I/O interface chips. In some cases all of the aforementioned are in one single IC. *[sec.1.8]*

- *Microcontroller* - Microcomputer that is designed to be used as a dedicated or embedded controller which helps monitor and control the operation of a machine, a piece of equipment, or a process. *[sec.1.8]*

- *Microprocessor* - A chip containing all of the circuits that make up the CPU portion of the computer; that is, the control unit and the arithmetic/logic unit. In other words, the microprocessor is a "CPU on a chip". *[sec.1.8]*

- *Most Significant Bit (MSB)* - The leftmost binary bit (largest weight) of a binary expressed quantity. *[sec.1.3]*

- *Most Significant Digit (MSD)* - The digit that carries the most weight in a particular number. *[sec.1.3]*

- *NMOS (N-channel Metal Oxide Semiconductor)* - Integrated-Circuit Technology which uses N-Channel MOSFETS as the principal circuit element. *[sec.1.5]*

- *Output Unit* - This unit receives data from the memory unit and presents it to the operator. *[sec.1.8]*

- *Parallel Transmission* - The simultaneous transfer of binary information from one place to another. *[sec.1.6]*

- *Positional-value system* - A system in which the value of a digit is dependent on its relative position. *[sec.1.3]*

- *Program* - A sequence of binary-coded instructions designed to accomplish a particular task by a computer. *[sec.1.2/1.8]*

- *Serial Transmission* - The transfer of binary information from one place to another a bit at a time. *[sec.1.6]*

- *Timing Diagram* - A depiction of logic levels as it relates to time. *[sec.1.5/1.6]*

- *Toggle* - The process of changing from one binary state to the other. *[sec.1.3]*

- *TTL (Transistor Transistor Logic)* - Integrated-Circuit technology which uses the bipolar transistor as the principal circuit element. *[sec.1.5]*

Problems

SECTION 1.1 *Numerical Representations*

1.1 Complete the following statements.

(a) _____ is the continuous representation of a quantity, while _____ is the discrete representation of a quantity.

(b) Systems in which both analog and digital quantities are manipulated are called _____ .

SECTION 1.2 *Digital and Analog Systems*

1.2 State six advantages of digital techniques.

1._____

2._____

3._____

4._____

5._____

6._____

SECTION 1.3 *Digital Number Systems*

1.3 Convert the following binary numbers to their equivalent decimal values:

(a) $10110_2 = $__26____ $_{10}$ **(b)** $11101_2 = $_____ $_{10}$ **(c)** $11011110110010_2 = $_____ $_{10}$

(d) $1101.1101_2 = $_____ $_{10}$ **(e)** $0.111011101_2 = $_____ $_{10}$

1.4 What is the largest number that can be represented using 12 bits?

1.5 How many binary bits are needed to represent 1015_{10}?

1.6 A certain digital circuit is supposed to count in a descending sequence from 15_{10} to 0. The binary counting sequence below is observed. What counts are missing from the expected correct sequence?

$1111_2, 1101_2, 1100_2, 1011_2, 1001_2, 1000_2, 0111_2, 0110_2, 0101_2, 0011_2, 0010_2, 0001_2, 0000_2.$

SECTION 1.6 *Parallel and Serial Transmission*

1.7 Binary number 10110110_2 is being transmitted serially from circuit A to circuit B of Figure 1.1(a). Draw the associated timing diagram for the data as it flows from circuit A to circuit B. (The first bit to be transmitted is the LSB.)

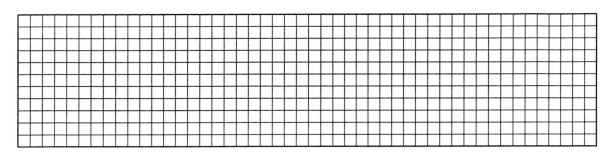

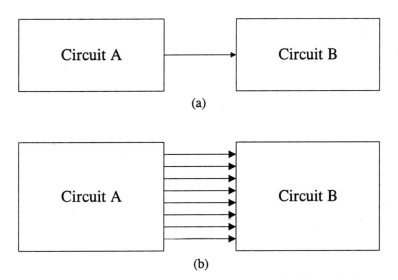

(a)

(b)

Figure 1.1 (a) Serial Transmission; (b) Parallel Transmission

1.8 If each bit in problem 1.7 takes 10 μs to transmit, how long will it take for the complete transmission of the data?

1.9 Generally speaking, how much faster is the transmission performed by the circuit of Figure 1.1(b) compared with that of Figure 1.1(a)?

1.10   Repeat problem 1.7 if the MSB is the first bit to be transmitted.

1.11   Binary number 1100011010_2 is transmitted from circuit X to circuit Y. How many lines between the transmitter and the receiver are required if a parallel transmission is to be performed.

SECTION 1.8 *Digital Computers*

1.12   What are the five major units of a computer?

1. _____ 2. _____ 3. _____ 4. _____ 5. _____

1.13   In a microcomputer what is the function of the CPU?

1.14   How is a microprocessor different from a microcontroller?

TEST 1

1. Digital representations of numerical values may best be described as having characteristics:

    (a) that vary in constant and direct proportion to the quantities they represent.
    (b) that vary constantly over a continuous range of values.
    (c) that are difficult to interpret because they are continuously changing.
    (d) that vary in discrete steps in proportion to the values they represent.

2. Which of the following represents the largest number that can be obtained in the decimal number system when the MSD positional value is 10^5?

    (a) $10,000_{10}$ (b) $9,999_{10}$ (c) $100,000_{10}$ (d) $99,999_{10}$

3. What is the largest count that can be obtained with six binary bits?

    (a) 31_{10} (b) 32_{10} (c) 63_{10} (d) 64_{10}

4. What is the largest number that can be obtained with six binary bits?

    (a) 31_{10} (b) 32_{10} (c) 63_{10} (d) 64_{10}

5. How many binary bits are needed to represent 185_{10}?

    (a) 5 (b) 6 (c) 7 (d) 8

6. Serial data transmission is faster than parallel data transmission.

    (a) True (b) False

7. If the LSB of a binary number is a 0, the equivalent decimal number is even.

    (a) True (b) False

8. The video display terminal of a computer system could be called:

    (a) an input unit (b) an output unit (c) the memory (d) the control unit

9. When counting in a binary sequence which of the binary bits toggle for each successive count?

    (a) MSB (b) ADC (c) LSB (d) DAC

10. A microcontroller can best be described as an IC chip that contains:

    (a) Both the ALU and the control unit.
    (b) Both a microprocessor and a microcomputer.
    (c) Both the ALU and the memory unit.
    (d) The CPU, I/O devices, and the memory unit.

2   NUMBER SYSTEMS AND CODES

Objectives

Upon completion of this chapter, you will be able to:

- Convert a number from one number system (decimal, binary, octal, hexadecimal) to its equivalent in one of the other number systems.

- Cite the advantages of the octal and hexadecimal number systems.

- Count in octal and hexadecimal.

- Represent decimal numbers using the BCD code; cite the pros and cons of using BCD.

- Understand the difference between BCD and straight binary.

- Understand the purpose of alphanumeric codes such as the ASCII code.

- Explain the parity method for error detection.

- Determine the parity bit to be attached to a digital data string.

Glossary of key terms covered in this chapter:

- *Alphanumeric Codes* - Codes that represent numbers, letters, punctuation marks and special characters. *[sec.2.8]*

- *ASCII Code* - A 7-bit alphanumeric code used by most computer manufacturers. *[sec.2.8]*

- *Binary-Coded-Decimal Code (BCD Code)* - Four-bit code used to represent each digit of a decimal number. *[sec.2.5]*

- *Byte* - A string of 8 bits. *[sec.2.7]*

- *Code* - A special group of symbols that represent numbers, letters or words. *[sec.2.5]*

- *Electrical Noise* - Spurious fluctuations in voltage and/or current in any electronic system. *[sec.2.9]*

- *Encoding* - When a group of symbols is used to represent numbers, letters or words. *[sec.2.5]*

- *Even Parity* - Total number of 1s (including the parity bit) that are contained in the code group is an even number. *[sec.2.9]*

- *Hexadecimal Number System* - Number system which has a base of sixteen. Digits 0 through 9 plus letters A through F are used to express a hexadecimal number. *[sec.2.4]*

- *Octal Number System* - Number system which has a base of eight. In this number system digits from 0 to 7 are used to express an octal number. *[sec.2.3]*

- *Odd Parity* - Total number of 1s (including the parity bit) that are contained in the code group is an odd number. *[sec.2.9]*

- *Padding* - The addition of an extra bit to the leftmost bit of an ASCII code in order to make it a byte. *[sec.2.8]*

- *Parity Bit* - Additional bit that is attached to each code group before being transferred from one location to another. *[sec.2.9]*

- *Parity Method* - Scheme used for error detection during the transmission of data. *[sec.2.9]*

- *Repeated Division* - Method used to convert a decimal number to its equivalent binary-system representation. *[sec.2.2]*

- *Straight Binary Coding* - Decimal number represented by its equivalent binary number. *[sec.2.5]*

Problems

SECTION 2.1 Binary-to-Decimal Conversions

2.1 Convert the following binary numbers to their decimal equivalent.

(a) 1101_2 (b) 1010_2 (c) 1100011010_2 (d) 1000001101_2 (e) 11101_2

SECTION 2.2 Decimal-to-Binary Conversions

2.2 Convert the following decimal numbers to their binary equivalent.

(a) 51_{10} (b) 13_{10} (c) 137_{10} (d) 567_{10} (e) 777_{10} (f) 1000_{10}

2.3 How many bits are required to express the decimal number 1023_{10}?

2.4 What is the highest decimal number that can be represented by a 16-bit binary number?

SECTION 2.3 Octal Number System

2.5 Convert the following octal numbers to their decimal equivalent.

(a) 217_8 (b) 55_8 (c) 5076_8 (d) 511_8 (e) 100_8 (f) 898_8

2.6 Convert the following decimal numbers to their octal equivalent.

(a) 323_{10} (b) 123_{10} (c) 898_{10} (d) 32536_{10} (e) 245_{10} (f) 2000_{10}

2.7 Convert each of the octal numbers from problem 2.5 to their binary equivalent.

2.8 Convert each of the binary numbers from problem 2.1 to their octal equivalent.

SECTION 2.4 Hexadecimal Number System

2.9 Convert the following hexadecimal numbers to their decimal equivalent.

(a) FF_{16} (b) $AD3_{16}$ (c) 589_{16} (d) $3AFD_{16}$ (e) $FEED_{16}$ (f) $00FA_{16}$

2.10   Convert each of the decimal numbers from problem 2.6 to their hexadecimal equivalent.

2.11   Convert each of the hexadecimal numbers from problem 2.9 to their binary equivalent.

2.12   Convert each of the binary numbers from problem 2.1 to their hexadecimal equivalent.

Apply the same techniques used in solving problems 2.9 and 2.10 to solve problems 2.13 and 2.14. (Hint: The only difference now is the <u>base</u> of the number system being used.)

2.13   Perform the following conversions between base-5 and decimal.

      (a) 1230_5 **(b)** 777_{10}

2.14   Perform the following conversions between base-4 and decimal.

      (a) 333_4 **(b)** 777_{10}

2.15   Complete the following counting sequence using the hexadecimal number system.
          $96_{16}, 97_{16}, 98_{16}, \ldots\ldots\ldots AF_{16}$.

2.16   What range of decimal values can be represented by an eight digit hexadecimal number?

SECTION 2.5 *BCD Code*

2.17   Encode the following decimal numbers into BCD.

(a) 63_{10} (b) 105_{10} (c) 757_{10} (d) 999_{10} (e) 36543_{10} (f) 777_{10}

2.18   Convert the following BCD numbers to their decimal equivalent.

(a) 0111010000101001_{BCD} (b) 101000100111_{BCD} (c) 010100111001_{BCD}

SECTION 2.6 *Putting it All Together*

2.19   What is the binary, octal, hexadecimal, and BCD equivalent of 1000_{10}?

SECTION 2.7 *The Byte*

2.20   How many bytes are needed to represent a 4 hex digit number?

2.21   What is the largest octal value that can be represented using three bytes?

SECTION 2.8 *Alphanumerical Codes*

2.22   Informational messages that come up on a video terminal during power-up are stored in the computer's memory. For a certain computer, the codes for each character that make up these messages are stored in successive memory locations as 7-bit ASCII codes with an even parity bit. List the binary contents of memory that stores the following message: *FLOPPY A - OK*

2.23   The word HELLO is stored in a computer's memory. Determine the five hex numbers stored in memory if each byte stored is a padded ASCII code.

SECTION 2.9 *Parity Method For Error Detection*

2.24   Add the required <u>even</u> parity bit to each of the following binary quantities.

(a) 00110001_2 (b) 100001_2 (c) 10011001_2 (d) 11111111_2

2.25   A digital circuit is going to transmit the binary data of problem 2.24. If the receiver were to check for <u>odd</u> parity, how would you reformat the transmitted data so that it would be comparable with the receiver.

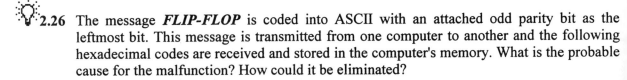

2.26   The message ***FLIP-FLOP*** is coded into ASCII with an attached odd parity bit as the leftmost bit. This message is transmitted from one computer to another and the following hexadecimal codes are received and stored in the computer's memory. What is the probable cause for the malfunction? How could it be eliminated?

$C6_{16}$, CC_{16}, $C9_{16}$, 50_{16}, $2D_{16}$, $C6_{16}$, CC_{16}, CF_{16}, 50_{16}

SECTION 2.10 *Applications*

2.27   How many ASCII codes can a 650-Megabyte CD-ROM hold?

2.28   A typical 8-bit Microcontroller uses a 16-bit address bus to address its memory locations.

(a) How many Hexadecimal digits are needed to represent a memory location?
(b) What is the total amount of memory locations that this Microcontroller can address?

TEST 2

1. Convert 11001101_2 to its decimal equivalent.

   (a) 515_{10} (b) 205_{10} (c) 221_{10} (d) 207_{10}

2. Convert 1050_{10} to binary.

   (a) 10001100100_2 (b) 11011100101_2 (c) 10000011010_2

3. Which of the following numbers represent the largest decimal number?

   (a) 65_{10} (b) FA_{16} (c) 77_8 (d) 111111_2

4. Which of the decimal numbers is equivalent to $3E23_{16}$?

   (a) $16,807_{10}$ (b) $15,907_{10}$ (c) $22,564_{10}$ (d) None of the above.

5. Which of the following numbers is not equivalent to the other three?

   (a) 125_{10} (b) 1111101_2 (c) 175_8 (d) $7F_{16}$

6. Translate the Hexadecimal counting $0FF_{16}$-104_{16} to an Octal equivalent sequence.

   (a) 377_8, 378_8, 379_8, 380_8, 381_8, 382_8.
   (b) 777_8, 1000_8, 1001_8, 1002_8, 1003_8, 1004_8.
   (c) 100_8, 101_8, 102_8, 103_8, 104_8, 105_8.
   (d) 377_8, 400_8, 401_8, 402_8, 403_8, 404_8.

7. Which of the following represents the binary equivalent of 321_4?

   (a) 0111101_2 (b) 0111001_2 (c) 0011001_2 (d) 111011_2

8. Which of the following represents the decimal equivalent of 321_4?

   (a) 56_{10} (b) 58_{10} (c) 128_{10} (d) None of the above

9. Number 9 does not exist in the number system whose base is nine.

   (a) True (b) False

10. When converting from decimal to octal using the repeated division method, the last remainder becomes the MSD.

    (a) True (b) False

3   LOGIC GATES AND BOOLEAN ALGEBRA

Objectives

Upon completion of this chapter, you will be able to:

• Perform the three basic logic operations.

• Describe the operation of and construct the truth tables for the AND, NAND, OR, and NOR gates, and the NOT (INVERTER) circuit.

• Draw timing diagrams for the various logic-circuit gates.

• Write the Boolean expression for the logic gates and combinations of logic gates.

• Implement logic circuits using basic AND, OR, and NOT gates.

• Appreciate the potential of Boolean algebra to simplify complex logic circuits.

• Use either of the universal gates (NAND or NOR) to implement a circuit   represented by a Boolean expression.

• Explain the advantages of constructing a logic circuit diagram using the alternate gate symbols, versus the standard logic-gate symbols.

• Describe the concept of active-LOW and active-HIGH logic signals.

• Draw and interpret logic that use the IEEE/ANSI standard logic gate symbols.

Glossary of key terms covered in this chapter:

- *Active logic levels* - When an input or output line of a logic circuit symbol has a bubble, that line is Active-Low. On the other hand, if it doesn't have a bubble, then that line is Active-High. *[sec.3.13]*

- *AND gate* - The digital circuit which implements the AND operation. The output of this circuit is HIGH (logic level 1), only if all of its inputs are HIGH. *[sec.3.4]*

- *AND operation* - A Boolean Algebra operation in which the symbol ( ) is used to indicate the ANDing of two or more logic variables. The result of the AND operation will be HIGH (logic level 1), only if all variables are HIGH. *[sec.3.1/3.4]*

- *Asserted* - Term used to describe the state of a logic signal. The term "Asserted" is synonymous with "Active." *[sec.3.14]*

- *Associative Laws* - Laws which state that the manner in which variables in an AND expression or OR expression are grouped together does not affect the final result. *[sec.3.10]*

- *Bi-State Signals* - Signals which have both an active-LOW and an active-HIGH state (i.e. $RD / \overline{WR}$). *[3.14]*

- *Boolean Algebra* - Algebraic process used as a tool in the design and analysis of digital systems. In Boolean Algebra only two values are possible, "0" and "1." *[sec.3.1]*

- *Boolean Theorems* - Rules that can be applied to Boolean Algebra in order to simplify logic expressions. *[sec.3.10]*

- *Bubbles* - Small circles on the input or output lines of logic circuit symbols which represent inversion of that particular signal. If a bubble is present, that input or output is said to be Active-Low. *[sec.3.13]*

- *Commutative laws* - Laws which state that the order in which two variables are ORed or ANDed is unimportant. *[sec.3.10]*

- *Complementation* - See NOT operation.

- *DeMorgan's Theorems* - The first theorem states that the complement of a sum (OR-operation) equals the product (AND-operation) of the complements. The second theorem states that the complement of a product (AND-operation) equals the sum (OR-operation) of the complements. *[sec.3.11]*

- *Dependency Notation* - A method used to pictorially represent the relationship between inputs and outputs of logic circuits. This method employs the usage of qualifying symbols embedded near the top center or geometric center of a symbol element. *[sec.3.15]*

- *Distributive Law* - Law which states that an expression can be expanded by multiplying term by term. This law also states that if we have a sum of two or more terms, each of which contains a common variable, the common variable can be factored out. *[sec.3.10]*

- *IEEE/ANSI* - Institute of Electrical and Electronics Engineers/American National Standards Institute. *[sec.3.15]*

- *INVERTER* - Also referred to as the NOT circuit, this logic circuit implements the NOT operation. An INVERTER has only one input, and its output logic level is always the opposite of this input's logic level. *[sec.3.5]*

- *Inversion* - See NOT operation.

- *Logic Level* - State of a voltage variable. The range of such voltage is expressed either by a "1" (HIGH) or a "0" (LOW). *[sec.3.1]*

- *Multivariable Theorems* - Boolean Theorems that involve more than one variable. *[sec.3.10]*

- *NAND gate* - Logic circuit which operates like an AND gate followed by an INVERTER. The output of a NAND gate is LOW (logic level 0), only if all inputs are HIGH (logic level 1). *[sec.3.9]*

- *NOR gate* - Logic circuit which operates like an OR gate followed by an INVERTER. The output of a NOR gate is LOW (logic level 0), when any or all inputs are HIGH (logic level 1). *[sec.3.9]*

- *NOT circuit* - See INVERTER. *[sec.3.5]*

- *NOT operation* - A Boolean Algebra operation in which the overbar $(\overline{X})$, or the prime (') symbol is used to indicate the Inversion of one or more logic variables. The result of a NOT operation is always the complement of the expression being NOTed. *[sec.3.1/3.5]*

- *OR gate* - The digital circuit which implements the OR operation. The output of this circuit is HIGH (logic level 1), if any or all of its inputs are HIGH. *[sec.3.3]*

- *OR operation* - A Boolean Algebra operation in which the symbol (+) is used to indicate the ORing of two or more logic variables. The result of the OR operation will be HIGH (logic level 1), if one or more variables is HIGH. *[sec.3.1/3.3]*

- *Truth Table* - A logic table which depicts a circuit's output response to the various combinations of the logic levels at its inputs. *[sec.3.2]*

- *Unasserted* - Term used to describe the state of a logic signal. The term "Unasserted" is synonymous with "Inactive." *[sec.3.14]*

Problems

SECTION 3.1 *Boolean Constants and Variables*

3.1 Complete the following statements.

    (a) Logical addition can also be referred to as _____ operation.

    (b) Inversion or logical complementation is often called the _____ operation.

    (c) The _____ operation can also be referred to as the logical multiplication.

SECTIONS 3.2-3.5 *Truth Tables/OR Operation With OR Gates/*
                                 AND Operation With AND Gates/NOT Operation

3.2 (a) Complete the truth table of Figure 3.1 (a) for a two-input **OR** gate.

     (b) Apply waveforms A and B of Figure 3.1(b) to a two-input **OR** gate and determine the resulting output waveform X.

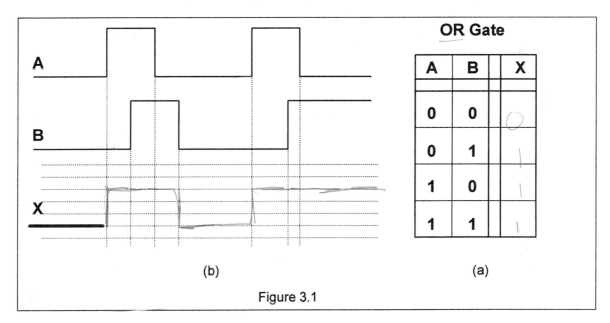

Figure 3.1

3.3 The input waveform A is applied to a two-input OR gate shown in Figure 3.2. Draw the input waveform at the B input that will produce the output X.

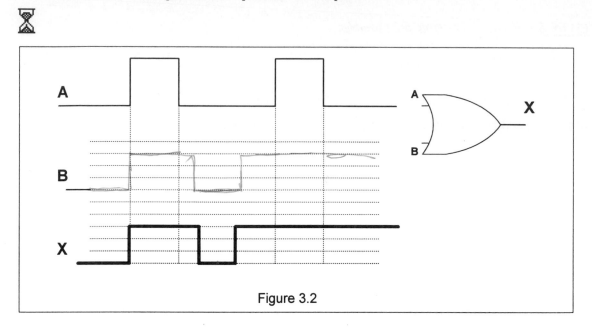

Figure 3.2

3.4 (a) Complete the truth table of Figure 3.3 (a) for a two-input **AND** gate.

    (b) Apply waveforms A and B of Figure 3. 3 (b) to a two-input **AND** gate and determine the resulting output waveform X.

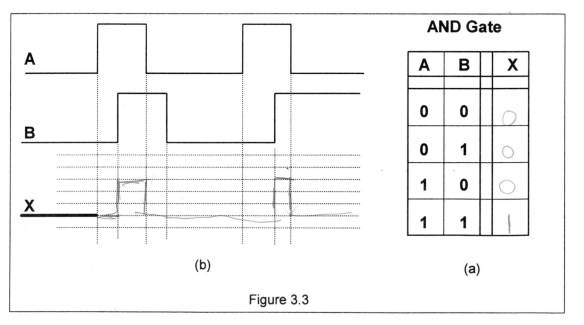

AND Gate		
A	B	X
0	0	
0	1	
1	0	
1	1	

(b)   (a)

Figure 3.3

3.5 The input waveform A is applied to a two-input AND gate shown in Figure 3.4. Draw the input waveform at the B input that will produce the output X.

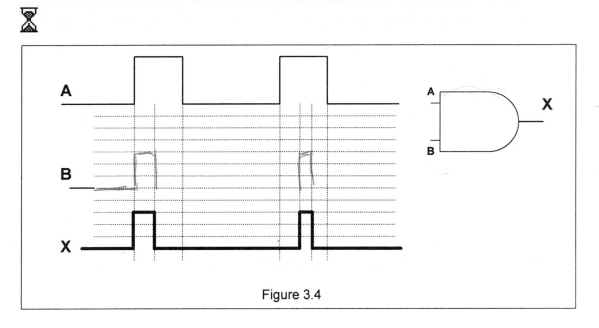

Figure 3.4

3.6 The Boolean expression at the output of a certain logic circuit is $X = \overline{A} + B$. Apply waveforms A and B of problem 3.4 to the inputs of that logic circuit and complete the truth table below.

A	B	$X = \overline{A} + B$
0	0	1
0	1	1
1	0	0
1	1	1

3.7 Determine whether the following statements are **True** or **False**:

(a) The output of a 3-input AND gate is HIGH when one or all of its inputs is HIGH. **[T]** , **[F]**

(b) The output of a 3-input OR gate is LOW when one or all of its inputs is LOW. **[T]** , **[F]**

(c) If the inputs of a 2-input AND gate are tied together, then the output waveform will follow the input signal. **[T]** , **[F]**

3.8 Write the Boolean expression for each of the following statements:

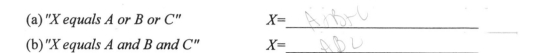

(a) *"X equals A or B or C"* $X=$ _____A+B+C_____

(b) *"X equals A and B and C"* $X=$ _____ABC_____

SECTIONS 3.6-3.7 *Describing Logic Circuits Algebraically/Evaluating Logic-Circuit Outputs*

3.9 For the circuit of Figure 3.5 insert INVERTERS at the outputs of the OR and AND gates respectively. Determine the output Boolean expression for X.

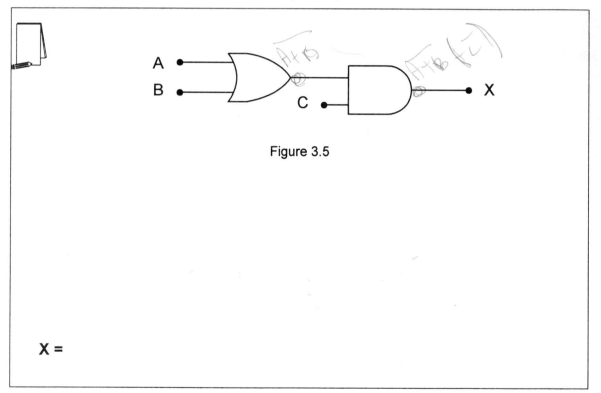

Figure 3.5

X =

3.10 A circuit's output expression is $Y = \overline{(ABC)} + D$. Fill in the truth table for that circuit.

A	B	C	D	$Y=\overline{(ABC)}+D$
0	0	0	0	1
0	0	0	1	0
0	0	1	0	1
0	0	0	1	0
0	1	0	0	1
0	1	0	1	0

3.11 Evaluate output Y of Figure 3.6 when A=0, B=1 and C=1.

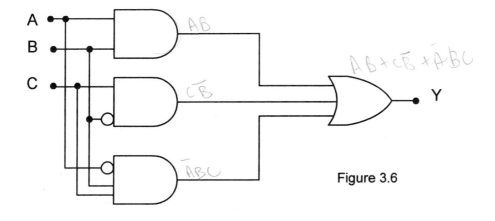

Figure 3.6

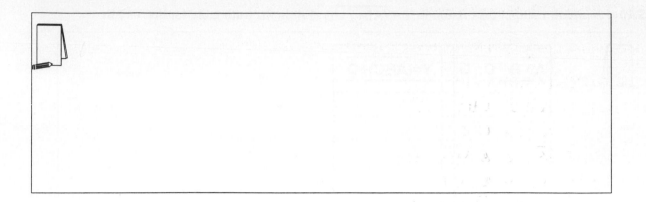

SECTIONS 3.8-3.9   *Implementing Circuits From Boolean Expressions/NOR gates and NAND Gates*

3.12   Draw the circuit diagrams that implement each of the following expressions.

(a) $X = \overline{\overline{A\,B}\,\overline{C}} + E\,F$

(b) $X = \overline{A + B + \overline{\overline{C + D}}}$

(c) $X = \overline{(A + B)\,(\overline{B}C)}$

(d) $X = \overline{(A\,B\,C)\,(A + D)}$

SECTIONS 3.10 *Boolean Theorems*

3.13 Simplify each of the following expressions using Boolean Theorems:

(a) $X = (\overline{A} + B)(A + \overline{B})$

(b) $Y = A\,B\,C + A\,B\,\overline{C} + A\,\overline{B}\,C$

(c) $Z = \overline{A}\,\overline{B}\,\overline{C} + \overline{B}\,\overline{C}\,\overline{C}$

(d) $W = \overline{A}\,B\,C + A\,\overline{B}\,C + \overline{A}\,\overline{B}\,C$

(e) $Q = A\,C\,D + \overline{A}\,B\,C\,D$

(f) $L = A\,\overline{B}\,C + \overline{A}\,\overline{B}\,\overline{C} + A\,C$

(g) $K = A\,B + C\,(A + C)$

SECTIONS 3.11 *DeMorgan's Theorems*

3.14 Simplify the following expressions using DeMorgan's theorems:

(a) $X = \overline{\overline{(A + B)} \; \overline{(C + D)}}$

(b) $Y = \overline{\overline{(A \, B)} + \overline{(C \, D)}}$

(c) $Z = \overline{(A + 0) + (A + B + C + D + 1)}$

(d) $W = \overline{\overline{A} \, B \, \overline{C}}$

(e) $Q = \overline{K \, L \; \overline{(M + N)} \; K \, L}$

(f) $L = \overline{\overline{A} \, \overline{B} \, (A + B)}$

(g) $K = \overline{A \, B \, \overline{C} \, D}$

SECTION 3.12 *Universality of NAND Gates and NOR Gates*

3.15   Covert the circuit of Figure 3.7 to one that uses only NAND gates.

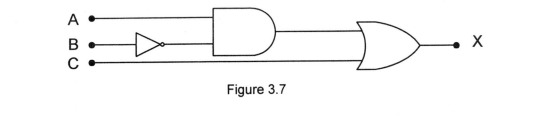

Figure 3.7

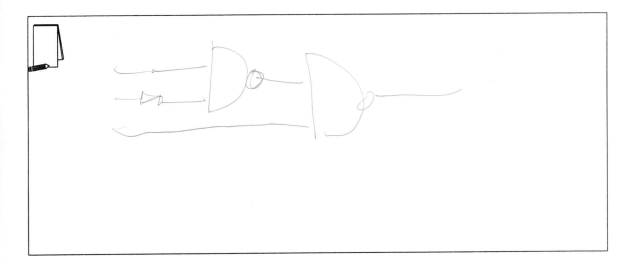

3.16   How many 2-input NOR gates are required to implement the Boolean expression $(A + B)(C + D)$?

3.17   Implement expression $X = ((A + \overline{B})\,(B + C)\,B)$ using one 7400 IC package.

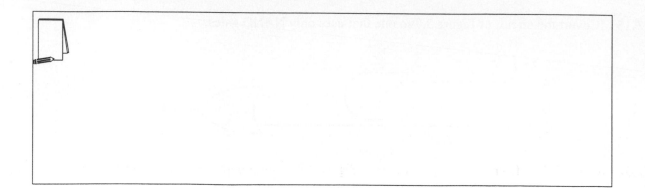

3.18   Show how $X = A + B + \overline{C}$ can be implemented using only one 2-input NOR gate and one 2-input NAND gate.

SECTIONS 3.13-3.15   *Alternate Logic-Gate Representation/Which Gate Representation to Use/New IEEE Standard Logic Symbols.*

3.19   Using the <u>Alternate Logic-Gate Representation,</u> modify the circuit of Figure 3.8 if output Z is to be active LOW.

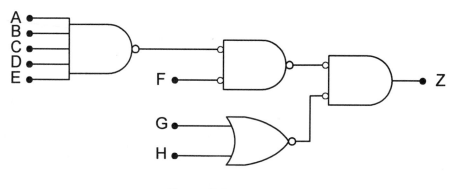

Figure 3.8

3.20 A logic LOW from output X of circuit of Figure 3.9 is needed to turn on an LED. Redraw the circuit so that it more accurately represents the circuit's operation.

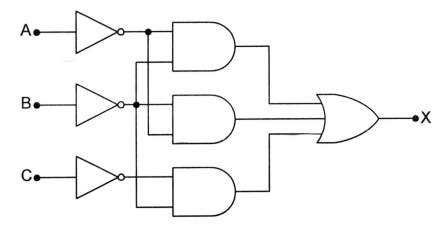

Figure 3.9

3.21 Under what conditions is the output $\overline{\text{LIGHT}}$ *unasserted* in Figure 3.10?

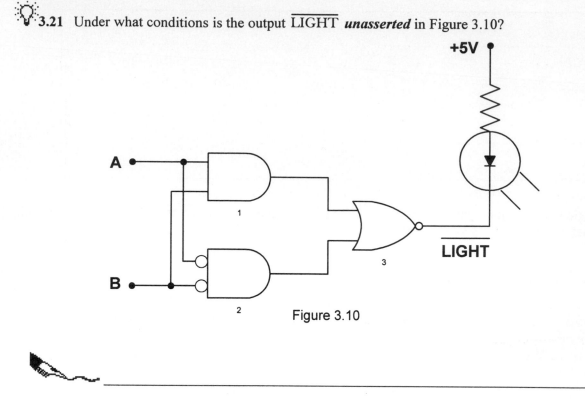

Figure 3.10

3.22 Draw the equivalent *IEEE/ANSI* symbol for each of the traditional logic symbols shown below.

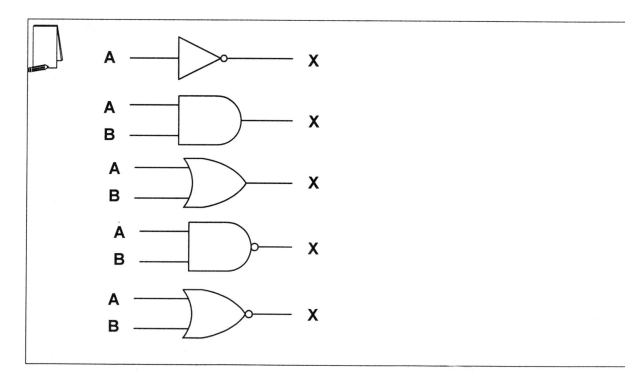

3.23   Using the dependency notation symbology, redraw the <u>simplified</u> circuit of problem 3.17.

3.24   Implement the Boolean expression $Z = ((A\,B + \overline{C})\,F + \overline{C} + D + E)$ by using dependency notation symbology.

TEST 3

1. The output of this gate is LOW, only if all inputs are HIGH.

   (a) AND   (b) NAND   (c) OR   (d) NOR

2. A 2-input NAND gate with its inputs tied together will function as what type of logic circuit?

   (a) AND   (b) INVERTER   (c) OR   (d) NOR

3. Three signals (A, B, and C) are ORed together. Their product is then ANDed with signals K, L, and Q Which of the following expressions indicates the correct order of operations?

   (a) A+B+CKLQ   (b) A+B+C(KLQ)   (c) A+(B+CKLQ)   (d) (A+B+C)KLQ

4. Given the Boolean expression $X = [(\overline{A + B}) + (\overline{CD + \overline{F} + \overline{G}}) + (E\overline{F} + G + \overline{H})]$ and the values A=0, B=1, C=1, D=0, E=1 F=1, G=0, H=0, the value of X is:

   (a) 0   (b) 1   (c) Undetermined

5. Which of the following Boolean expressions represents the DeMorganized version of the expression $X = (\overline{\overline{A + B}}) + (\overline{\overline{C} + \overline{D}})$?

   (a) (A+B)+(C+D)   (b) (AB)+(CD)   (c) (A+B)(CD)   (d) (AB)(C+D)

6. Which of the following Boolean expressions represents a three input OR gate?

   (a) $\overline{A} \cdot \overline{B} \cdot \overline{C}$ (b) $\overline{\overline{A} + \overline{B} + \overline{C}}$ (c) $\overline{A \cdot B \cdot C}$ (d) $\overline{\overline{A} \cdot \overline{B} \cdot \overline{C}}$

7. Suppose that a Boolean expression represents the output of a logic circuit and that it contains four variables (four inputs). How many different input combinations must be listed in this circuit's truth table?

   (a) 4_{10} (b) 8_{10} (c) 16_{10} (d) 32_{10}

   For the next three questions determine whether the statement is True or False

8. The term "Unasserted" is synonymous to "Active."   (a) [T]   (b) [F]

9. The Boolean expression $X = \overline{\overline{\overline{A + B + C}}}$ represents the output of a three input NOR gate fed to an INVERTER whose output is also fed to another INVERTER.   (a) [T]   (b) [F]

10. You would need a minimum of four universal two-input NAND gates to perform the logical operation of a two-input OR gate.   (a) [T]   (b) [F]

4 COMBINATIONAL LOGIC CIRCUITS

Objectives

Upon completion of this chapter, you will be able to:

- Convert a logic expression into a sum-of-products expression.

- Perform the necessary steps to reduce a sum-of-products expression to its simplest form.

- Use Boolean algebra and the Karnaugh map as a tool to simplify and design logic circuits.

- Explain the operation of both exclusive-OR and exclusive-NOR circuits.

- Design simple logic circuits without the help of a truth table.

- Implement enable circuits.

- Cite the basic characteristics of TTL and CMOS digital ICs.

- Use the basic troubleshooting rules of digital systems.

- Deduce from observed results the faults of malfunctioning combinational   logic circuits.

- Describe the fundamental idea of programmable logic devices (PLDs).

- Outline the steps involved in programming a PLD to perform a simple combinational logic function.

- Go to the CUPL User's Manual to acquire the information needed to do a simple programming experiment in the laboratory.

Glossary of key terms covered in this chapter:

- *Bipolar ICs* - Integrated Digital Circuits in which NPN and PNP transistors are the main circuit elements. *[sec.4.9]*

- *CAD*- Computer Aided Drafting. *[sec.4.14]*

- *CMOS* - Complementary metal-oxide semiconductor. A logic family which belongs to the category of unipolar digital ICs. *[sec.4.9]*

- *Combinational logic circuits* - Circuits made up of combinations of logic gates. *[sec.4.4]*

- *Contention* - See signal contention.

- *CUPL*- Universal Compiler for Programmable Logic. *[sec.4.14]*

- *Current Tracer* - Digital troubleshooting tool that detects a changing current in a wire or PC-board trace. *[sec.4.10/4.13]*

- *DIP* - "Dual-in-line package." The most common type of IC packages. *[sec.4.9]*

- *Don't Care* - An input condition of a logic variable in which neither a 1 (HIGH) nor a 0 (LOW) will affect the final output result. *[sec.4.5]*

- *Enable/Disable circuits* - Logic circuits (gates) that control the passage of an input signal through to the output. *[sec.4.8]*

- *Exclusive-NOR (XNOR) circuit* - A two input logic circuit that produces a HIGH output only when the inputs are equal. *[sec.4.6]*

- *Exclusive-OR (XOR) circuit* - A two input logic circuit which produces a HIGH output only when the inputs are different. *[sec.4.6]*

- *Floating inputs* - Input signals which are left disconnected in a logic circuit. *[sec.4.9]*

- *GSI* - Giga-Scale Integration. *[sec.4.9]*

- *HDL* - The syntax used to describe a PLD's operation is often referred to as the **H**ardware **D**escription **L**anguage *[sec.4.14]*

- *Indeterminate* - Whenever a logic voltage level of a particular logic family falls out of the required range of voltages for either a logic 0 or logic 1. *[sec.4.9.]*

- *JEDEC* - **J**oint **E**lectronic **D**evice **E**ngineering **C**ouncil. *[sec.4.14]*

- *Karnaugh map* - A two-dimensional form of a truth table used to simplify a Sum-of-products expression. *[sec.4.5]*

- *Logic compilers* - Software designed for PLD development. *[sec.4.14]*

- *Logic probe* - Digital troubleshooting tool which senses the logic level at a particular point in a circuit. *[sec.4.10]*

- *Logic pulser* - Digital troubleshooting tool that generates a short-duration pulse/s when manually actuated. *[sec.4.10]*

- *Looping* - When adjacent squares in a Karnaugh map containing 1s are combined for purpose of simplification of a sum-of-products expression. *[sec.4.5]*

- *LSI* - Large-Scale Integration. *[sec.4.9]*

- *MSI* - Medium-Scale Integration. *[sec.4.9]*

- *Octets* - A group of eight 1s that are adjacent to each other within a Karnaugh map. *[sec.4.5]*

- *Output Loading* - When a digital IC has its output connected to too many IC inputs. *[sec.4.12]*

- *Pairs* - A group of two 1s that are adjacent to each other within a Karnaugh map. *[sec.4.5]*

- *Parity Checker* - A logic circuit that checks transmitted data for the proper parity, and produces an error output (E) when a single-bit error has occurred. *[sec.4.7]*

- *Parity Generator* - A logic circuit that generates an even and an odd parity bit. *[sec.4.7]*

- *Product-of-sums (POS)* - A logic expression that consists of two or more OR terms (sums) that are ANDed together. *[sec.4.1]*

- *Programmable logic Device (PLD)* - An IC that contains a large number of logic gates whose interconnections can be programmed by the user to generate the desired logic relationship between inputs and outputs. *[sec.4.14]*

- *Quads* - A group of four 1s that are adjacent to each other within a Karnaugh map. *[sec.4.5]*

- *Signal contention* - A condition that occurs when two logic signals are "fighting" each other. That is, when one signal is trying to go to a logic LOW while at the same time and at the same point in the logic circuit a different signal is trying to go to a logic HIGH. *[sec.4.11]*

- *Simulator*- A computer program that calculates the correct output logic states based on a description of the logic circuit and the current inputs. *[sec.4.14]*

- *Solder bridges* - Splashes of solder that short two or more points together. *[sec.4.12]*

- *SSI* - Small-Scale Integration. *[sec.4.9]*

- *Substrate* - A piece of semiconductor material which is part of the building block of any digital IC. *[sec.4.9]*

- *Sum-of-products form (SOP)* - Logic expression consisting of two or more AND terms (products) that are ORed together. *[sec.4.1]*

- *Test vectors*- A set of hypothetical inputs that will prove that the PLD works as expected. *[sec.4.14]*

- *TTL* - Transistor-transistor logic. Logic family which belongs to the category of bipolar digital ICs. *[sec.4.9]*

- *ULSI* - Ultralarge-Scale Integration. *[sec.4.9]*

- *Unipolar ICs* - Integrated Digital Circuits where unipolar Field Effect Transistors (MOSFETs) are the main circuit elements. *[sec.4.9]*

- *VLSI* - Very Large-Scale Integration. *[sec.4.9]*

- *Zero Insertion Force (ZIF) socket* - A special socket that allows you to drop the IC chip in and then clamp the contacts onto the pins. *[sec.4.14]*

Problems

SECTIONS 4.1-4.3 *Sum-of-Products Form/Simplifying Logic Circuits/Algebraic Simplification*

4.1 Simplify the following expressions using Boolean algebra.

(a) $X = A\overline{B}\,\overline{C} + \overline{A}\,\overline{B}\,\overline{C}$

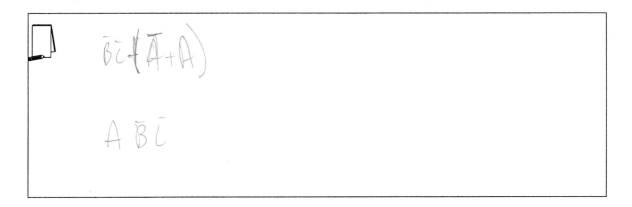

$$\overline{B}\,\overline{C} \cdot (\overline{A} + A)$$

$$A\,\overline{B}\,\overline{C}$$

(b) $X = AB + A\overline{B} + BC + \overline{B}\,\overline{C}$

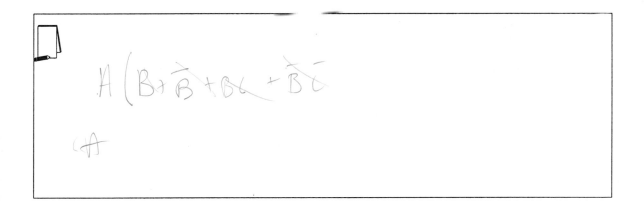

$$A(B + \overline{B} + BC + \overline{B}\overline{C}$$

$$A$$

(c) $X = A\overline{B}\,\overline{C} + \overline{A}\,\overline{B}\,\overline{C} + \overline{A}\,\overline{B}\,C$

(d) $X = ABC + A\overline{B}C + \overline{A}BC + (\overline{A+B})C$

(e) $K = \overline{X}\,\overline{Y}Z + \overline{X}YZ + X\overline{Y}\,\overline{Z} + X\overline{Y}Z + (\overline{\overline{X}+\overline{Y}+\overline{Z}})$

(f) $W = (K + N + M)(K + \overline{N} + M) + (\overline{K} + N + M)(\overline{K} + \overline{N} + M)$

(a) Refer to Figure 4.1. Let DRIV=A; $\overline{\text{BELTP}} = \overline{\text{BELTD}} = $ B; PASS=C; IGN=E; $\overline{\text{ALARM}} = $ X.
Determine the Boolean expression for the output X using the newly assigned variables *(Don't simplify it, yet!)*

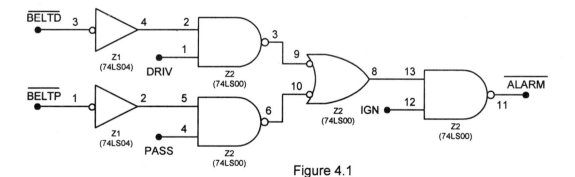

Figure 4.1

(b) Now, simplify the expression of step (a).

(c)   Implement the simplified expression using only 3-input NOR gates.

SECTION 4.4 *Designing Combinational Logic Circuits*

4.3 Design a logic circuit whose output is HIGH when inputs A and B are LOW, or when inputs C and D are HIGH.

Step 1: Set up the truth table

Step 2: Write the AND term for each case where the output is a 1.

Step 3: Write the SOP (sum-of-products) expression for the output.

Step 4: Simplify the output expression.

Step 5: Implement the circuit for the final expression.

4.4 A certain logic circuit in the NASA's Shuttle turns ON a green LED in the astronauts' cabin to indicate that the pressure in the external fuel tanks has reached the desirable value for lift-off. The desired pressure is set by the on-board computers and is encoded in a 3-bit binary number whose LSB is equivalent to 100 p.s.i. A pressure transducer monitors the fuel tanks and relays its information to the on-board computers via a 3-bit binary number whose LSB is equivalent to 100 p.s.i. When the pressure from the fuel tanks match the pre-programmed computer pressure for lift-off the green LED lights up. Design the logic circuit necessary to turn on the green indicator.

Use the step-by-step procedure used in problem 4.3

Step 1: Set up the truth table

Step 2: Write the AND term for each case where the output is a 1.

Step 3: Write the SOP (sum-of-products) expression for the output.

Step 4: Simplify the output expression.

Step 5: Implement the circuit for the final expression.

4.5 Design the necessary logic for the situation in Problem 4.4, if a red indicator is to turn ON when the pressure inside the tanks rises above 600 p.s.i.

4.6 Design a circuit whose output X is HIGH only when inputs A and B are HIGH but A and C are different.

4.7 Design a circuit whose output Z is HIGH when inputs C and D are LOW and inputs A or B are HIGH.

4.8 A burglar alarm is required to sound off whenever an intrusion takes place. The alarm should sound off when the entrance door (E) or the window (W) is opened. It should also sound off when the entrance door and the window are closed, but a motion detector (M) detects any movement inside of the house. And finally, the alarm must go off if a panic button (P) is depressed, regardless of the status of the other sensors in the house. Design the necessary logic circuit for the desired burglar alarm.

4.9 A late-model automobile has an 8-bit microcontroller that is used to check certain sensors in the car's system before the engine can be started. Each sensor has an associated name and its 16-bit corresponding µcomputer address. The corresponding addresses are as follows (Xs mean don't care conditions):

(I)   Doors Closed and Locked (DCL) _____ $FCXX_{16}$.
(II) Seat Belts Buckled-up (SBB) _____ $FDXX_{16}$.
(III) Electrical System Check (ESC) _____ $FEXX_{16}$.
(IV) Ignition ON ($\overline{ION}$) _____ $FFXX_{16}$.

The µcomputer sends the proper logic HIGH signal to each of the sensors (I thru IV) and monitors each response. If all the responses are appropriate then a final logic <u>LOW</u> signal is sent to start the engine (IV). Naturally, all of this is checked in microseconds as the ignition key is turned on to start the car. Design the necessary logic that will decode the address bus of the 8-bit µcomputer and whose outputs control each of the sensors used.

<u>**SECTIONS 4.5-4.6**</u> *The Karnaugh map Method/Exclusive-OR and Exclusive-NOR Circuits*

4.10 Simplify the following SOP expressions using Karnaugh mapping.

(a) $X = \overline{A}\overline{B}\overline{C}\overline{D} + \overline{A}\overline{B}C\overline{D} + A\overline{B}C\overline{D} + \overline{A}B\overline{C}D + \overline{A}BCD + A\overline{B}\overline{C}\overline{D}$

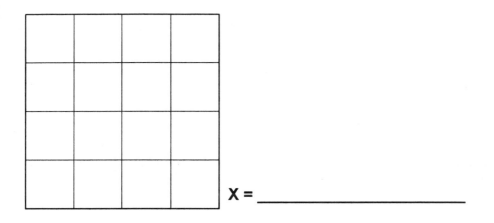

X = _____

(b) $Z = \overline{K}\overline{N}M + \overline{K}\overline{N}\overline{M} + \overline{K}N\overline{M}$

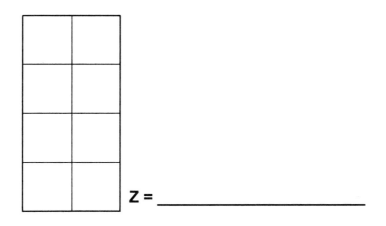

Z = _____

(c) $Y = \overline{P}Q\overline{R}S + \overline{P}QRS + PQ\overline{R}S + PQRS$

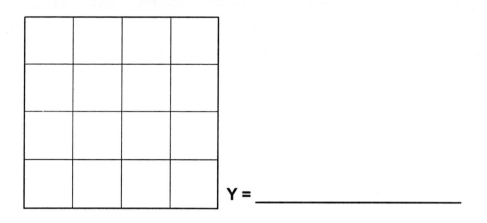

Y = _____

4.11   *Write and implement* the SOP expression for the following statements using Karnaugh maps:

(a)   A,B,C and D are the inputs of a counter. Z is the output and it is to be HIGH for counts 0,1,2,3,7 and 15.

Step 1: Set up the truth table.

Step 2: Write the AND term for each case where the output Z is 1.

Step 3: Write the SOP expression for the output Z.

 *Step 4: Simplify the output expression using the Karnaugh map.*

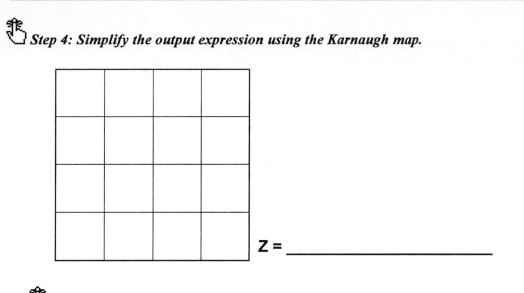

Z = _____

 *Step 5: Implement the final circuit.*

(b) The output Z of a circuit whose inputs are K, L, M and N, is to be HIGH whenever all of the inputs are equal, or whenever K is equal to M.

Step 1: Set up the truth table.

Step 2: Write the AND term for each case where the output Z is 1.

👆 *Step 3: Write the SOP expression for the output Z.*

👆 *Step 4: Simplify the output expression using the Karnaugh map.*

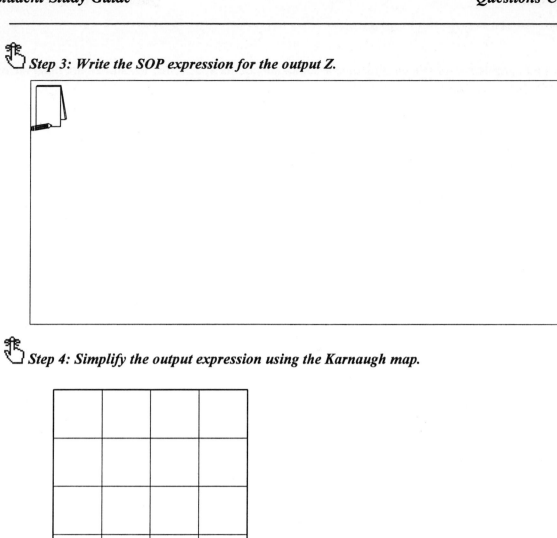

Z = _____

👆 *Step 5: Implement the final circuit.*

4.12 (a) Redo problem 4.11 (a), but this time assume that counts 4, 5, 6, 12, 13, and 14 are *don't care* conditions.

Step 1: Set up the truth table.

Step 2: Write the AND term for each case where the output Z is 1.

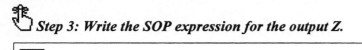 *Step 3: Write the SOP expression for the output Z.*

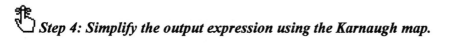 *Step 4: Simplify the output expression using the Karnaugh map.*

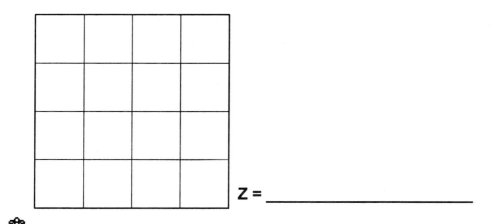

Z = _____

 *Step 5: Implement the final circuit.*

(b) Use a K map to simplify $X = AB(\overline{C}D + \overline{D}) + \overline{C}\,\overline{D} + \overline{A}\,B\,\overline{C} + A$

Step 1: Get the expression into SOP form if it is not already so.

Step 2: For each product term in the SOP expression, place a 1 in each K map square whose label contains the same combination of input variables. Place a 0 in all other squares.

X = _____

SECTION 4.6 *Exclusive-OR and Exclusive-NOR Circuits*

4.13 (a) Implement the Boolean expression X = AB using <u>one</u> two input NAND gate and <u>one</u> XOR gate.

(b) Repeat part (a) by using <u>one</u> two input NAND gate and <u>one</u> XNOR gate.

(c) Use the following words in order to complete the statements below: (equal, different, tie, HIGH, LOW, INVERTER)

1. The output of an XOR gate is LOW when the inputs are _____.

2. The output of an XOR gate is HIGH when the inputs are _____.

3. The output of an XNOR gate is _____ when the inputs are different

4. The output of an XNOR gate is _____ when the inputs are equal

5. If *one* of the inputs of an XNOR gate is grounded, the XNOR gate behaves as an _____.

6. One way to make an XOR gate behave like an INVERTER is to _____ both inputs together.

SECTION 4.7 *Parity Generator and Checker*

4.14 Design a parity generator that has three data inputs (A, B, C) and two outputs (Y and Z). Output Y will be HIGH if there is an even number of 1s in the input data. Output Z will be HIGH if there is an odd number of 1s in the data input.

4.15 Design the Parity Checker Circuit for the Parity Generator circuit of problem 4.14.

This circuit should check for both ODD and EVEN parity.

SECTIONS 4.9 *Basic Characteristics of Digital ICs*

4.16 Complete the following statements by filling in the blanks.

(a) Bipolar transistors are used by the _____ logic family, while the _____ logic family uses P-channel and N-channel MOSFETs.

(b) If a TTL input is left unconnected, that input acts like a logic ____ .

(c) If a _____ input is left floating, the IC may become overheated and eventually destroy itself.

(d) If an IC has 50,000 gates built on its substrate, then it's considered _____ _____ _____ Integration. However, if it has over 1,000,000 gates built on its substrate, then the IC falls into the category of _____ _____ Integration.

SECTIONS 4.10 *Troubleshooting Digital Systems*

4.17 A technician has just wire-wrapped the circuit of Figure 4.2(a). Determine what are the most probable causes for the malfunction demonstrated by the logic probe indications in the table of Figure 4.2(b).

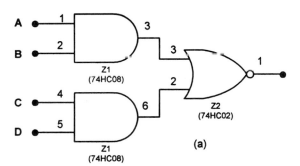

pin	Condition
Z1-1	Pulsing
Z1-2	HIGH
Z1-3	Pulsing
Z1-4	HIGH
Z1-5	HIGH
Z1-6	LOW
Z2-3	Pulsing
Z2-2	LOW
Z2-1	Pulsing

(b)

Figure 4.2

_____

_____

_____

_____

_____

_____

_____

4.18 Refer to the TTL circuit of Figure 4.3(a). The logic probe conditions in the table of Figure 4.3(b) are observed. Determine the most probable cause for the malfunctioning.

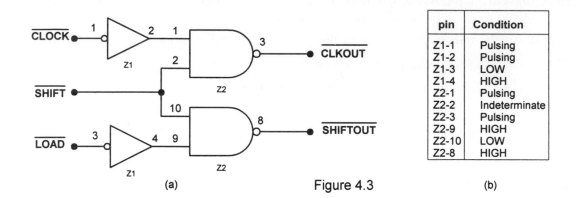

pin	Condition
Z1-1	Pulsing
Z1-2	Pulsing
Z1-3	LOW
Z1-4	HIGH
Z2-1	Pulsing
Z2-2	Indeterminate
Z2-3	Pulsing
Z2-9	HIGH
Z2-10	LOW
Z2-8	HIGH

(a)   Figure 4.3   (b)

_____

_____

_____

_____

_____

4.19 Refer to the TTL circuit of Figure 4.4(a). A technician constructs the circuit, plugs the ICs into the IC sockets, and then tests the circuit. The logic probe conditions listed in the table of Figure 4.4(b) are viewed. Determine the most probable cause for the observed circuit malfunction.

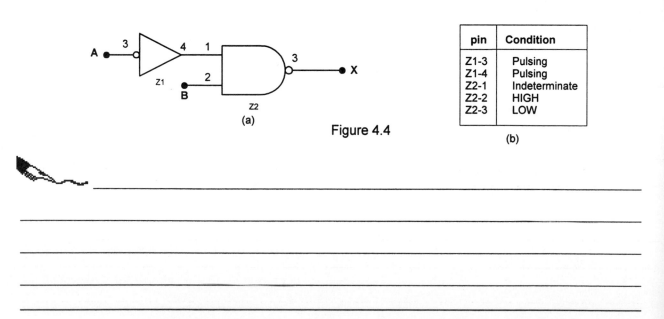

pin	Condition
Z1-3	Pulsing
Z1-4	Pulsing
Z2-1	Indeterminate
Z2-2	HIGH
Z2-3	LOW

(a)   Figure 4.4   (b)

_____

_____

_____

_____

_____

4.20 Refer to circuit of Figure 4.5. Output X should be HIGH only when the output from the BCD counter is equal to decimal counts 2, 3 or 9. The technician designed the "Logic Circuit" and upon testing it, he notices that the BCD counter is working properly, but output X is always HIGH. State 5 possible causes for the malfunction.

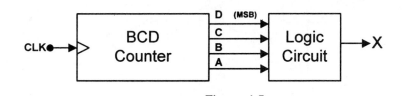

Figure 4.5

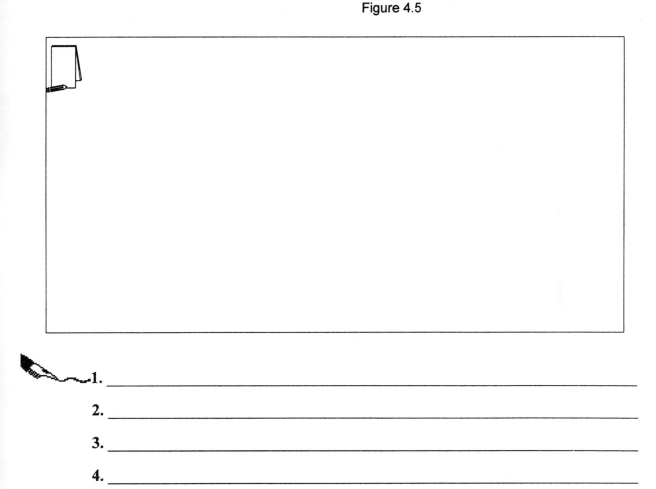

1. _____

2. _____

3. _____

4. _____

5. _____

4.21 The logic probe conditions listed in Figure 4.6(b) are observed for the TTL circuit of Figure 4.6(a). Consider the following list of possible problems. For each one indicate 'yes' or 'no'. Explain your reasoning for each 'no' response.

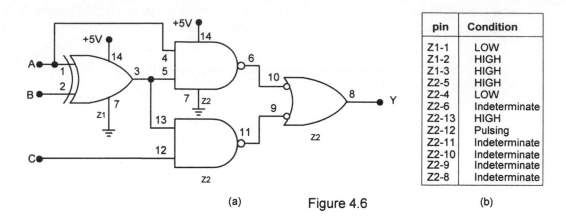

pin	Condition
Z1-1	LOW
Z1-2	HIGH
Z1-3	HIGH
Z2-5	HIGH
Z2-4	LOW
Z2-6	Indeterminate
Z2-13	HIGH
Z2-12	Pulsing
Z2-11	Indeterminate
Z2-10	Indeterminate
Z2-9	Indeterminate
Z2-8	Indeterminate

(a)   Figure 4.6   (b)

(a) Integrated circuit Z2 has pin 13 broken.

_____

_____

_____

_____

(b) Integrated circuit Z2 has pin 13 internally shorted to ground.

_____

_____

_____

(c) Connection from Z2-9 to Z2-11 is broken.

_____

_____

_____

_____

(d) Z2-9 is shorted to Z2-10.

_____

_____

_____

(e) Integrated circuit Z2 doesn't have Vcc applied to it.

_____

_____

_____

4.22 A technician builds the circuit of Figure 4.6 (a) using CMOS ICs. She uses an XOR gate (Z1) and three 3-input NAND gates (Z2). During the testing of the circuit, she finds that the outputs of the NAND gates are undetermined and at unpredictable logic levels. She also notices that IC Z2 is getting excessively warm. What is the most probable cause for the malfunction?

_____

_____

_____

_____

_____

_____

SECTIONS 4.14 *Programmable Logic Devices*

4.23 (a) Program the PLD of Figure 4.7 so that its output X is HIGH when the majority of its inputs A, B, and C are HIGH.

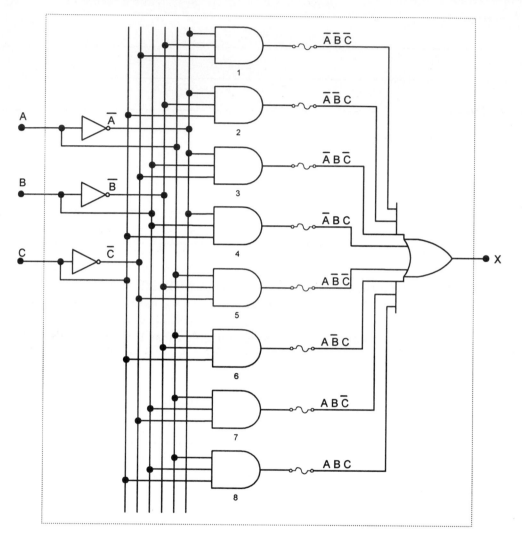

Figure 4.7

(b) Write the CUPL source file hardware description in Boolean equation entry mode to implement the following SOP expressions:

1. $X = ABC + CDE \rightarrow$ X = _____

2. $X = \overline{A}\,\overline{B} + \overline{A}\,B + \overline{B} \rightarrow$ X = _____

3. $X = \overline{A}\,B + A\,\overline{B} \rightarrow$ X = _____

(c) Show how you would write the statement *The SOP Expression* in a CULP input file.

_____

(d) Complete the following statements:

1. A _____ is a computer program that calculates the correct output logic states based on a description of the logic circuit and the current inputs.

2. A set of hypothetical inputs that will prove that the PLD works as expected are called _____ _____

3. An IC that contains a large number of logic gates whose interconnections can be programmed by the user to generate the desired logic relationship between inputs and outputs is called a _____.

4. A _____ socket allows you to drop the IC chip in and then clamp the contacts onto the pins.

5. The syntax used to describe a PLD's operation is often referred to as the _____ _____ _____.

TEST 4

1. Simplify the expression $Y = \overline{W}\,\overline{F}\,Z + \overline{W}\,F\,Z + W\,\overline{F}\,Z$

   (a) $Y = Z\,(\overline{W} + \overline{F})$ (b) $Y = Z\,(\overline{W}\,\overline{F})$ (c) $Y = Z\,(\overline{W} + F)$ (d) $Y = \overline{Z}\,(\overline{W}\,\overline{F})$

2. The Boolean expression $X = A\,B + \overline{\overline{C}} + A\,\overline{C} + B$ can be implemented using one three input:

   (a) OR gate   (b) AND gate   (c) NAND gate   (d) None of the above

3. Which of the following represent a sum-of-products expression?

   (a) $X = \overline{A\,B\,C} + A\,B\,C + \overline{A}\,B\,C$ (b) $X = \overline{A}\,K\,L + A\,K\,L + \overline{(A + \overline{K} + L)}$ (c) $X = \overline{A}\,B\,C + A\,\overline{B}\,C + \overline{A}\,B\,\overline{C}$
   (d) None of the above

4. How many variables are eliminated when a quad is formed in a Karnaugh map?

   (a) One   (b) Two   (c) Three   (d) Four

5. The logic gate that produces a LOW output only when the inputs are equal is the:

   (a) XNOR   (b) XOR   (c) NAND   (d) NOR

6. Which two-input gate acts as an inverter when one of its inputs is permanently tied to ground?

   (a) XNOR   (b) XOR   (c) NAND   (d) NOR

7. What are the minimum amount of gates needed to implement the expression $X = A\,B + \overline{A}\,\overline{B}$?

   (a) 5   (b) 4   (c) 3   (d) 1

8. A four variable truth table yields an output X that is HIGH for fifteen conditions and LOW for one condition. The <u>easiest and fastest</u> way to implement the circuit whose output is X, is to:

   (a) write the S-of-P expression for all cases where X=1, then simplify the X expression using Boolean algebra, and then draw the circuit.
   (b) write the S-of-P expression for all cases where X=1, then simplify the X expression using the Karnaugh map, and then draw the circuit.
   (c) write the S-of-P expression for the case where X=0, then invert the expression using DeMorgan's theorems, simplify the expression using Boolean algebra, and then draw the circuit.
   (d) write the S-of-P expression for the case where X=0, then invert the expression using DeMorgan's theorems, simplify the expression using the Karnaugh map, and then draw the circuit.

9. The CUPL source file hardware description in Boolean equation entry mode representing the SOP $X = A\,B + \overline{A}\,\overline{B}\,\overline{C}$ is:

   (a) A # B&A # B # C   (b) A&B&!A&!B&!C   (c) A&B # !A&!B&!C   (d) A$B # !A&!B&!C

10. The syntax used to describe a PLD's operation is often referred to as:

    (a) HDL   (b) ZIF   (c) CUPL   (d) JEDEC

5   FLIP-FLOPS AND RELATED DEVICES

Objectives

Upon completion of this chapter, you will be able to:

- Construct and analyze the operation of a latch flip-flop made from NAND or NOR gates.

- Describe the difference between synchronous and asynchronous systems.

- Understand the operation of edge-triggered flip-flops.

- Analyze and apply the various flip-flop timing parameters specified by the manufacturers.

- Understand the major differences between parallel and serial data transfers.

- Draw the output timing waveforms of several types of flip-flops in response to a set of input signals.

- Recognize the various IEEE/ANSI flip-flop symbols.

- Use state transition diagrams to describe counter operation.

- Use flip-flops in synchronous circuits.

- Connect shift registers as data transfer circuits.

- Employ flip-flops as frequency-division and counting circuits.

- Understand the typical characteristics of Schmitt triggers.

- Apply two different types of one-shots in circuit design.

- Design a free-running oscillator using a 555 timer.

- Recognize and predict the effects of clock skew on synchronous circuits.

- Troubleshoot various types of flip-flop circuits.

- Program a PLD using CUPL's state transition format for circuit description.

Glossary of key terms covered in this chapter:

- **555 Timer** - A TTL-compatible IC which can wired to operate in several different modes such as a One-Shot and an Astable Multivibrator. *[sec.5.24]*

- **Astable Multivibrator** - Digital circuit which oscillates between two unstable output states. *[sec.5.24]*

- **Asynchronous Active Pulse Width** - The minimum time duration that a DC SET or DC CLEAR input has to be kept in its active state in order to reliably SET or CLEAR the flip-flop. *[sec.5.11]*

- **Asynchronous Inputs** - flip-flop inputs which can affect the operation of the flip-flop independently of the synchronous and Clock inputs. *[sec.5.9]*

- **Asynchronous Systems** - Systems in which outputs can change states any time one or more of the inputs change. *[sec.5.4]*

- **Asynchronous Transfer** - Data transfer performed without the aid of the Clock. *[sec.5.17]*

- **Binary Counter** - A group of flip-flops connected in a special arrangement in which the states of the flip-flops represent the binary number equivalent to the number of pulses that have occurred at the input of the counter. *[sec.5.19]*

- **Bistable Multivibrator** - Name which is sometimes used to describe a flip-flop. *[sec.5.24]*

- **CLEAR** - Asynchronous flip-flop input used to clear Q immediately to 0. *[sec.5.9]*

- **Clear State** - When the inputs of a flip-flop cause it to go to the Q=0 state. *[sec.5.1]*

- **Clock** - A digital signal in the form of a rectangular pulse train or a squarewave. *[sec.5.4]*

- **Clock Pulse HIGH [$t_{W(H)}$]** - The minimum time duration that a Clock signal must remain HIGH before going LOW. *[sec.5.11]*

- **Clock Pulse LOW [$t_{W(L)}$]** - The minimum time duration that a Clock signal must remain LOW before going HIGH. *[sec.5.11]*

- **Clock Skew** - When because of propagation delays a Clock signal arrives at the Clock inputs of different flip-flops at different times. *[sec.5.25]*

- **Clock Transition Times** - Duration given by the manufacturer of a particular IC for the rise and fall times of the Clock signal transitions used by that IC. *[sec.5.11]*

- **Clocked D flip-flop** - Type of flip-flop where the D (Data) input is the synchronous input. *[sec.5.7]*

- **Clocked flip-flops** - flip-flops which have a Clock input. *[sec.5.4]*

- *Clocked J-K flip-flop* - Type of flip-flop where the inputs J and K are the synchronous inputs. *[sec.5.6]*

- *Clocked S-C flip-flop* - Type of flip-flop where the inputs SET and CLEAR are the synchronous inputs. *[sec.5.5]*

- *Common-Control Block* - Symbol used by the IEEE/ANSI standard to describe when one or more inputs are common to more than one of the circuits in an IC. *[sec.5.10]*

- *Contact Bounce* - Random voltage transitions produced by operating a mechanical switch. *[sec.5.1]*

- *Control Inputs* - Control input signals synchronized with the active Clock transition determine the output state of a flip-flop. *[sec.5.4]*

- *D Latch* - Circuit which contains a NAND gate latch and two steering NAND gates. *[sec.5.8]*

- *Data Lock-Out* - Feature on some Master/Slave flip-flops by which the Master flip-flop is disable a short time after the positive-going Clock transition. *[sec.5.13]*

- *Direct RESET (R_D)* - Term synonymous with CLEAR. *[sec.5.9]*

- *Direct SET (S_D)* - Term synonymous with PRESET. *[sec.5.9]*

- *Edge-Detector* - Circuit that produces a narrow positive spike that occurs coincident with the active transition of a Clock input pulse. *[sec.5.5]*

- *Edge-Triggered* - The manner in which a flip-flop is activated by a signal transition. It may be either a positive or negative edge-triggered flip-flop. *[sec.5.4]*

- *Free-Running Multivibrator* - See Astable Multivibrator. *[sec.5.24]*

- *Hold Time (t_H)* - Time interval immediately following the active transition of the Clock signal during which the control input has to be maintained at the proper level. *[sec.5.4/5.11]*

- *Jam Transfer* - See Asynchronous Transfer. *[sec.5.17]*

- *Latch* - A term synonymous with flip-flop. *[sec. 5.1]*

- *Master/Slave flip-flops* - flip-flops which have as their internal structure two flip-flops - a Master and a Slave. *[sec.5.13]*

- *Maximum Clocking Frequency (f_{MAX})* - The highest frequency that may be applied to the Clock input of a flip-flop and still have trigger reliably. *[sec.5.11]*

- *MOD Number* - The number of different states that a counter can sequence through. *[sec.5.19]*

- *Monostable Multivibrator* - See One-Shot. *[sec.5.22]*

- *NAND Gate Latch* - A flip-flop constructed from two NAND gates. *[sec.5.1]*

- *Negative-Going Threshold (V_{T-})* - A voltage level inherent to a Schmitt Trigger circuit which if dropped below will cause the output to change. *[sec.5.21]*

- *Negative-Going Transition (NGT)* - When a Clock signal changes from a logic 1 to a logic 0. *[sec.5.4]*

- *Noise* - Spurious voltage fluctuations that may be present in the environment and cause digital circuits to malfunction. *[sec.5.25]*

- *Nonretriggerable One-Shot* - Type of One-Shot that will not respond to a trigger input signal while in its quasi-state. *[sec.5.22]*

- *NOR Gate Latch* - A flip-flop constructed from two NOR gates. *[sec.5.2]*

- *One-Shot* - A circuit which belongs to the flip-flop family but which has only one stable state (normally Q=0). *[sec.5.22]*

- *Open Inputs*- Unconnected or floating inputs of any logic circuit. *[sec.5.25]*

- *Override Inputs* - Synonymous with Asynchronous inputs. *[sec.5.9]*

- *Parallel Data Transfer* - Operation by which the contents of a register are transferred simultaneously to another register. *[sec.5.7/5.17]*

- *Positive-Going Threshold (V_{T+})* - A voltage level inherent to a Schmitt Trigger circuit which if exceeded will cause the output to change. *[sec.5.21]*

- *Positive-Going Transition (PGT)* - When a Clock signal changes from a logic 0 to a logic 1. *[sec.5.4]*

- *PRESET* - Asynchronous flip-flop input used to set Q immediately to 1. *[sec.5.9]*

- *Propagation Delays (t_{PLH}/t_{PHL})* - Delay from the time a signal is applied to the time when the output makes its change. *[sec.5.11]*

- *Pulse-Steering Circuit* - Circuit that steers a spike through to the SET or CLEAR input of a latch in accordance with the levels present at the S and C, or J and K. *[sec.5.5/5.6]*

- *Quartz Crystal* - A piece of quartz crystal that vibrates at an extremely precise and stable frequency once it is electrically excited. *[sec.5.25]*

- *Quasi-Stable* - State in which a One-Shot stays momentarily (normally Q=1) before returning to its normal state (normally Q=0). *[sec.5.22]*

- *Registers* - A group of flip-flops capable of storing data. *[sec.5.17]*

- *Retriggerable One-Shot* - Type of One-Shot that will respond to a trigger input signal while in its quasi-state. *[sec.5.22]*

- *Schmitt-Trigger* - Digital circuit which accepts a slow-changing input signal and produces a rapid oscillation-free transition at the output. *[sec.5.21]*

- *Sequential Circuits* - A circuit in which the outputs follow a predetermined sequence of states, with a new state occurring each time a clock pulse occurs. *[sec.5.14]*

- *Serial Data Transfer* - When data are transferred from one place to another one bit at a time. *[sec.5.17/5.18]*

- *Set State* - When the inputs of a flip-flop cause it to go to the Q=1 state. *[sec.5.1]*

- *Set-Up Time (t_S)* - The time interval immediately preceding the active transition of the Clock signal during which the control input has to be maintained at the proper level. *[sec.5.4/5.11]*

- *Shift Register* - Digital circuit which accepts binary data from some input source and then shifts these data through a chain of flip-flops one bit at a time. *[sec.5.18]*

- *State Transition Diagram* - A way to show how the states of flip-flops change with each applied clock pulse. Each circle in the state transition diagram represents one possible state as indicated by the binary number inside the circle. *[sec.5.19/5.26]*

- *Synchronous Inputs* - See Control Inputs. *[sec.5.9]*

- *Synchronous Systems* - Systems in which the output can change states only when a Clock occurs. *[sec.5.4]*

- *Synchronous Transfer* - Data transfer performed by using the synchronous and the Clock inputs of a flip-flop. *[sec.5.17]*

- *Toggle Mode* - When a flip-flop changes states for each Clock pulse. *[sec.5.6]*

- *Transparent Mode* - In a D-latch if input D changes while EN is HIGH, the Q output will look exactly like D; in this mode, the D latch is said to be transparent. *[sec.5.8]*

- *Trigger* - Input signal to a flip-flop that causes its output to change states depending on the conditions of the control signals. *[sec.5.5]*

Problems

SECTIONS 5.1-5.3 *NAND Gate Latch/NOR Gate Latch/Troubleshooting Case Study*

5.1   Complete the following statements.

(a)   The output of a _NOR_ gate latch is invalid, when the SET and CLEAR inputs are HIGH.

(b)   The Q output of a NAND gate latch is LOW, when the SET input is _high_ and the CLEAR input is _LOW_.

(c)   The output of a _NAND_ gate latch will not change if both inputs are HIGH.

5.2

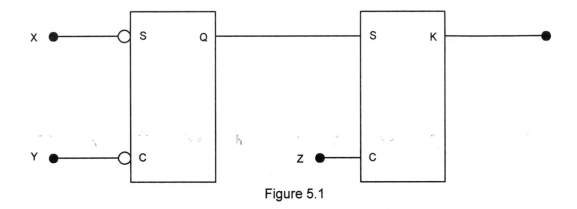

Figure 5.1

(a)   Use the NAND and the NOR latch representations and redraw the logic circuit of Figure 5.1.

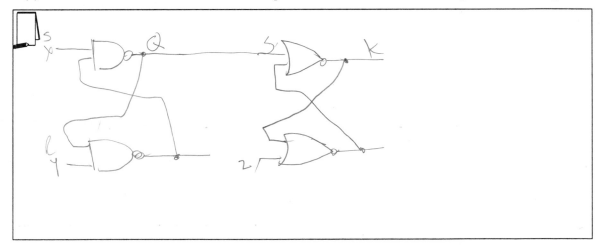

(b) Apply waveforms X, Y and Z to the TTL circuit of Figure 5.1 and draw the timing diagram for the outputs Q and K. Assume that initially Q=K=1

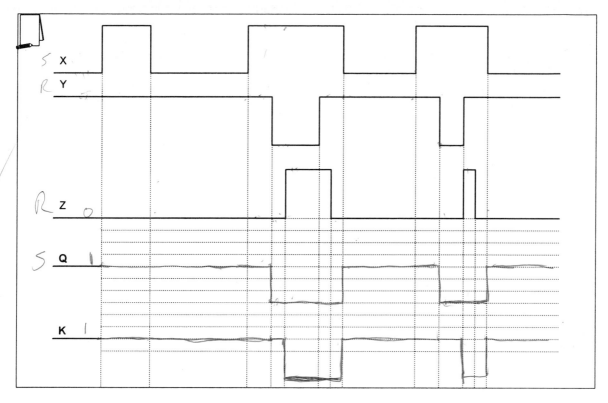

5.3 An oscilloscope is used to test the circuit of Figure 5.1. The technician notices that the K output is always HIGH. Determine some possible reasons for the malfunction.

SECTIONS 5.4-5.5 *Clock Signals and Clocked Flip-Flops/Clocked S-C Flip-Flop*

5.4 (a) Figure 5.2(a) shows a negative edge-triggered S-C flip-flop. Apply the waveforms of Figure 5.2(b) to the inputs of the S-C flip-flop and determine the output waveform Q. Assume that Q=0 initially.

The output of a negative edge triggered S-C flip-flop changes only when the clock signal goes from a logic HIGH to a logic LOW (NGT)

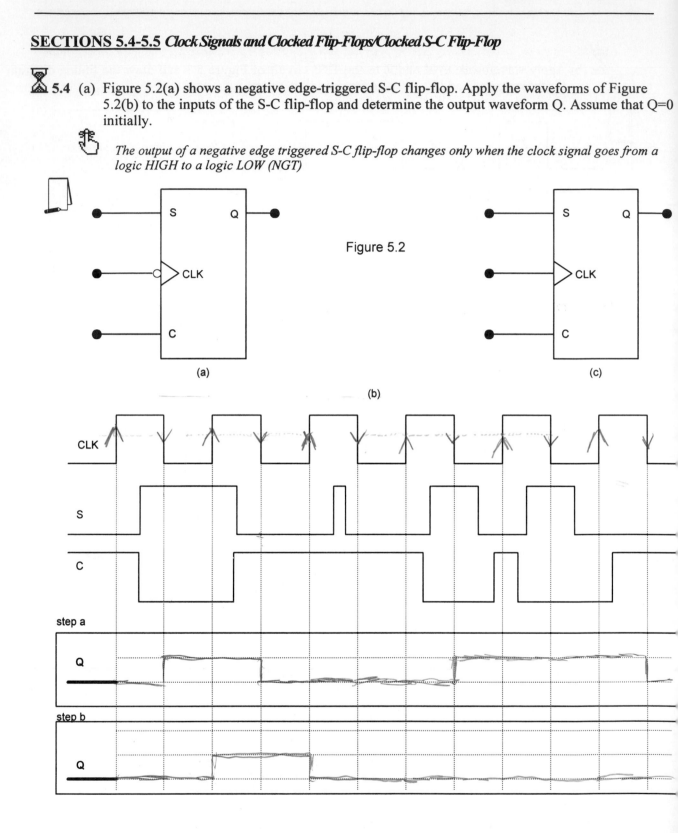

Figure 5.2

(a)

(c)

(b)

The output of a positive edge triggered S-C flip-flop changes only when the clock signal goes from a logic LOW to a logic HIGH (PGT)

(b) Repeat step (a) for the positive edge-triggered Set-Clear flip-flop of Figure 5.2(c).

5.5 The following statements are all false. Change *ONE* word in each of the following two statements in order to make each one a true statement.

(a) In asynchronous digital systems, the time during which the output of a circuit can change is determined by a signal called CLOCK.

Synch

(b) The Set-Up time requirement of a flip-flop is that time interval immediately following the active transition of the CLK signal during which the synchronous inputs have to be maintained at the proper level.

(c) The internal circuitry of the edge-triggered S-C flip-flop consists of an edge-detector circuit, a pulse-steering circuit, and a basic NOR latch.

_____

SECTIONS 5.6-5.8; 5.25   *Clocked J-K flip-flop / Clocked D flip-flop /D Latch (Transparent Latch / Troubleshooting flip-flop Circuits.*

5.6 A technician uses waveforms of Figure 5.3(b) to test the J-K flip-flop Q of Figure 5.3(a). With an oscilloscope, she measures a <u>5KHz 50%</u> duty-cycle waveform at output Q.

Consider the following list of possible causes for the circuit's malfunction. For each one indicate 'yes' or 'no'. Explain your reasoning for each response. Determine waveform Q to justify each of your answers (Assume Q=0 initially).

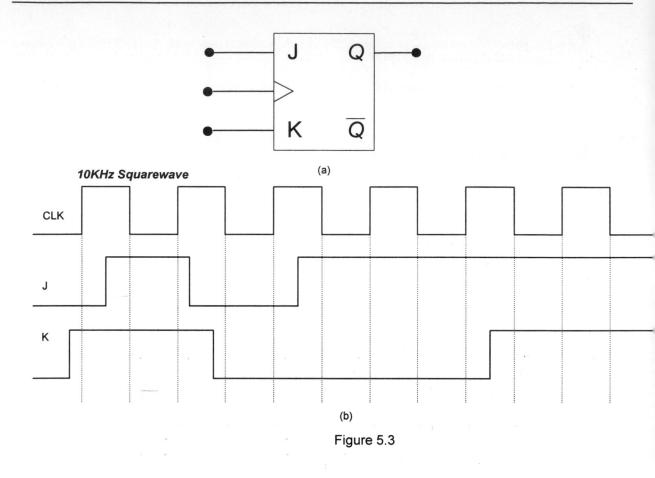

Figure 5.3

(a) The technician unintentionally used a negative edge-triggered J-K flip-flop.

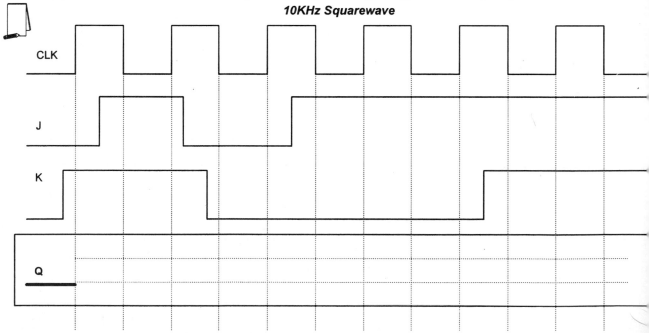

_____

_____

_____

_____

_____

(b) Input J is shorted to ground.

10KHz Squarewave

CLK

J   0

K

Q

_____

_____

_____

_____

_____

(c) Input K is internally shorted to Vcc.

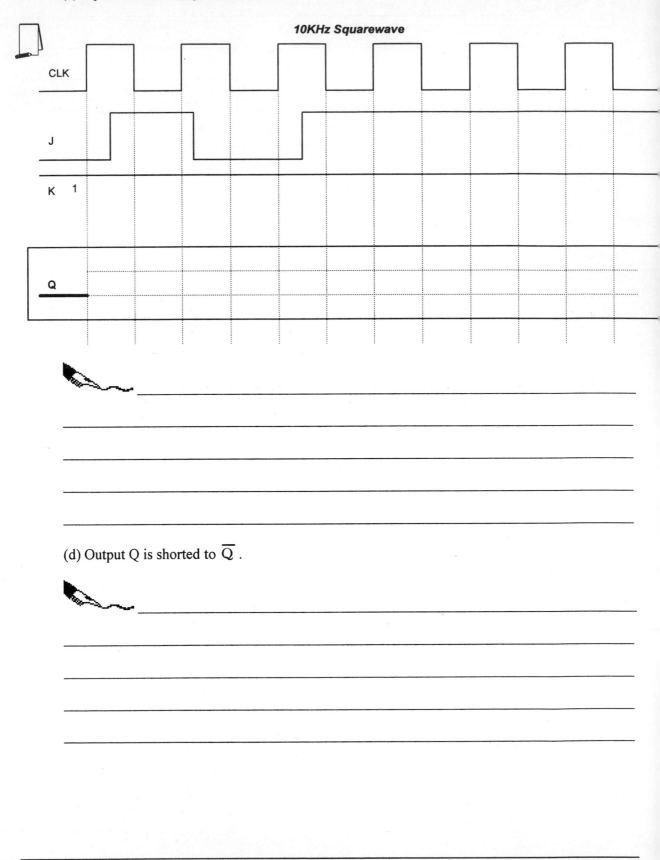

10KHz Squarewave

CLK

J

K   1

Q

_____

_____

_____

_____

_____

_____

(d) Output Q is shorted to $\overline{Q}$.

_____

_____

_____

_____

_____

_____

5.7 Refer to flip-flops of Figure 5.4(a), (b) and waveforms (c). Sketch the output waveforms X and L. (Assume X=L=0 initially)

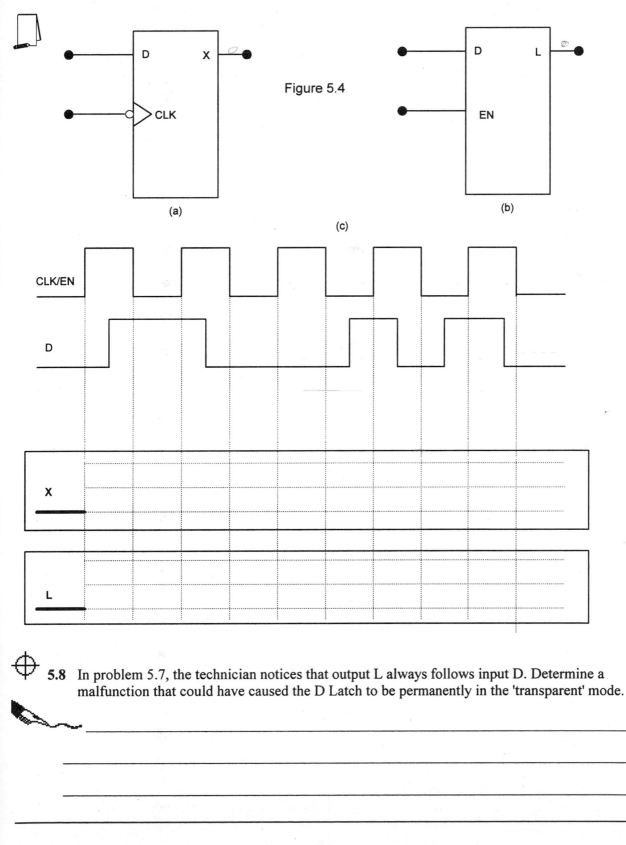

Figure 5.4

(a)   (b)

(c)

CLK/EN

D

X

L

5.8 In problem 5.7, the technician notices that output L always follows input D. Determine a malfunction that could have caused the D Latch to be permanently in the 'transparent' mode.

_____

_____

_____

_____

SECTIONS 5.9-5.10 *Asynchronous Inputs/IEEE-ANSI Symbols*

5.9 (a) Refer to the circuit represented by the IEEE/ANSI symbol of Figure 5.5(b). Complete the state table of Figure 5.5(a) for each NGT of the clock. Assume that initially Q=0 for each condition.

(b) Apply the waveforms of Figure 5.5(c) to the flip-flop of Figure 5.5(a) and draw the output waveform for Q. Assume that J=K=1 and Q=0 initially.

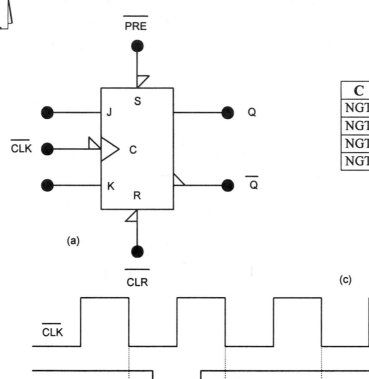

(a)

C	J	K	R	S	Q
NGT	1	1	1	0	
NGT	1	0	1	1	
NGT	0	0	0	1	
NGT	1	1	1	1	

(b)

(c)

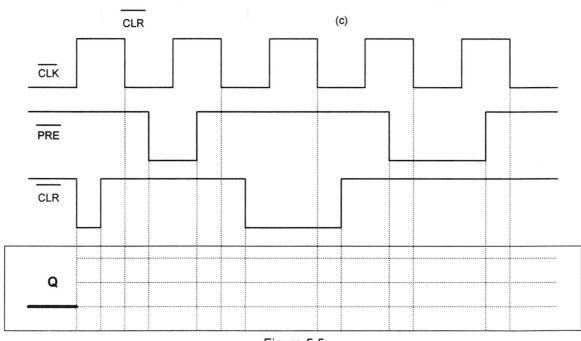

Figure 5.5

SECTIONS 5.11-5.12   *Flip-flop Timing Considerations/Potential Timing Problem in FF Circuits*

5.10 Refer to the table of flip-flop values of Figure 5.6.

flip-flop timing values (ns)	74C74	7474
t_S	60	20
t_H	0	5
t_{pHL}- from CLK to Q	200	40
t_{pLH}- from CLK to Q	200	25
t_{pHL} - from $\overline{CLR}$ to Q	225	40
t_{pLH}- from $\overline{PRE}$ to Q	225	25
$t_{W(L)}$ - CLK LOW time	100	37
$t_{W(H)}$ - CLK HIGH time	100	30
$_{W(L)}$ - at $\overline{PRE}$ or $\overline{CLR}$	60	30
f_{MAX} - in MHz	5	15

Figure 5.6

A 74C74 flip-flop is wired as a toggle flip-flop. The clock signal used is a 1MHz, 7.5% Duty Cycle. On the oscilloscope, the Q of the flip-flop is not a 500KHz squarewave, but is instead a non-repetitive ambiguous waveform. Why do you think the reason is for the apparent malfunction?

_____

_____

_____

5.11 The flip-flops of Figure 5.7(a) and (b) have the parameters listed in the table of Figure 5.6. The waveforms of Figure 5.7(c) are applied to both flip-flops. Assume that Z=M=0 initially. Sketch outputs Z and M.

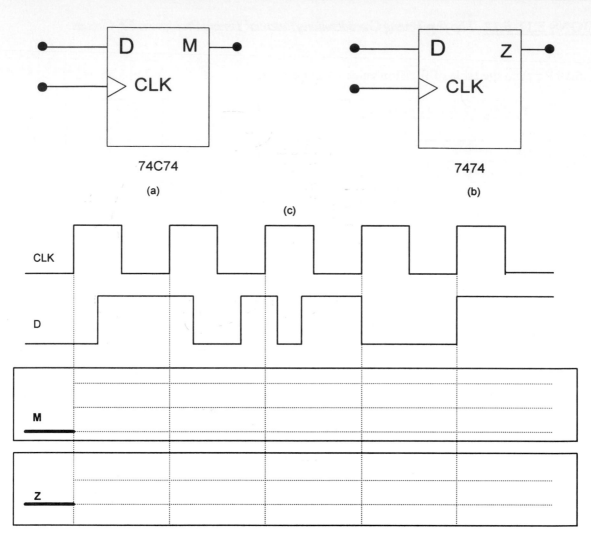

Figure 5.7

SECTION 5.13-5.14 *Master-Slave flip-flops/Flip-Flop Applications*

5.12   Complete the following:

(a) Master/slave flip-flops have been replaced with a new master/slave version called a _____ _____ _____ _____ _____.

(b) A _____ circuit is one in which the outputs follow a predetermined _____ of states, with a new state occurring each time a clock pulse occurs.

SECTIONS 5.17-5.18 *Data Storage and Transfer/Serial Data Transfer: Shift Registers*

5.13 The table below was observed as shift pulses were applied to the shift register of Figure 5.8.

(a) Determine the most probable cause for the malfunction.

X_3	X_2	X_1	X_0	Y_3	Y_2	Y_1	Y_0	
1	0	1	1	0	0	0	0	← Before pulses applied.
0	1	0	1	1	0	0	0	← After the first pulse.
0	0	1	0	1	1	0	0	← After the second pulse.
0	0	0	1	0	1	1	0	← After the third pulse.
0	0	0	0	1	0	1	0	← After the fourth pulse.

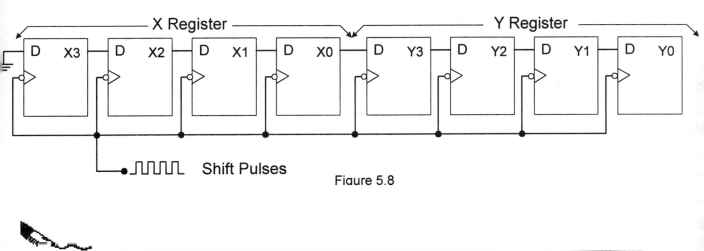

Figure 5.8

_____

_____

_____

_____

(b) Disconnect the D input of flip-flop X_3 (MSB of the X-Register) from ground, and connect it to the output Y_0. Complete the table below.

X_3	X_2	X_1	X_0	Y_3	Y_2	Y_1	Y_0	
1	0	1	1	0	0	0	0	← Before pulses applied.
								← After the first pulse.
								← After the second pulse.
								← After the third pulse.
								← After the fourth pulse.

SECTION 5.19 *Frequency Division and Counting*

5.14 Draw the state transition diagram for a three bit counter that has the following counting sequence: 0,1,2,4,6,7,3,5,0,1...repeats.

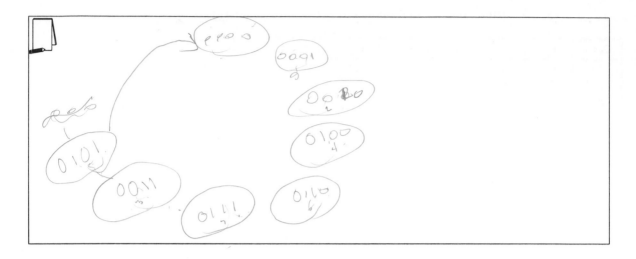

5.15   What is the MOD number of the counter described in problem 5.14?

_____

5.16   Refer to the counter of problem 5.14 and answer the following:

(a) If the counter starts at count 000_2, what count will it hold after 16 pulses?

(b) If the counter starts at count 111_2, what count will it hold after 842 pulses?

(c) If the counter starts at count 100_2, what count will it hold after 358 pulses?

(d) If the counter starts at count 101_2, what count will it hold after 3673 pulses?

5.17 The input clock to the counter of Figure 5.9 is a 100KHz, 10% Duty-Cycle waveform.

Figure 5.9

(a) What is the frequency and Duty-Cycle of the waveforms at the outputs X0, X1 and X2?

(b) Change the counter of Figure 5.9 so that it has *eight* J-K flip-flops (X0-X7). What is the total number of different states that the counter can go through?

(c) What is the maximum binary count that the counter in step (b) can reach?

SECTION 5.20 *Microcomputer Application*

5.18 Add the necessary *"Decoding Logic"* circuitry to the microcomputer of Figure 5.10 so that the four decoded outputs X, Y, Z, and W correspond to the MPU addresses $\overline{0F}xx_{16}$, $0Fxx_{16}$, $0Dxx_{16}$, and $0Cxx_{16}$ respectively.

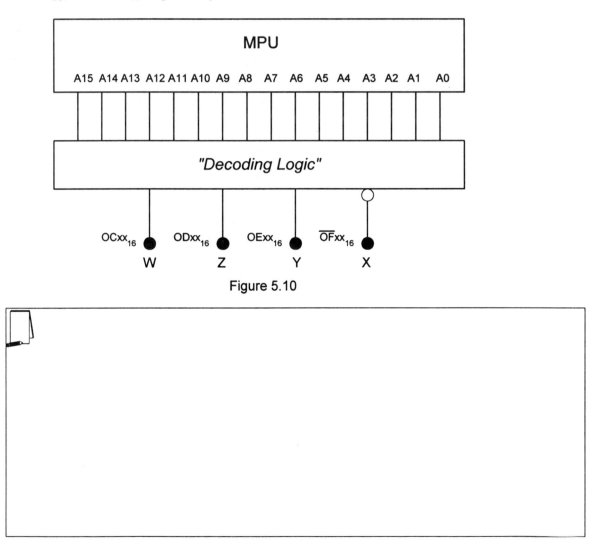

Figure 5.10

5.19 Describe the operational affects of an external open on the address bus line A9 of Figure 5.10. *Assume that the "Decoding Logic" circuitry is TTL.*

_____

_____

_____

_____

_____

SECTION 5.22 *One-Shot (Monostable Multivibrator)*

5.20 (a) State the major operational difference between a *Retriggerable* and a *Nonretriggerable* One-Shot.

_____

_____

_____

(b) Apply the waveforms of Figure 5.11 to both a *Retriggerable* and a *Nonretriggerable* One-Shot. If each OS is a positive-edge trigger device and each is set up for a pulse duration of 4.5ms determine the Q output for both types.

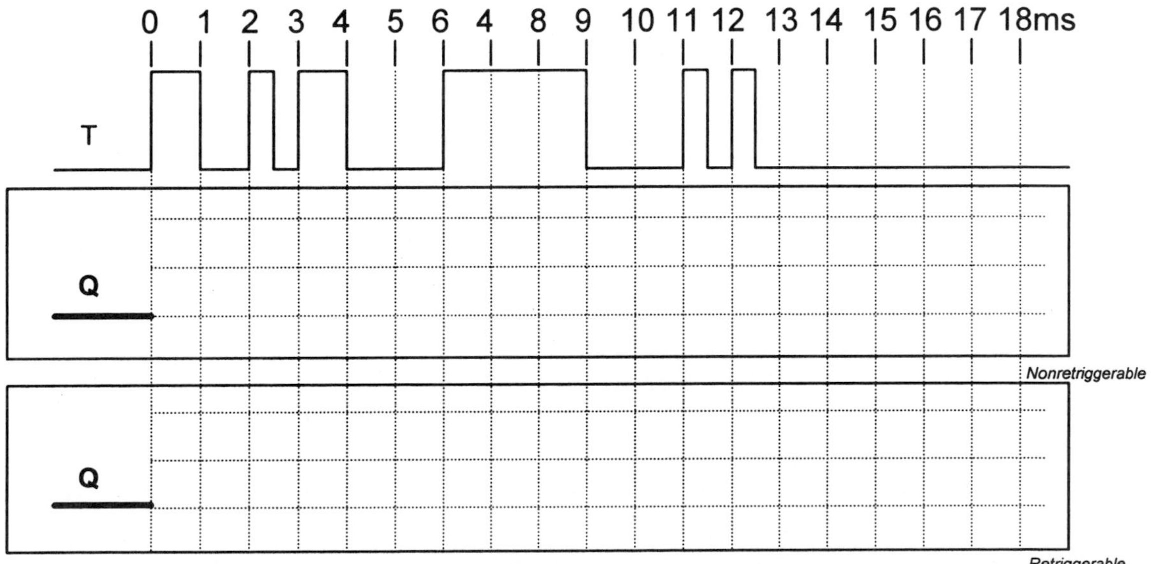

Figure 5.11

SECTION 5.25 *Troubleshooting flip-flop Circuits*

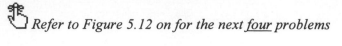 *Refer to Figure 5.12 on for the next four problems*

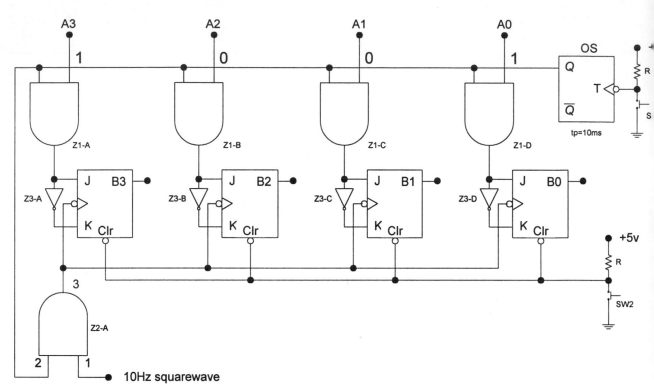

Figure 5.12

5.21 The TTL shift register circuit of Figure 5.12 was designed so that the parallel transfer of input data A_0-A_3 to outputs B_0-B_3 would occur upon actuation of switch SW1. When switch SW2 is momentarily depressed, the parallel register is cleared.

   (a)   What binary data will be present at outputs B_0 - B_3 after SW1 is depressed?

(b)   Why are the INVERTERs needed between the J and the K inputs of each flip-flop?

_____

_____

_____

5.22   During the testing of the circuit, the technician records the following results:

A_3	A_2	A_1	A_0	B_3	B_2	B_1	B_0	
1	0	0	1	0	0	0	0	← After SW2 is depressed.
1	0	0	1	1	0	0	1	← After SW1 is depressed.
1	1	0	0	1	0	0	1	← After #A_0-A_3 is changed.
1	1	0	0	0	1	0	0	← After SW1 is depressed.
1	1	0	0	1	1	0	0	← After SW1 is depressed again.
1	1	1	1	1	1	0	0	← After #A_0-A_3 is changed.
1	1	1	1	0	1	1	1	← After SW1 is depressed.
1	1	1	1	1	1	1	1	← After SW1 is depressed again.
1	1	1	1	0	0	0	0	← After SW2 is depressed.

Determine the cause for the malfunction observed in the recorded data.

_____

_____

_____

_____

_____

_____

5.23   After the technician repaired the problem that caused the malfunction observed in the previous question, he discovered that sometimes the binary number A_0 - A_3 doesn't get transferred to outputs B_0 - B_3.

(a)   Analyze the circuit design and offer a possible explanation as to the reason why data don't always get transferred.

Describe the necessary steps required for a data transfer to occur.

_____

_____

_____

_____

_____

_____

_____

_____

_____

_____

(b)   List two different ways of fixing the problem.

_____

_____

_____

_____

5.24   Once in a while, it appears that pressing SW1 has the same affect as pressing SW2, that is, the shift register gets cleared. At other times, what gets transferred to the output does not reflect the data at the inputs. Determine what is the most probable cause for the problem and how it can be fixed.

_____

_____

_____

_____

_____

_____

SECTION 5.26 *Applications Using Programmable Logic Devices*

5.25 Complete the following statements by filling in the blank:

    (a) The preprocessor command _____ allows a constant numeric value to be assigned a name at the top of the source file.

    (b) The word _____ tells the compiler that we are using the state transition mode of hardware description.

5.26 (a) Refer to the NAND latch of Figure 5.13 and write the CUPL equations for each output.

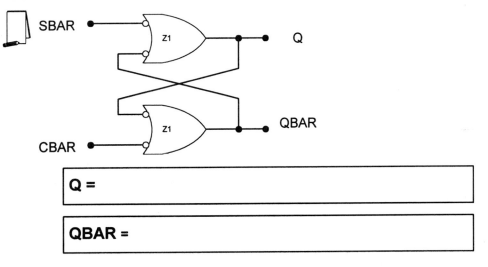

    Q =

    QBAR =

Figure 5.13

    (b) Redraw the latch of Figure 5.13 using the standard representation for NAND gates and write the new CUPL equations for each output.

    Q =

    QBAR =

5.27   Draw the circuit represented by following CUPL equations:
Q = (D & EN) # !QBAR;   QBAR = (!D & EN) # !Q;

5.28   A certain 4-bit counter (Q3 Q2 Q1 Q0) counts in the following sequence before it recycles: 0, 1, 2, 15, 5, 11, 3, 7, 12, 9. All of the other states, if they occur, should advance the counter to 8. Complete the following CUPL source file for the counter by filling in the blanks.

Sequence [Q3, Q2, Q1, Q0]

```
{                               0                    1
            present 'b'0000          next'b'0001
            present 'b'0001          0010
            present 'b'0010          next'b'1111
            present 'b'0011          0111
            present 'b'0100          next'b'1000
            present 'b'0101          next'b'1011
            present 'b'0110          1000
            present 'b'0111          _____
            present 'b'1000          next'b'1000
            present 'b'1001          _____
            present 'b'1010          next'b'1000
            present 'b'1011          _____
            present 'b'1100          next'b'1001
            present 'b'1101          _____
            present 'b'1110          next'b'1000
            present 'b'1111          _____
}
```

TEST 5

1. The two possible output states of a flip-flop, regardless of its type are:

    (a) Q=0 and the $\overline{Q}$ =0 (b) Q=0 and $\overline{Q}$ =1 (c) The Q=1 and $\overline{Q}$ =1 (d) The Q=1 and $\overline{Q}$ =0 (e) b and d.

2. If a D-type flip-flop is clocked with a 10KHz signal with a D.C. (duty-cycle) of 30%, and its $\overline{Q}$ output is tied to the D input, then the signal at the output Q is:

    (a) 10KHz, 30% D.C. (b) 10KHz, 50% D.C. (c) 5KHz, 30% D.C. (d) 5KHz, 50% D.C. (e) None of the above.

3. The major difference between a J-K flip-flop and any other type of flip-flop is that the J-K flip-flop has:

    (a) asynchronous inputs (b) a toggle mode (c) a t_H=0 (d) both synchronous and asynchronous inputs.

4. Which of the following require an external resistor and capacitor for proper operation?

    (a) Master slave J-K flip-flop.   (b) Schmitt-trigger.   (c) One-shot.   (d) NOR latch.

5. Which of the following flip-flop timing parameters indicate the time requirements of the synchronous inputs prior and after the clocking of the flip-flop?

    (a) t_s (b) t_{PHL} (c) $t_{W(L)}$ (d) t_H (e) a and d   (f) b and c

6. Which of the following are true about a MOD 32 counter?

    (a) It has a max. count of 32 (b) It has 31 states (c) Fout = Fin/31 (d) None of the above.

7. Determine the output frequency for a 4-bit serial binary counter with an input clock of 160KHz.

    (a) 40KHz (b) 10.66KHz (c) 20KHz (d) 10KHz (e) None of the above

8. Which of the following is true about a Retriggerable one-shot.

    (a) Its normal state is the Clear state. (b) Its quasi-stable state is the Set state. (c) It can be retriggered while it is in its quasi-stable state. (d) If it is triggered by a waveform that has a period (T) less than the one-shot's pulse duration (t_P), then the one-shot will always be in its quasi stable state. (e) All of the above.

9. How many shift pulses will be needed to serially shift the contents of a 4-bit shift register to another 4-bit shift register?

    (a) 1 (b) 2 (c) 4 (d) 8 (e) None of the above

10. What logic circuit does the CUPL equations *Q=!(C # QBAR)* and *QBAR=!(S # Q)* represent?
    (a) D flip-flop (b) NOR latch (c) NAND latch (d) D latch

6 DIGITAL ARITHMETIC: OPERATIONS AND CIRCUITS

Objectives

Upon completion of this chapter, you will be able to:

- Perform binary addition, subtraction, multiplication, and division on two binary numbers.

- Add and subtract hexadecimal numbers.

- Know the difference between binary addition and OR addition.

- Compare the advantages and disadvantages among three different systems of representing signed binary numbers.

- Manipulate signed binary numbers using the 2's-complement system.

- Understand the BCD adder circuit and the BCD addition process.

- Describe the basic operation of an arithmetic-logic unit.

- Employ full adders in the design of parallel binary adders.

- Cite the advantages of parallel adders with the look-ahead carry feature.

- Explain the operation of a parallel adder/subtractor circuit.

- Use an ALU integrated circuit to perform various logic and arithmetic operations on input data.

- Read and understand the IEEE/ANSI symbol for a parallel adder.

- Analyze several troubleshooting case studies of adder/subtractor circuits.

- Program a PLD to operate as a 4-bit full adder.

Glossary of key terms covered in this chapter:

- *1's-Complement Form* - The result obtained when each bit of a binary number is complemented. *[sec.6.2]*

- *2's-Complement Form* - The result obtained when a 1 is added to the least significant bit position of a binary number in the 1's-complement form. *[sec.6.2]*

- *2's-Complement System* - See 2's-complement form.

- *Accumulator Register* - The principal register of an Arithmetic Logic Unit. *[sec.6.9]*

- *Addend* - A number to be added to another. *[sec.6.3]*

- *Arithmetic Logic Unit (ALU)* - A digital circuit used in computers to perform various arithmetic and logic operations. *[sec.6.9/6.17]*

- *Augend* - The number to which an addend is added. *[sec.6.3]*

- *BCD Adder* - A special adder containing two 4-bit parallel adders and a correction detector circuit. Whenever the addition of two BCD code groups is greater than 1001_2 (9_{10}), the correction detector circuit senses it, adds to the result the correction factor 0110_2 (6_{10}) and generates a carry to the next decimal position. *[sec.6.16]*

- *Carry* - A digit or a bit that is generated when two numbers are added and the result is greater than that of the base for that number system. *[sec.6.1]*

- *Carry Propagation* - It is the intrinsic circuit delay of some parallel adders that prevents the Carry bit (C_{OUT}) and the result of the addition from appearing at the output simultaneously. *[sec.6.13]*

- *Carry Ripple* - See Carry Propagation. *[sec.6.13]*

- *Dividend* - The number to be divided. *[sec.6.6]*

- *Divisor* - The number by which a dividend is divided. *[sec.6.6]*

- *Full Adder* - Logic circuit with three inputs and two outputs. The inputs are a carry bit (C_{IN}) from a previous stage, a bit from the Augend, and a bit from the addend respectively. The outputs are the sum bit produced by the addition of the bit from the addend with the bit from the Augend and the resulted carry (C_{OUT}) bit which will be added to the next stage. *[sec.6.10]*

- *Half Adder* - Logic circuit with two inputs and two outputs. The inputs are a bit from the Augend, and a bit from the addend respectively. The outputs are the sum bit produced by the addition of the bit from the addend with the bit from the Augend and the resulted carry (C_{OUT}) bit which will be added to the next stage. *[sec.6.11]*

- *Look-Ahead Carry* - The ability of some parallel adders to predict, without having to wait for the carry to propagate through the Full Adders, whether or not a carry bit (C_{OUT}) will be generated as result of the addition, thus reducing the overall propagation delays. *[sec.6.13]*

- *Minuend* - The number from which the subtrahend is to be subtracted. *[sec.6.4]*

- *Negation* - The operation of converting a positive number to its negative equivalent or a negative number to its positive equivalent. *[sec.6.2]*

- *Arithmetic Overflow* - When in the process of adding two binary numbers a 1 is generated from the MSB position of the number into the sign bit position. *[sec.6.4/6.12]*

- *Parallel Adder* - A digital circuit made from full adders and used to add all the bits from the addend and the Augend together and simultaneously. *[sec.6.10]*

- *Set* - Name given to a group of several individual variable bits. *[sec.6.20]*

- *Sigma (Σ)* - A Greek letter which represents addition and is often used to label the Sum Output bits of a parallel adder. *[sec.6.14/6.18]*

- *Sign Bit* - A binary bit that is added to the leftmost position of a binary number to indicate whether that number represents a positive or a negative quantity. *[sec.6.2]*

- *Sign-Magnitude System* - Number system consisting of a sign-bit and the necessary magnitude bits. In this system the magnitude bits are the true binary equivalent of the decimal value being represented. *[sec.6.2]*

- *Subtrahend* - The number that is to be subtracted from a minuend. *[sec.6.4]*

Problems

SECTION 6.1 *Binary Addition*

6.1   Add the following groups of binary numbers using binary addition:

     (a) $110110_2 + 10010_2$ (b) $10101.001_2 + 1011_2$ (c) $11101_2 + 10000_2$

SECTION 6.2 *Representing Signed Numbers*

6.2   Using the 2's complement system, represent each of the following signed decimal numbers:

     (a) +14   (b) -32   (c) -8   (d) +55   (e) -355   (f) +123

SECTIONS 6.3-6.4 *Addition in the 2's-Complement System/Subtraction in the 2's-Complement System*

6.3 The following signed binary numbers are expressed in the 2's-complement system. Determine the equivalent decimal number for each of the binary numbers.

(a) 010110_2 (b) 110111_2 (c) 01110011_2 (d) 11000_2 (e) 111001_2

6.4 Perform the following operations using the 2's Complement system:

(a) [8+5] (b) [-12+15] (c) [+32-(-8)] (d) [9-13]

SECTIONS 6.5-6.6 *Multiplication of Binary Numbers/Binary Division*

6.5   Perform the following arithmetic operations using binary numbers:

(a) 23 x 5   (b) 12.5 x 2.25   (c) 64/8   (d) 217/11

SECTIONS 6.7-6.8 *BCD Addition/Hexadecimal Arithmetic*

6.6   Perform the following additions after converting each decimal number to its BCD code:

(a) 25+26   (b) 50+32   (c) 2357+1250   (d) 9+9

6.7   Add or subtract the following hexadecimal numbers:

(a) $75F_{16}+32D_{16}$ (b) $12A_{16}-FF_{16}$ (c) $7834_{16}+ABCD_{16}$

SECTIONS 6.9-6.15 *Arithmetic Circuits/Parallel Binary Adder/Complete Parallel Adder with Registers/ Integrated-Circuit Parallel Adder/2's Complement System*

6.8   When the contents of register $[A]_{(A0-A3)}$ and register $[B]_{(B0-B3)}$ of the 4-bit TTL parallel adder circuit of Figure 6.1 are added, the following results are obtained. Determine the cause for the circuit's malfunction.

A_3	A_2	A_1	A_0	B_3	B_2	B_1	B_0	C_4	S_3	S_2	S_1	S_0
1	1	0	1	0	1	1	0	1	0	0	1	1
1	0	0	0	0	1	1	1	1	0	1	1	1
0	1	0	0	0	1	0	1	0	1	0	0	1
0	0	1	1	0	1	0	0	0	1	1	1	1

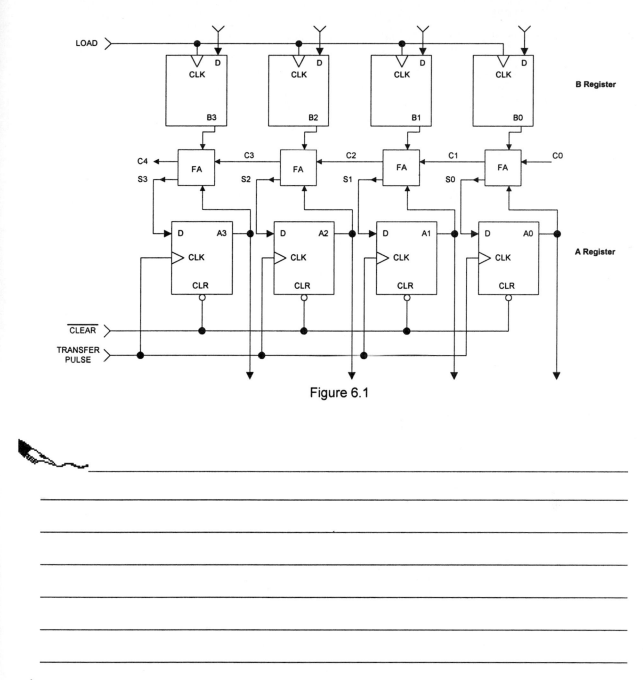

Figure 6.1

⊕ **6.9**   Refer to the 8-bit parallel adder/subtractor circuit of Figure 6.2 and complete the table below for each of the following set of conditions:

A7	A6	A5	A4	A3	A2	A1	A0	B7	B6	B5	B4	B3	B2	B1	B0	SW1	Outputs
0	1	1	0	0	1	1	1	1	0	0	0	1	0	1	1	GND	
1	1	0	0	0	0	0	1	1	0	1	0	0	0	1	0	+5V	
1	0	1	0	0	1	0	1	1	1	0	0	0	0	1	0	GND	
1	1	1	0	0	1	1	0	1	1	0	0	0	1	1	0	+5V	

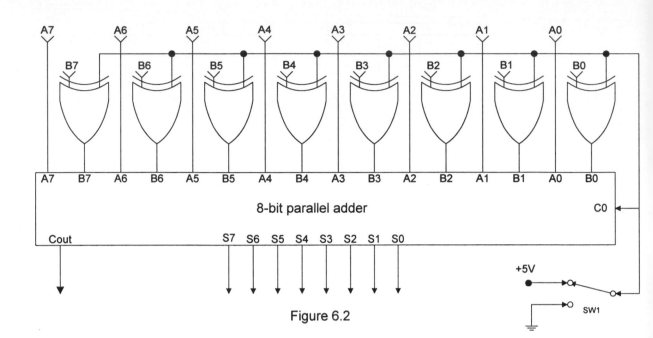

Figure 6.2

SECTION 6.16 *BCD Adder*

Refer to Figure 6.3 for all the problems in this section.

6.10 Complete the table below for each of the following conditions of the BCD circuit of Figure 6.3:

A_3	A_2	A_1	A_0	B_3	B_2	B_1	B_0	S_3	S_2	S_1	S_0	X	Σ_3	Σ_2	Σ_1	Σ_0
1	0	0	1	1	0	0	1									
1	0	0	0	0	0	1	1									
0	1	1	1	0	1	0	1									
0	1	1	0	0	0	1	1									

6.11   How would the results of the BCD sum be affected, if input C_0 of the 'Correction adder' circuit became stuck to Vcc?

_____

_____

_____

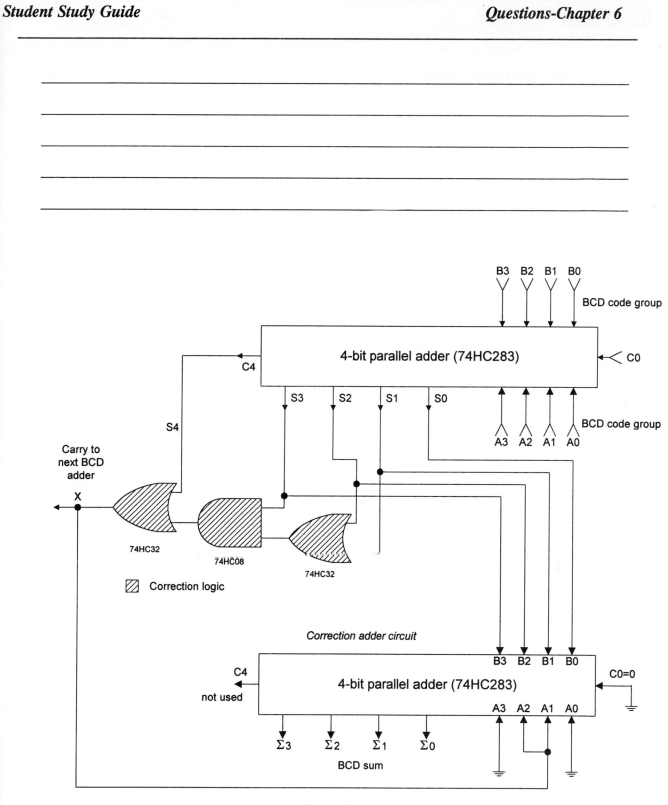

Figure 6.3

6.12   Redraw the *'Correction adder circuit'* of Figure 6.3 using only one Full-Adder and two Half-Adders.

6.13   The following table of results were obtained by a technician while testing the BCD adder circuit of Figure 6.3. Determine the cause for the malfunction.

B₃	B₂	B₁	B₀	A₃	A₂	A₁	A₀	X	BCD Sum
0	1	0	1	0	1	0	1	1	0 0 0 0
0	0	1	0	0	1	1	1	0	1 1 0 1
0	1	1	1	0	1	0	1	1	0 0 1 0
0	0	1	0	0	0	1	1	0	1 0 0 1
0	0	0	0	0	0	0	0	0	0 1 0 0

_____

_____

_____

_____

_____

_____

_____

SECTION 6.17 *ALU Integrated Circuits*

Refer to Figure 6.4 for all the problems in this section.

6.14 (a) Determine the 74HC382 ALU outputs $F_3F_2F_1F_0$ for the following inputs:
$A_3A_2A_1A_0 = 1100$, $B_3B_2B_1B_0 = 0101$, $S_2S_1S_0 = 010$, $C_N = 1$

(b) Repeat (a) for $S_2S_1S_0 = 101$

(c) Repeat (a) for $S_2S_1S_0 = 100$

6.15 What has to be done to the given conditions of Problem 6.14 if we want the *A plus B* operation to be performed?

_____

_____

_____

_____

_____

_____

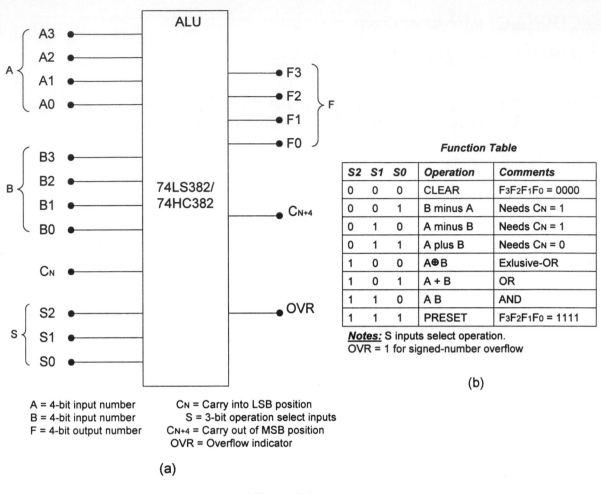

Figure 6.4

6.16   Using the Exclusive-OR operation ($S_2S_1S_0 = 100$) show how the 74HC382 can be wired to always produce [F] = [A].

6.17   Repeat Problem 6.15 for $[F] = [\overline{A}]$.

SECTION 6.18 *IEEE-ANSI Symbols*

6.18   Draw the IEEE/ANSI symbol for a four-bit parallel adder IC.

SECTION 6.20 *A PLD full adder*

6.19   (a)   In CUPL notation a _____ can be ,made up of several individual variable bits.

      (b)   The notation *pin [1..3] = [X0..2]* assigns pin 1 to _____, pin 2 to _____, and pin 3 to _____.

      (c)   In a CUPL source file, the $ symbol represents the _____ operation.

      (d)   *A3, A2, A1, A0* is an example of a group of _____ variables in CUPL notation.

6.20   (a)   Assume that A3, A2, A1, A0 has the value 1100 and B3, B2, B1, B0 has the value 0011. Let us define *Anum = [B3, B2, B1, B0]*, *Bnum = [A3, A2, A1, A0]*, and *Z = [Z3, Z2, Z1, Z0]*. If **Z = Anum \$ Bnum**, what is the value of Z after this operation?

      (b)   Repeat (a) if **Z = Anum & Bnum.**

      (c)   Repeat (a) if **Z = Anum # Bnum.**

TEST 6

1. How many bits are required to represent -150_{10}, as a signed binary number is the 2's-compl. form?

    (a) 10   (b) 9   (c) 8   (d) 7

2. What is the decimal value of the 2's-complement system signed binary number 11111111_2?

    (a) -127   (b) -255   (c) 255   (d) -1

3. When performing subtraction by addition in the 2's-complement system:

    (a)   Both the minuend and the subtrahend are changed to the 2's-complement form.
    (b)   The minuend is changed to the 2's-complement form and the subtrahend is left unchanged.
    (c)   Both the minuend and the subtrahend are left unchanged.
    (d)   The subtrahend is changed to the 2's-complement form and the minuend is left unchanged.

4. Which of the following represents the sum of $4CA5_{16}+FEA5_{16}$?

    (a) $15B4A_{16}$ (b) $2FB4A_{16}$ (c) $14B4A_{16}$ (d) $14B40_{16}$

5. Convert 255_{10} and 989_{10} to BCD and then add them together. Select the BCD final answer.

    (a) 0001 0010 0100 0100   (b) 0010 0100 0100   (c) 1011 1101 1110   (d) 1111 0010 0100 0100

6. The 74HC382 ALU is capable of:

    (a)   performing several different arithmetic operations on binary data inputs.
    (b)   performing several different arithmetic and logic operations on binary data inputs.
    (c)   performing several different logic operations on binary data inputs.
    (d)   None of the above

7. Which of the following represents the four possible conditions for the addition of two binary numbers?

    (a) 0+0=0, 1+0=1, 1+1=0+carry, 1+1+1=0+carry   (b) 0+0=0, 1+0=1, 1+1=1+carry, 1+1+1=1+carry
    (c) 0+0=0, 1+0=1, 1+1=0+carry, 1+1+1=1+carry   (d) 0+0=0, 1+0=1, 1+1=1+carry, 1+1+1=1+carry

8. The decimal equivalent of the signed binary number 11001011_2 is:

    (a) 203   (b) -53   (c) -203   (d) 52

9. Negation is the operation of converting a positive number to its negative equivalent.

    (a) [TRUE]   (b) [FALSE].

10. Assume that the sets A and B have been defined in a CUPL source file. If A = [1110] and B = [0001], determine the value for the set X for the CUPL expression X=!(A # B):

    (a) 1111 (b) 0000 (c) 1010 (d) 0101

7   COUNTERS AND REGISTERS

Objectives

Upon completion of this chapter, you will be able to:

- Understand the operation and characteristics of synchronous and asynchronous counters.

- Construct counters with MOD numbers less than 2^N.

- Identify IEEE/ANSI symbols used in IC counters and registers.

- Construct both up and down counters.

- Connect up multistage counters.

- Analyze and evaluate various types of presettable counters.

- Design arbitrary-sequence synchronous counters.

- Understand several types of schemes used to decode different types of counters.

- Anticipate and eliminate the effects of decoding glitches.

- Compare the major differences between the ring and Johnson counters.

- Analyze the operation of a frequency counter and of a digital clock.

- Recognize and understand the operation of various types of IC registers.

- Apply existing troubleshooting techniques used for combinational logic systems to troubleshoot sequential logic systems.

- Program a GAL16V8 to operate as a counter.

Glossary of key terms covered in this chapter:

- ⟶ - When used inside an IEEE/ANSI symbol, ⟶ in the label for an input indicates that when an active transition exists at that input a Shift-Right operation will result. *[sec. 7.23]*

- + - When used inside an IEEE/ANSI symbol and on a clock input, it indicates that the counter will be incremented by 1 when clocked. *[sec. 7.3/7.10]*

- "-" - When used inside an IEEE/ANSI symbol and on a clock input, it indicates that the counter will be decremented by 1 when clocked. *[sec. 7.3/7.10]*

- / - When used inside an IEEE/ANSI symbol, the slash (/) in the label for an input indicates the separation of two functions. *[sec. 7.23]*

- *Active-HIGH decoder* - A decoder which produces a logic HIGH at the output when detection occurs. *[sec. 7.11]*

- *Active-LOW decoder* - A decoder which produces a logic LOW at the output when detection occurs. *[sec. 7.11]*

- *&* - When used inside an IEEE/ANSI symbol, it indicates an AND gate or AND function. *[sec. 7.3]*

- *Asynchronous Counter* - Type of serial counter where the flip-flops do not change states in exact synchronism with the applied clock pulses. *[sec. 7.1]*

- *BCD Counter* - A binary counter that counts from 0000_2 to 1001_2 before it recycles. *[sec. 7.2]*

- *Bidirectional Universal Shift Register* - A shift register that can perform shift-left, shift-right, parallel in, and parallel out operations. *[sec. 7.22]*

- *Buffer Register* - A register that holds digital data temporarily. *[sec. 7.16]*

- *C* - When used inside an IEEE/ANSI symbol, the letter C in the label for an input indicates that, the input controls the entry of data into a storage element. *[sec. 7.10]*

- *C1* - When used inside an IEEE/ANSI symbol, the designation C1 in the label indicates that, this input controls the entry of data into any storage element that has the prefix 1 in its label. *[sec. 7.23]*

- *Circulating Shift Register* - A shift register where one of the outputs of the last Flip-Flop in the shift register is connected to the input of the first Flip-Flop in the shift register. *[sec. 7.15]*

- *CT=0* - When used inside an IEEE/ANSI symbol, CT=0 in the label for an input indicates that the counter will clear when that input goes active. *[sec. 7.3]*

- *CTR* - When used inside an IEEE/ANSI symbol, it indicates that the IC is a counter. *[sec. 7.3]*

- *D* - When used inside an IEEE/ANSI symbol, the letter D in the label indicates Data. *[sec. 7.10/7.23]*

- *Decade Counter* - Any counter which is capable of going through ten different logic states. *[sec. 7.2]*

- *DIVn* - When used inside an IEEE/ANSI symbol, it indicates that it is a MODn counter. *[sec. 7.3/7.10]*

- *Down Counter* - A counter that counts downward from a maximum count to zero. *[sec. 7.4]*

- *Equality Operator (:)* - Operator used in a CUPL file that checks for bit equality between an set of variables and a binary constant. *[sec. 7.25]*

- *Frequency Counter* - A circuit that can measure and display the frequency of a signal. *[sec. 7.16]*

- *G* - When used inside an IEEE/ANSI symbol, the letter G in the label for an input indicates AND dependency. *[sec. 7.10]*

- *Glitch* - Momentary narrow spurious and sharply defined change in voltage. *[sec. 7.2]*

- *Johnson Counter* - A shift register where the inverted output of the last Flip-Flop in the shift register is connected to the input of the first Flip-Flop in the shift register. *[sec. 7.15]*

- *LED* - Light Emitting Diode. *[sec. 7.11]*

- *Parallel Counter* - See Synchronous counter. *[sec. 7.6]*

- *Parallel In/Parallel Out Register* - A type of register that can be loaded with parallel data and has parallel outputs available. *[sec. 7.18/7.19]*

- *Parallel In/Serial Out* - A type of register that can be loaded with parallel data and has only one serial output. *[sec. 7.18/7.21]*

- *Presettable Counter* - A counter which can be preset to any starting count either synchronously or asynchronously. *[sec. 7.8]*

- *R* - When used inside an IEEE/ANSI symbol, the letter R in the label for an input indicates a Reset function. *[sec. 7.23]*

- *Ring Counter* - A shift register where the output of the last Flip-Flop in the shift register is connected to the input of the first Flip-Flop in the shift register. *[sec. 7.15]*

- *Ripple Counter* - One type of asynchronous counter. *[sec. 7.1]*

- *Sampling Interval* - The time window during which a frequency counter samples and thereby determines the unknown frequency of a signal. *[sec. 7.16]*

- *Sequential Logic Systems* - A logic system in which its logic outputs' states and sequence of operations depend on both the present and past input conditions. *[sec. 7.24]*

- *Serial In/Parallel Out* - A type of register that can be loaded with data serially and has parallel outputs available. *[sec. 7.18/7.22]*

- *Serial In/Serial Out* - A type of register that can be loaded with data serially and has only one serial output. *[sec. 7.18/7.20]*

- *Spike* - See Glitch. *[sec. 7.2]*

- *SRG 8* - When used inside an IEEE/ANSI symbol, SRG 8 in the common-control block indicates that this IC is an 8-bit shift register. *[sec. 7.23]*

- *State Transition Diagram* - Diagram that shows how flip-flops in a counter change states as input pulses are applied. *[sec. 7.2]*

- *Stepper Motor* - A motor which rotates in steps rather than in a continuous motion. *[sec. 7.14]*

- *Strobing* - A technique often used to eliminate decoders' spikes. *[sec. 7.12]*

- *Synchronous Counter* - A counter where all of its Flip-Flops are clocked simultaneously. *[sec. 7.6]*

- *Tristate Outputs* - A special type of logic circuit output that allows device outputs to be safely tied together. *[sec. 7.22]*

- *Twisted Ring Counter* - See Johnson Counter. *[sec. 7.15]*

- *Up Counter* - A counter that counts upward from zero to a maximum count. *[sec. 7.4]*

- *Variable Frequency-Divider* - A presettable counter that can be easily wired for different MOD numbers without the need for additional logic circuitry. *[sec. 7.9]*

Problems

PART I

SECTION 7.1 *Asynchronous (Ripple) Counters*

7.1   Figure 7.1 is a four-bit asynchronous counter circuit. The table below pertains to similar asynchronous counters. Complete the table by filling in the blanked spaces.

All J and K inputs are tied HIGH

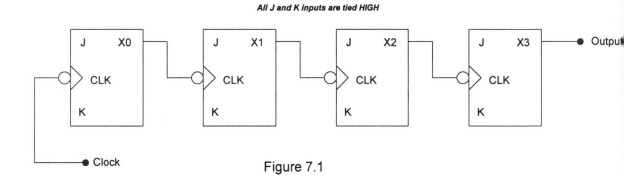

Figure 7.1

MOD-#	Clock Frequency	Output Frequency	# of JK flip-flops
16	256 KHz	4 KHz	
32	350 KHz		
		100 KHz	3
	500 KHz		7

SECTIONS 7.2,7.3,7.24   *Counters With MOD Numbers < 2^N/IC Asynchronous Counters/Troubleshooting.*

7.2   For each of the following modifications in the MOD-14 Ripple Counter of Figure 7.2, determine the new MOD number:

(a) The inputs to gate Z1 are A, B, C.   [MOD number is _7_]
(b) The inputs to gate Z1 are A, C, D.   [MOD number is _13_]
(c) The inputs to gate Z1 are A, B, +Vcc.   [MOD number is _16_]

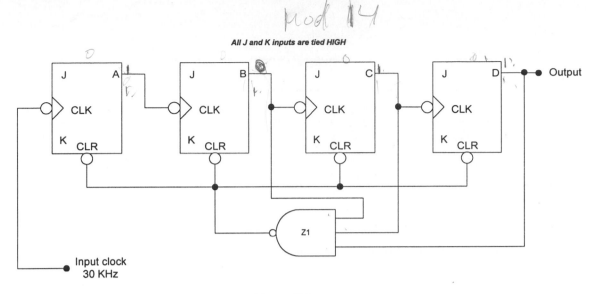

Figure 7.2

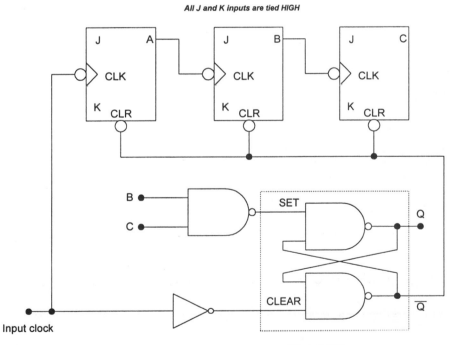

7.3 The 3-bit asynchronous counter of Figure 7.3 is tested and the technician determines that it is working as a MOD-8 counter (000_2-111_2). Find two different possible faults for the malfunction.

Figure 7.3

1._____

_____

_____

_____

_____

2._____

_____

_____

_____

_____

7.4 A technician wires and tests the 8-bit binary counter of Figure 7.4. When its output X is displayed on the oscilloscope, the technician finds that it is a 54Hz squarewave. Determine the most probable cause for the malfunction.

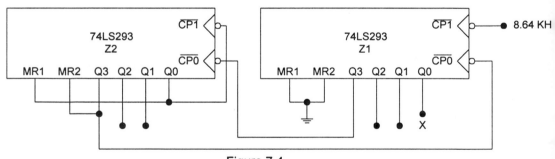

Figure 7.4

_____

_____

_____

_____

SECTIONS 7.5, 7.24 *Propagation Delay in Ripple Counters/Troubleshooting*

7.5 If the counter of Figure 7.5 holds count 7 (111_2) and the clock input goes through a negative-going transition, how long will it take for FF C to change states?

 (See TTL Data Manual or CD-ROM for 74LS112 timing specifications)

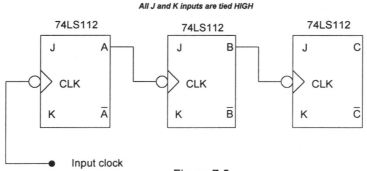

Figure 7.5

7.6 The circuit of Figure 7.5 is built and tested. As the technician applies clock pulses, he notices that the counter goes through the following binary counting sequence: 000_2, 001_2, 110_2, 111_2, 100_2, 101_2, 010_2, 011_2, 000_2 ... (repeats). Why do you think the counter behaves this way?

_____

_____

_____

_____

_____

_____

SECTIONS 7.6-7.9,7.24   *Synchronous (Parallel) Counters/Synchronous Down and Up/Down Counters Presettable Counters/The 74ALS193/HC193 Counter/Troubleshooting.*

7.7   State the major *advantages* and *disadvantages* between synchronous and asynchronous counters.

<u>*Asynchronous Counter:*</u>

Advantage- _____

_____

_____

_____

Disadvantage- _____

_____

_____

_____

_____

<u>*Synchronous Counter:*</u>

Advantage- _____

_____

_____

Disadvantage- _____

_____

_____

7.8   Complete the timing diagram for a SN74HC193 counter so that it goes through the <u>sequence</u> listed below.

        (See TTL Data Manual or CD-ROM for 74HC193 timing specifications)

        1.   Clear the counter.
        2.   Load the counter with binary fourteen.
        3.   Count up by four counts.
        4.   Count down by three counts.

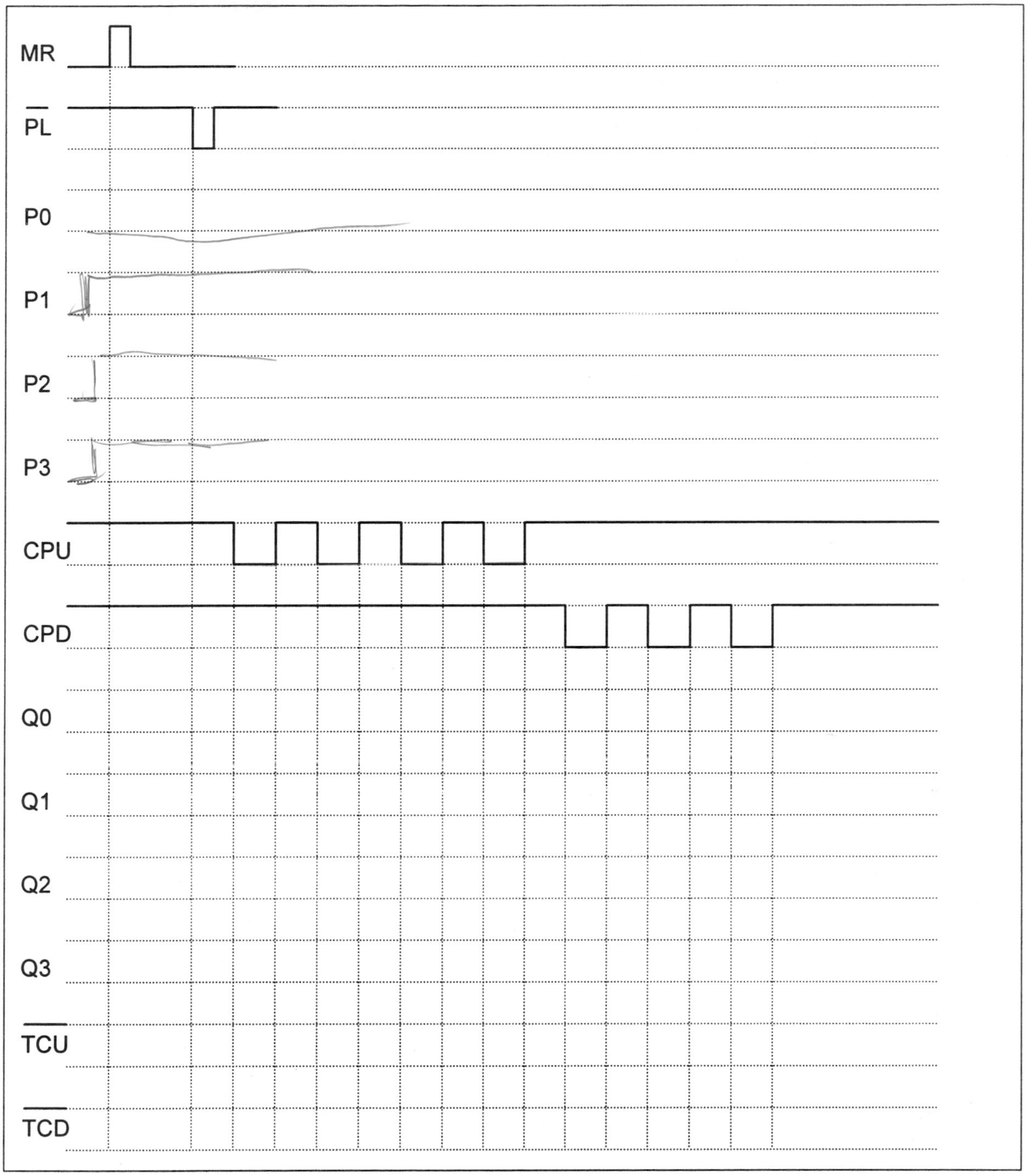
MR
$\overline{PL}$
P0
P1
P2
P3
CPU
CPD
Q0
Q1
Q2
Q3
$\overline{TCU}$
$\overline{TCD}$

7.9   Design an UP/DOWN counter that operates according to the following set of specifications:

1. SN74ALS193s are to be used in its design.
2. The counter is a MOD-256 when counting UP.
3. The counter is a MOD-34 when counting DOWN.
4. A switch (SW1) controls whether the counter counts UP or DOWN.
5. A maximum of three external gates can be used in the design of this counter.

7.10   While testing the counter built for problem 7.9, the technician applies a 10KHz signal to the input of the counter and notices that the frequency at the MSB of the counter is around 39Hz regardless of the position of SW1. Determine three possible causes for the malfunction.

1._____

2._____

3._____

SECTION 7.10 *More on the IEEE/ANSI Dependency Notation*

7.11   Refer to the IEEE/ANSI symbol of Figure 7.6 and answer the following questions:

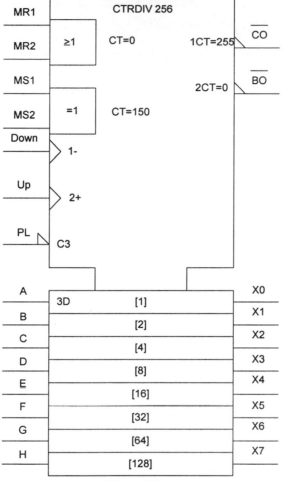

Figure 7.6

(a)   What is the maximum count that this counter can reach?

_____

(b)   What happens when MS1=MS2=1?

_____

(c)   What happens when MR1=1?

_____

(d)   What does '3D' mean at input A?

_____

(e)   What happens at count 255?

_____

(f)   What must be done to clear this counter?

_____

(g)   What does it mean when output $\overline{BO}$ =0?

_____

(h)   What would have to be changed in this IEEE/ANSI symbol, if MR1=MR2=1 was needed to clear the counter?

_____

(i)   What does the '+' symbol at the *Up* input mean?

_____

SECTIONS 7.11-7.13, 7.24   *Decoding a Counter/Decoding Glitches/Cascading BCD Counters/ Troubleshooting*

7.12   The inputs to the circuit of Figure 7.7 come from the ripple counter of Figure 7.5. The clock input frequency for this counter is a 1MHz squarewave. Output Q of flip-flop Z2 is to be Set whenever the binary count of zero (000_2) is decoded and cleared whenever the binary count of three (011_2) is decoded.

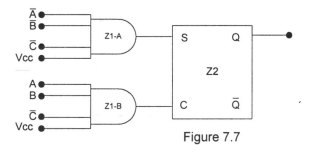

Figure 7.7

(a) Draw the expected Q waveform, keeping in mind the effects of propagation delays of the flip-flops of figure 7.5. (Assume that initially: Q=1 and the counter of figure 7.5 is clear).

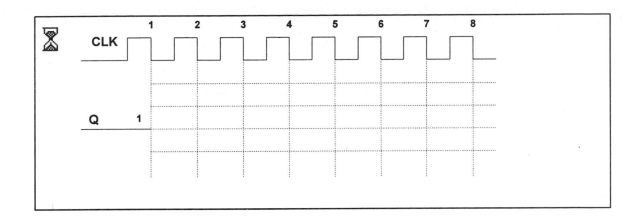

(b)   Modified the circuit of Figure 7.7 so that it operates as intended. (*Hint*: Add a One-Shot to strobe gates Z1-A and Z1-B)

7.13   A technician builds the circuit of Figure 7.8 (a). She tests the circuit and records the results shown in table of Figure 7.8 (b). Find the cause for the circuit's malfunction.

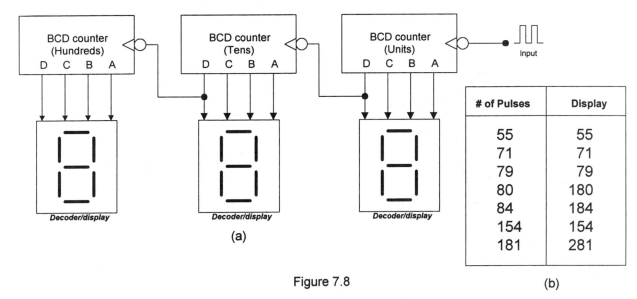

# of Pulses	Display
55	55
71	71
79	79
80	180
84	184
154	154
181	281

(a)

Figure 7.8

(b)

SECTION 7.14 *Synchronous Counter Design*

7.14 (a) Design a synchronous counter that has the following counting sequence: 001_2, 010_2, 110_2, 111_2 and then repeats. The undesired (unused) states are: 000_2, 011_2, 100_2, 101_2. The counter must always go to 001_2 on the NEXT clock pulse after an undesired state.

To design the synchronous counter perform each of the following steps:

Step 1:   Determine the desired number of bits and the desired counting sequence.

Step 2:   Draw the state transition diagram showing all possible states, including those that are not part of the desired counting sequence.

<u>*Step 1*</u>   <u>*Step 2*</u>

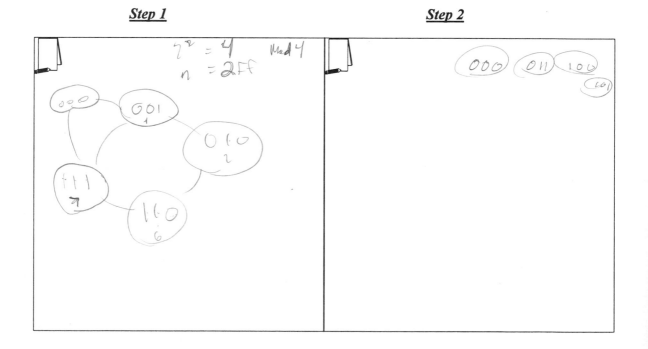

Step 3: Use the state transition diagram to set up a table that lists all present states and their next
states.

Step 4: Add a column to this table for each J and K input. For each present state, indicate the levels
required at each J and K input in order to produce the transition to the next state.

Step 5: Design the logic circuits to generate the levels required at each J and K input.

Step 6:　　Implement the final expression.

(b)   Using the procedure described in problem 7.14 (a), redesign the counter without any requirement on the unused states; that is, their NEXT states can be "don't care" states.

Step 1:   Determine the desired number of bits and the desired counting sequence.

Step 2:   Draw the state transition diagram showing all possible states, including those that are not part of the desired counting sequence.

<u>*Step 1*</u>   <u>*Step 2*</u>

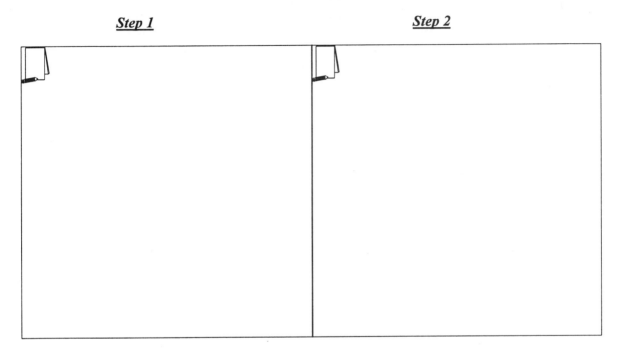

Step 3: Use the state transition diagram to set up a table that lists all present states and their next states.

Step 4: Add a column to this table for each J and K input. For each present state, indicate the levels required at each J and K input in order to produce the transition to the next state.

Step 5: Design the logic circuits to generate the levels required at each J and K input.

Step 6:   Implement the final expression.

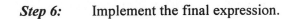

SECTIONS 7.15 *Shift-Register Counters*

7.15   The waveforms of Figure 7.9 represent the input clock and the output signal Q_0 of a Ring counter. How many flip-flops are being used by the Ring counter?

_____

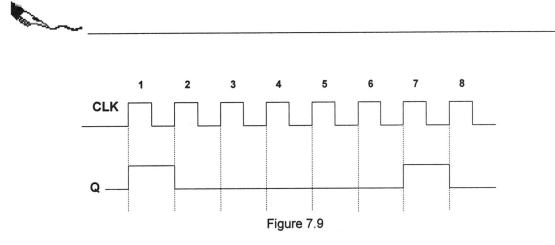

Figure 7.9

7.16   Complete each of the following statements:

(a)   To build a MOD- _____ Ring Counter, it requires 23 Flip-Flops.

(b)   To decode any state of a MOD-14 Johnson Counter, it requires a _____ input AND gate.

(c)   If the frequency of the input clock of a 6-bit Johnson Counter is _____ KHz, then the output signal at any of the flip-flops in the counter is equal to 5KHz, _____ Duty Cycle.

PART II

SECTIONS 7.16, 7.17, 7.24   *Counter Applications: Frequency Counter and Digital Clock/Troubleshooting*

7.17   When the frequency counter circuit of Figure 7.10 was tested, it showed that regardless of width (t_p) of the SAMPLE pulses, the Decoder/Display always displayed a number which was twice as large as the actual input frequency. What could have caused the malfunction?

_____

_____

_____

_____

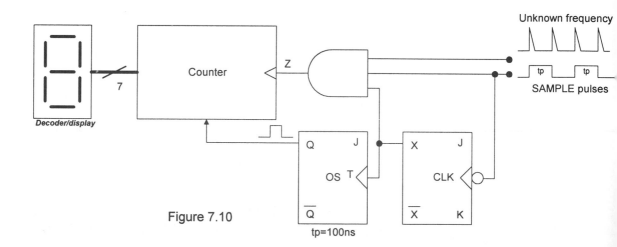

Figure 7.10

7.18   The hours section circuit of a digital clock (figure 7.11) is built and tested. After observing the clock's operation for a couple of hours, it is noticed that the minute's section works properly but the hours section of the clock changes back and forth between 11:00 and 12:00 with each "Pulse/Hour"pulse. Determine the cause for the malfunction.

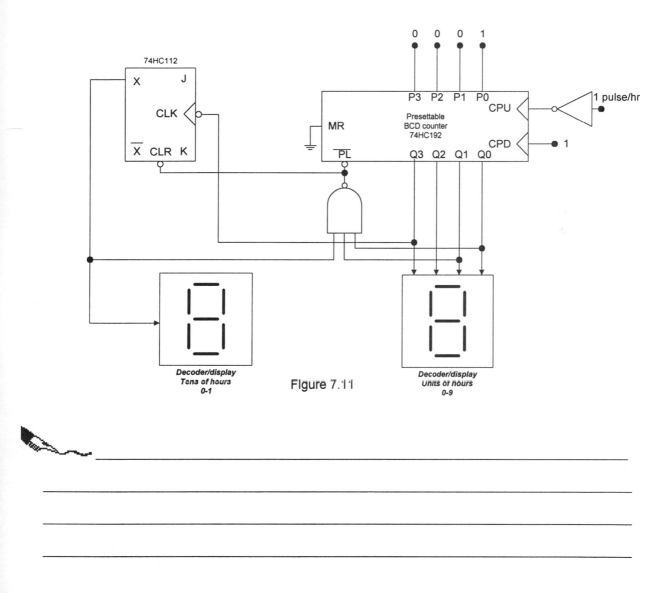

Figure 7.11

_____

_____

_____

_____

SECTIONS 7.20, 7.21, 7.24   *Serial In/Serial Out - The 4731B*
                                   Parallel In/Serial Out - The 74ALS165/74HC165/Troubleshooting.

7.19   Design a MOD-512 Johnson counter using a 4731B IC and any additional logic circuitry needed.

7.20   Refer to the parallel in/serial out 8-bit register 74HC165 (Figure 7.12) and the associated waveforms. Complete the timing diagram by drawing the output waveform Q7. (Assume that Q7=0 initially.)

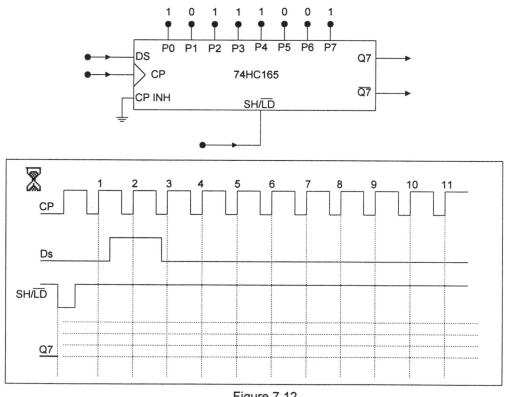

Figure 7.12

SECTION 7.23 *IEEE-ANSI Register Symbols.*

7.21 Describe in detail the function of each of the 5 arrowhead blocks in the IEEE/ANSI symbol of Figure 7.13.

1. _____

2. _____

3. _____

4. _____

5. _____

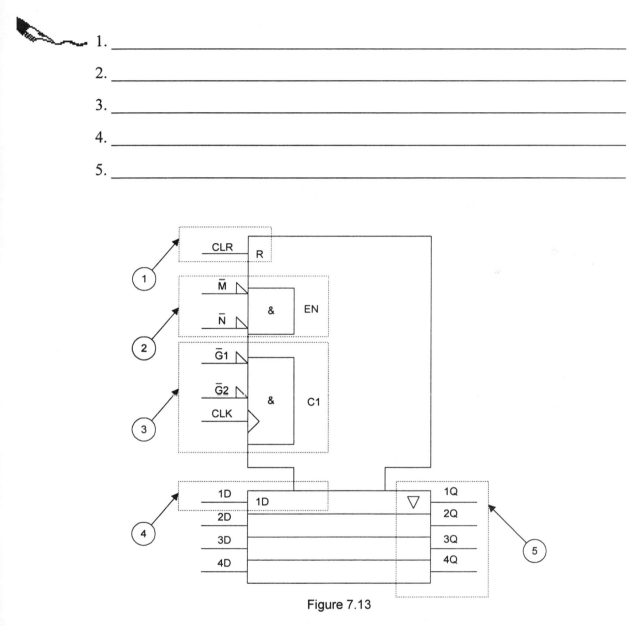

Figure 7.13

SECTION 7.25 *Programming PLDs as Counters Using Boolean Equations*

7.22 (a) Design a 3-bit MOD-8 serial counter using a GAL16V8. The counter should count in the following sequence: 5, 4, 2, 1, 0, 3, 6, 7, repeats

Step 1: Draw the Present State, Next State table.

Step 2: Write the unsimplified SOP expressions for each D input in terms of the present states of the flip-flops:

Q2.D = _____

Q1.D = _____

Q0.D = _____

(b) Write the CUPL file to create the counter described in step (a) using the *Equality Operator*.

TEST 7

1. How many Flip-Flops are needed to make a MOD-64 ripple counter?

    (a) 4   (b) 5   (c) 6   (d) 7

2. An asynchronous counter has an input clock frequency of 256KHz and an output frequency of 64KHz. What is the MOD number of this counter?

    (a) 4   (b) 25   (c) 3   (d) 2

3. What would the dependency notation CTRDIV 256 mean on a IEEE/ANSI counter symbol?

    (a) It indicates a counter that divides the input frequency by 256.   (b) It indicates a MOD-256 counter.
    (c) It indicates a counter with a F_{max} of 256KHz.   (d) (a) and (b).

4. Synchronous counters eliminate the delay problems found with asynchronous counters because the:

    (a)   Individual Flip-Flops used in this type of counter are much faster than those used by asynchronous counters.
    (b)   Input pulses are applied simultaneously to each Flip-Flop.
    (c)   Input pulses are applied simultaneously to both the least and the most significant Flip-Flops.
    (d)   Input pulses are applied only to the least significant Flip-Flop of the counter.

5. How many BCD counters are needed to provide a decimal count of 9,999?

    (a) 4   (b) 14   (c) 2^4 (d) 5

6. A ten bit Ring counter is clocked with a 200KHz. The output frequency is:

    (a) 195.5Hz   (b) 195.3Hz   (c) 20KHz   (d) 10KHz

7. A ten bit Johnson counter is clocked with a 200KHz. The output frequency is:

    (a) 195.5Hz   (b) 195.3Hz   (c) 20KHz   (d) 10KHz

8. A MOD-16 asynchronous counter uses Flip-Flops that have "worst case" propagation delay of $t_{PHL}=15ns$. The maximum input frequency for this counter is:

    (a) 4.1MHz   (b) 16.6MHz   (c) 66.6MHz   (d) 22.2MHz

9. A line in the CUPL file for a certain MOD-8 counter using field directive and equality operator shows *b' 110 & twisted: 3.* What does it cause to happen?

    (a) twisted.D=110 whenever the present state of twisted is 011 (3)
    (b) twisted.D=011 whenever the present state of twisted is 110 (6)
    (c) twisted.D=111 whenever the present state of twisted is 111 (7)
    (d) None of the above

10. The + sign on a counter symbol by the $\overline{CP}$ indicates a count-down operation.   (a) [TRUE]   (b) [FALSE]

8   INTEGRATED-CIRCUIT LOGIC FAMILIES

Objectives

Upon completion of this chapter, you will be able to:

• Read and understand digital IC technology as specified in manufacturers' data sheets.

• Compare the characteristics of standard TTL and the various TTL series.

• Determine the fan-out for a particular logic device.

• Use logic devices with open-collector outputs.

• Analyze circuits containing tristate devices.

• Compare the characteristics of the various CMOS series.

• Analyze circuits that use a CMOS bilateral switch to allow a digital system to control analog signals.

• Describe the major characteristics and differences among TTL, ECL, MOS, and CMOS logic families.

• Cite and implement the various considerations that are required when interfacing digital circuits from different logic families.

• Use voltage comparators to allow a digital system to be controlled by analog signals.

• Use a logic pulser and a current tracer as digital circuit troubleshooting tools.

Glossary of key terms covered in this chapter:

- ***4000/1400 Series*** - This is the oldest CMOS series. These devices have very low power dissipation and can operate over a wide range of power-supply voltages (3 to 15V). They have very low output current capabilities and are very slow when compared to TTL and other CMOS series. *[sec.8.10]*

- ***74AC/ACT (Advanced CMOS)*** - This series is functionally equivalent to the various TTL series but is not pin-comparable with TTL. ACT offers advantages over the HC series in noise immunity, propagation delay, and maximum clock speed. *[sec.8.10]*

- ***74AHC/AHCT (Advanced High speed CMOS)*** - This newest series of CMOS devices can be used as direct replacements for HC series devices. The AHC series is three times faster and can be used as direct replacements for HC series devices. *[sec.8.10]*

- ***74ALB (Advanced Low-Voltage BiCMOS)*** - This series has been designed for 3.3V bus interface applications. *[sec.8.11]*

- ***74ALVC (Advanced Low Voltage CMOS)*** - This series is intended for bus interface applications that use 3.3V logic only. *[sec.8.11]*
- ***74AVC (Advanced Very-Low-Voltage CMOS)*** - This series has been introduced with 2.5 volt systems in mind. It can operate on supplies as low as 1.2 volts or as high as 3.3 volts. *[sec.8.11]*

- ***74ALVT (Advanced Low-Voltage BiCMOS Technology)*** - This series is an improvement over the LVT series. Like the LVT series, the ALVT series is also intended for bus-interface applications and is pin compatible with existing ABT and LVT series. *[sec.8.11]*

- ***74C Series*** - This CMOS series is pin compatible and functionally equivalent with TTL devices having the same number. For example, the 74C74 is equivalent to the TTL 7474. The performance characteristics of the 74C series are about the same as the 4000 series. *[sec.8.10]*

- ***74HC/HCT (High-Speed CMOS)*** - This is an improved version of the 74C series, which has a tenfold increase in switching speed, comparable to the 74LS devices, and a much higher output current capability than the 74C series. *[sec.8.10]*

- ***74LVC (Low Voltage CMOS)*** - This series operates from a nominal power supply voltage of 3.3V instead of the current 5V standard. However, this series can handle 5V logic levels on its inputs and is capable of driving 3V systems with its outputs, provided the current drive is kept low enough. *[sec.8.11]*

- ***74LVT (Low Voltage BiCMOS Technology)*** - This series contains CMOS parts that are intended for 8- and 16-bit bus-interface applications. *[sec.8.11]*

- ***ABT*** - See Advanced BiCMOS Technology. *[sec.8.10]*

- ***Advanced BiCMOS Technology (ABT)*** - This is the second generation of BiCMOS bus-interface devices. *[sec.8.10]*

- *Low-Power Schottky TTL (LS-TTL)* - A TTL subfamily which uses the identical Schottky TTL circui except that uses larger resistor values. *[sec.8.4]*

- *LVT* - See Low-Voltage Technology. *[sec.8.11]*

- *Low-Voltage Technology (LVT)* - A new technology that uses a nominal 3.3V as its operating powe supply voltage in order to increase the overall chip density, increase the circuit's operating speed, an decrease the power dissipation. *[sec.8.11]*

- *LS-TTL* - See Low-Power Schottky TTL. *[sec.8.4]*

- *MOS* - Metal-Oxide-Semiconductor. *[sec.8.7]*

- *MOSFET* - Metal-Oxide-Semiconductor-Field-Effect-Transistor. *[sec.8.7]*

- *Multiple-Emitter Transistor* - The type of input transistor used in the design of TTL AND and NAN gates. *[sec.8.2]*

- *Noise Immunity* - A circuit's ability to tolerate noise without causing spurious changes in the outp voltage. *[sec.8.1]*

- *Noise Margin* - A quantitative measure of Noise Immunity. *[sec.8.1]*

- *Open-Collector Buffer* - See Buffer/Drivers. *[sec.8.12]*
- *Open-Collector Output* - A type of output structure of some TTL circuits in which only one transist with a floating collector is used. *[sec.8.12]*

- *Open-Drain Buffer* - See Buffer/Drivers. *[sec.8.12]*

- *Open-Drain Output* - See Open-Collector Output. *[sec.8.12]*

- *PLCC* - Plastic Leaded Chip Carrier. *[sec.8.1]*

- *Power-Supply Decoupling* - When a small RF capacitor is connected between Ground and Vcc near ea TTL IC on a circuit board. *[sec.8.6]*

- *Propagation Delays* - Delay encounter by a signal as it goes through a circuit. There are two types propagation delays as far as logic circuits are concerned: t_{PLH} (delay time in going from logical LOW a logical HIGH state) and t_{PHL} (delay time in going from logical HIGH to a logical LOW state). *[sec.8.1]*

- *Pull-Down Transistor* - See Current-Sinking Transistor. *[sec.8.2]*

- *Pull-Up Transistor* - See Current-Sourcing Transistor. *[sec.8.2]*

- *QFT* - Quad Flat Pack. *[sec.8.1]*

- *SBD* - Schottky Barrier Diode. *[sec.8.4]*

- *Schottky TTL* - A TTL subfamily that employs the same basic TTL standard logic circuit with the exception that it uses a Schottky barrier diode (SBD) connected between the base and collector of each transistor. *[sec.8.4]*

- *SOIC* - Small Outline Integrated Circuit. *[sec.8.1]*

- *Speed-Power product* - A numerical value (in Joules) often used to compare different logic families. It is obtained by multiplying the propagation delay by the power dissipation of a logic circuit. *[sec.8.1]*

- *SSOP* - Shrink Small Outline Package. *[sec.8.1]*

- *Static Sensitivity* - See Electrostatic discharge (ESD). *[sec.8.10]*

- *Surface-mount technology* - A method of manufacturing circuit boards whereby ICs are soldered to conductive pads on the surface of the board. *[sec.8.1]*

- *Totem-Pole Output* - A term used to describe the way in which two bipolar transistors are arranged at the output of most TTL circuits. *[sec.8.2]*

- *TQFP* - Thin Quad Flat Pack. *[sec.8.1]*

- *Transmission Gate* - Same as Bilateral Switch. *[sec.8.16]*

- *Tristate Buffer* - A circuit that is used to control the passage of a logic signal from input to output. *[sec.8.13]*

- *Tristate Logic Outputs* - A type of output structure which allows three types of output states - HIGH, LOW, and High-Impedance (Hi-Z). *[sec.13]*

- *TSSOP* - Thin Shrink Small Outline Package. *[sec.8.1]*

- *TVSOP* - Thin Very Small Outline Package. *[sec.8.1]*

- *Voltage Level-Translator* - Circuit that takes a low-voltage input and translates it to a high-voltage output. *[sec.8.18/8.19]*

- *Wired-AND Connection* - Term used to describe the logic function created when Open-Collector outputs are tied together. *[sec.8.12]*

Problems

SECTIONS 8.1-8.3   *Digital IC Terminology/The TTL Logic Family/TTL Data Sheets*

8.1   Complete each of the following definitions:

(a) V_{OL} , stands for the voltage level at the output of a TTL logic circuit in the LOW state.

(b) I_{IL}, stands for the current that flows ___In___ a TTL input when a specified low-level voltage is applied to that input.

(c) t_{PLH} , stands for the delay time from a logic 0 to a logic 1.

(d)   _Fan__ _Out_ stands for the maximum number of logic inputs that an output can reliably drive.

(e)   PGA stands for: _____ _____ _____

(f)   BGA stands for: _____ _____ _____

(g)   Transistor Q4 on the output of a standard TTL gate is often referred to as the current- _sinking_ transistor.

(h)   Transistor Q3 on the output of a standard TTL gate is often referred to as the current- _sourcing_ transistor.

(i)   The NOR TTL circuit does not use a _multiple_ - _emitter_ transistor.

8.2

Table 8.1

	74	74S	74LS	74AS	74ALS	74F	Units
$V_{CC(max)}$	5.25	5.25	5.25	5.5	5.5	5.5	V
$V_{OL(max)}$	0.4	0.5	0.5	0.5	0.5	0.5	V
$V_{OH(min)}$	2.4	2.7	2.7	2.5	2.5	2.5	V
$V_{IL(max)}$	0.8	0.8	0.8	0.8	0.8	0.8	V
$V_{IH(min)}$	2.0	2.0	2.0	2.0	2.0	2.0	V
$t_{PLH(max)}$	22	4.5	15	4.5	11	6	ns
$t_{PHL(max)}$	15	5.0	15	4.0	8	5.3	ns
$I_{CCH(max)}$	8	16	1.6	3.2	0.85	2.8	mA
$I_{CCL(max)}$	22	36	4.4	17.4	3	10.2	mA

Using the **74AS** IC values in table 8.1 above determine the following:

(a) worst-case dc noise.

(b) the maximum propagation delay.

(c) the maximum power dissipation for the IC.

SECTIONS 8.4-8.6 *TTL series Characteristics /TTL Loading and Fan-Out/Other TTL Characteristics.*

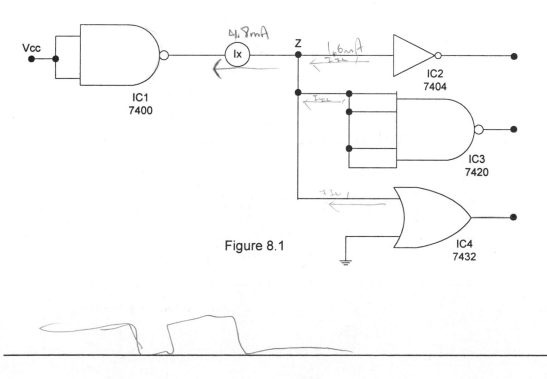

Figure 8.1

Table 8.2

TTL Series	Outputs		Inputs	
	$I_{OH(max)}$	$I_{OL(max)}$	$I_{IH(max)}$	$I_{IL(max)}$
74	-0.4 mA	16 mA	40 μA	1.6 mA
74S	-1 mA	20 mA	50 μA	2 mA
74LS	-0.4 mA	8 mA	20 μA	0.4 mA
74AS	-2 mA	20 mA	20 μA	0.5 mA
74ALS	-0.4 mA	8 mA	20 μA	0.1 mA
74F	-1 mA	20 mA	20 μA	0.6 mA
4000B	-0.4 mA	0.4 mA	1 μA	1 μA
74HC/HCT	-4 mA	4 mA	1 μA	1 μA
74AC/ACT	-24 mA	24mA	1 μA	1 μA
74AHC/AHCT	-8 mA	8 mA	1 μA	1 μA

*Refer to Figure 8.1 and table 8.2. Assume that **all** of the ICs in the circuit of Figure 8.1 are of the **74** logic family.*

8.3

(a)   Calculate the value and direction of current Ix.

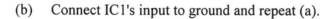

(b)   Connect IC1's input to ground and repeat (a).

(c)   Change IC1 to a **74HCT04** and repeat (a). Would this situation cause any problems with the circuit's operation?

8.4 In the circuit of Figure 8.1, determine the total amount of current that the output of IC1 must sink and supply if all of the ICs are of the *74ALS* logic family.

8.5 How does the *74F* series compare with the *74LS* series' dc noise margins?

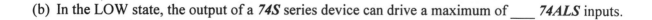

8.6 Refer to Table 8.2 and fill-in the blanks (*number of inputs*) in the following statements.

(a) In the HIGH state, the output of a *74* series device can drive a maximum of ____ *74F* inputs.

(b) In the LOW state, the output of a *74S* series device can drive a maximum of ____ *74ALS* inputs.

(c) In the LOW state, the output of a *74F* series device can drive a maximum of ____ *74LS* inputs.

(d) The output of a *74AS* series device can drive ____ *74ALS* inputs without exceeding its fan out.

(e) In the LOW state, the output of a *74ALS* series device can drive a maximum of ____ *74* inputs.

(f) In the LOW state, the output of a *74ALS* series device can drive a maximum of ____ *74S* inputs.

(g) The output of a *74ALS* series device can drive ____ *74HC* inputs without exceeding its fan out.

(h) The output of a *74HC* series device can drive ____ *74ALS* inputs without exceeding its fan out.

SECTIONS 8.7-8.10   *MOS Technology/Digital MOSFET Circuits/Complementary MOS Logic/ CMOS Series Characteristics*

8.7 Complete the following statements by filling the blanks:

(a) _____ logic uses bipolar transistors, while CMOS uses _____ _____ transistors.

(b) In a circuit that utilizes _____ logic, the power dissipation is directly proportional to the operating frequency.

(c) CMOS should be chosen over _____, if the main consideration is packing density.

(d) Among all the MOSFET circuits, _____-_____ has the lowest packing density.

(e) The usage of negative voltages is a disadvantage of _____-_____ MOSFETs.

(f) Current spikes are drawn from biasing power supply each time a CMOS output switches from _____ to _____.

(g) In both the HIGH and LOW states, the _____ _____ _____ of _____ logic can be determined by multiplying V_{DD} by 30%.

(h) Damage can occur to a _____ circuit, if its inputs are left floating.

(i) _____-_____ _____ is an improved version of the 74C series, which has a tenfold increase in switching speed.

(j) _____ logic combines the best of features of bipolar and CMOS logic.

(k) Because of parasitic PNP and NPN transistors embedded in the substrate of CMOS ICs, _____-_____ can occur under certain circumstances.

8.8   *Table 8.3 below shows Input/Output voltage levels (in volts) with VDD = VCC = +5V.*

Table 8.3

	CMOS							TTL			
	4000B	74HC	74HCT	74AC	74ACT	74AHC	74AHCT	74	74LS	74AS	74ALS
VIH(min)	3.5	3.5	2.0	3.5	2.0	3.85	2.0	2.0	2.0	2.0	2.0
VIL(max)	1.5	1.0	0.8	1.5	0.8	1.65	0.8	0.8	0.8	0.8	0.8
VOH(min)	4.95	4.9	4.9	4.9	4.9	4.4	3.15	2.4	2.7	2.7	2.7
VOL(max)	0.05	0.1	0.1	0.1	0.1	0.44	0.1	0.4	0.5	0.5	0.4
VNH	1.45	1.4	2.9	1.4	2.9	0.55	1.15	0.4	0.7	0.7	0.7
VNL	1.45	0.9	0.7	1.4	0.7	1.21	0.7	0.4	0.3	0.3	0.4

Which of the logic families in Table 8.3 has the best dc noise margin?

8.9 Which of the logic families in Table 8.3 has the worst dc noise margin?

SECTIONS 8.11-8.14 *Low-Voltage Technology/Open-Collector/Open-Drain Outputs/ Tristate (Three-State) Logic Outputs/High Speed Interface Logic*

8.10

Table 8.4

	LVC	ALVC	LV	LVT	Units
$V_{CC(recom.)}$	2.0 to 3.6	2.3 to 3.6	2.7 to 3.6	2.7 to 3.6	V
t_{Pd}	6.5	3	18	4	ns
$V_{IH\ range}$	2.0 to 6.5	2.0 to 4.6	2.0 to Vcc + 0.5	2.0 to 7	V
$V_{IL(max)}$	0.8	0.8	0.8	0.8	V
I_{OH}	24	12	6	32	mA
I_{OL}	24	12	6	64	mA

Use Table 8.4 and complete the following statements by filling the blanks with the proper Low-Voltage logic family:

(a) The _____ Low-Voltage logic family offers the best performance.

(b) The _____ Low-Voltage logic family offers the widest range of operating voltages.

(c) The output levels of the _____ Low-Voltage logic family are equivalent to TTL levels.

8.11 How many *74TTL* inputs can a typical *74LVT*-device drive in the HIGH state? In the LOW state?

8.12 (a) The 7400 NAND gates used in the circuit of Figure 8.2 have totem-pole outputs. After building the circuit the technician determines that the circuit is not working properly. State the problem with the design.

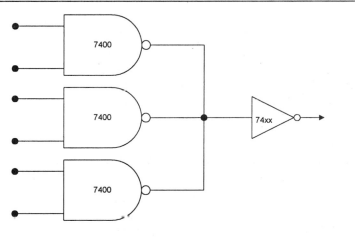

Figure 8.2

(b) Change the design so that the circuit functions properly.

8.13   In the circuit of Figure 8.3 we have CMOS Inverters driving CMOS tristate buffers. The circuit conditions were recorded in Table 8.5. Point out the fault with the circuit, and explain the most probable reason for the malfunction.

_____

_____

_____

_____

_____

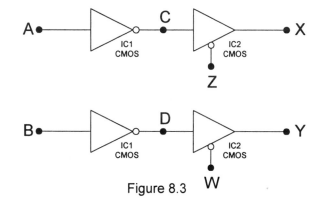

Figure 8.3

Table 8.5

A	B	Z	W	C	D	X	Y
0	0	0	0	1	1	1	1
0	0	0	1	1	1	1	Hi-Z
0	0	1	0	1	1	Hi-Z	1
0	0	1	1	1	1	Hi-Z	Hi-Z
0	1	0	0	?	?	?	?
0	1	0	1	?	?	?	Hi-Z
0	1	1	0	?	?	Hi-Z	?
0	1	1	1	?	?	Hi-Z	Hi-Z
1	0	0	0	?	?	?	?
1	0	0	1	?	?	?	Hi-Z
1	0	1	0	?	?	Hi-Z	?
1	0	1	1	?	?	Hi-Z	Hi-Z
1	1	0	0	0	0	0	0
1	1	0	1	0	0	0	Hi-Z
1	1	1	0	0	0	Hi-Z	0
1	1	1	1	0	0	Hi-Z	Hi-Z

8.14 The TTL circuit of Figure 8.4 shows three MOD-8 counters (Z1-Z3) which are connected to a common 3-bit data bus (A, B, C) through tristate buffers. Ring-Counter Z4 selects which MOD-8 counter places data on the data bus via the tristate buffers (Z5-Z7). A technician uses a logic probe to obtain the Table 8.6. Determine a cause for the circuit's malfunction.

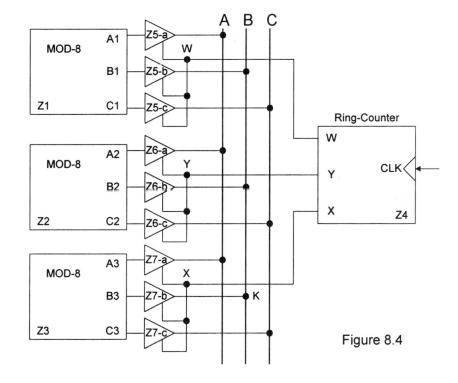

Figure 8.4

Table 8.6

Ring Counter			Z1			Z2			Z3			Data Bus		
W	Y	X	A1	B1	C1	A2	B2	C2	A3	B3	C3	A	B	C
0	0	1	1	1	0	0	1	0	0	1	1	0	1	1
0	1	0	1	1	1	0	0	1	1	0	0	0	0	1
1	0	0	1	1	0	1	1	0	0	1	0	1	1	0
0	0	1	1	1	0	0	0	0	1	0	1	1	1	1
0	0	1	0	1	1	1	1	1	0	0	0	0	1	0

8.15 What would happen if connection W from Ring counter Z4 to the tristate buffers Z5 of Figure 8.4 became open?

_____

_____

_____

_____

8.16 Complete the following statements by filling the blanks:

(a) If the physical distance between components in a system is more than about _____ inches, the bus wires between them need to be viewed as _____ _____.

(b) _____ series is more suitable for high-speed busses within a single circuit board or between boards in small enclosures like a personal computer case.

(c) _____ series is specially designed to drive the relatively long busses that connect modules in the back of an industry standard 19-inch rack mounting system.

SECTIONS 8.15-8.20 *The ECL Digital IC Family/CMOS Transmission Gate (Bilateral Switch)/IC Interfacing TTL Driving CMOS/CMOS Driving TTL/Analog Voltage Comparators*

8.17 Complete the following statements by filling the blanks:

(a) The latest ECL series by Motorola is called _____.

(b) The transistors in the ECL logic circuit never _____, and so switching speed is very high.

(c) The worst case ECL noise margins are approximately _____.

(d) In ECL logic the typical voltage for a logic LOW is _____ V, and _____ V for a logic HIGH.

(e) There is no need for Inverters in the ECL logic family because an ECL logic block produces an output and its _____.

(f) A special type of CMOS gate that passes signals digital as well as analog in both directions is called a _____ _____.

8.18 The circuit of Figure 8.5 shows TTL driving CMOS and CMOS driving TTL. Explain why the circuit would not function properly? Add the necessary circuitry in order to fix the designer's mistakes. *(Use the data from Table 8.3 in this Study Guide)*

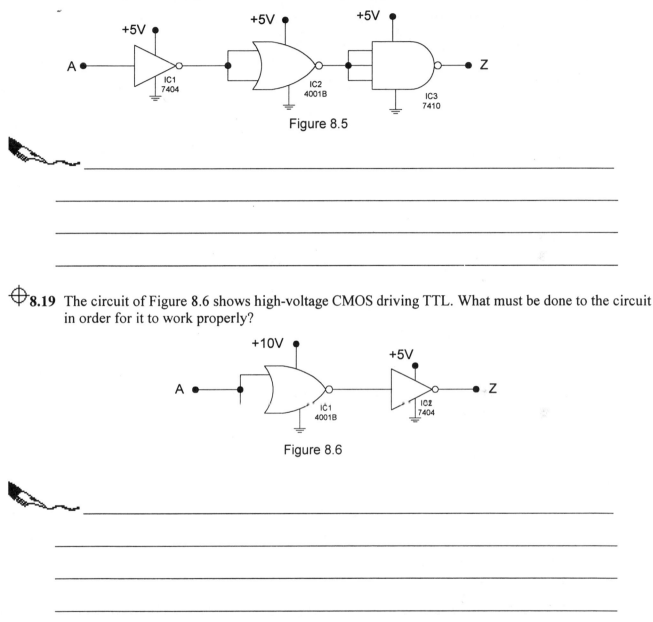

Figure 8.5

_____

_____

_____

_____

8.19 The circuit of Figure 8.6 shows high-voltage CMOS driving TTL. What must be done to the circuit in order for it to work properly?

Figure 8.6

_____

_____

_____

_____

8.20 Consider the high-pressure detector circuit of Figure 8.7. The output of the pressure sensor goes up 20μV per P.S.I. When the output of the LM339 Voltage Comparator goes HIGH, the alarm goes ON. Determine at what pressure the alarm goes ON.

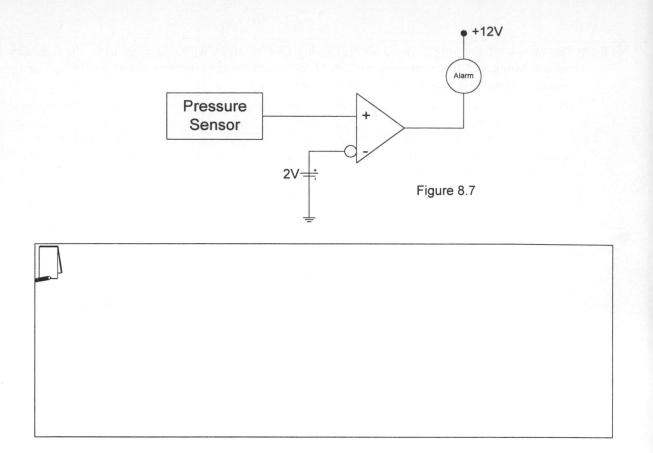

Figure 8.7

SECTION 8.21 *Troubleshooting.*

The Logic Probe, Logic Pulser and Current Tracer will be used as troubleshooting tools for the problems in this Section:

8.21 For problem 8.13, describe a procedure for using a logic pulser and a logic probe to verify the suspected fault.

_____

_____

_____

_____

_____

_____

8.22 Assume that in the circuit of Figure 8.4 bus line B is shorted to ground at node K. Develop a procedure for using the current tracer and the logic pulser to isolate the short.

_____

_____

_____

_____

_____

_____

8.23 After the circuit of Figure 8.5 is redesigned properly, the technician finds that output Z is always HIGH. List at least three possible causes for the circuit's malfunction. Using the troubleshooting tools mentioned at the beginning of this section, describe how you would find the problem with the circuit?

1. _____

2. _____

3. _____

_____

_____

_____

_____

TEST 8

1. The typical dc noise margin for the 74 TTL series is:

    (a) > 3.5V (b) 0.4V (c) 200mV (d) 1.5V

2. Which of the following statements is **not** true about the TTL logic family?

    (a) Totem-pole outputs cannot be tied together.
    (b) When the current-sinking transistor is ON it may sink as much as I_{OL} without exceeding V_{OL}(max).
    (c) If a totem-pole TTL output goes from HIGH to LOW, a high amplitude current spike is drawn from Vcc.
    (d) When NOR gate inputs are tied together, they are always treated as a single load on the signal source.

3. The output of a logic family X is rated at $I_{OH} = 640\mu A$ and $I_{OL} = 46.4mA$. The input of a logic family Y is rated at $I_{IH} = 40\mu A$ and $I_{IL} = 1.6mA$. If the logic family X is driving logic family Y, how many inputs can it drive reliably?

    (a) HIGH state = 64 inputs, LOW state = 4.6 inputs.   (b) HIGH state = 400 inputs, LOW state = 1.125 inputs.
    (c) HIGH state = 16 inputs, LOW state = 29 inputs.   (d) HIGH state = 8 inputs, LOW state = 14.5 inputs.

4. The unused input of a 3-input CMOS AND gate should:

    (a) be left floating since it will assume a logic HIGH.   (b) be tied to Ground to prevent it from picking up noise
    (c) any unused CMOS input should be tied to ground.   (d) be tied to V_{DD}.

5. A 74ALS output is LOW. The IC parameter that describes the current that flows from a TTL logic input to that output is:

    (a) I_{OL} (b) I_{IL} (c) I_{OH} (d) I_{IH}

6. Tristate buffers are commonly used to:

    (a) Simultaneously connect multiple signals to a common bus line.
    (b) Sequentially connect multiple signals to a common bus line.
    (c) Randomly connect multiple signals to a common bus line.
    (d) Replace open-collector devices.

7. A current tracer:

    (a) Cannot be used to manually inject pulses into a circuit in order to test the circuit's operation.
    (b) Can be used in conjunction with a logic pulser to trace the precise location of shorts to ground or Vcc.
    (c) Can detect a changing current in a wire or printed circuit-board trace without breaking the circuit.
    (d) All of the above.

8. Totem-pole outputs of various AND gates can be tied together to form "wired-AND" connection. (a) [T]   (b) [F]

9. Bus contention is a term used to describe a condition where two or more active devices are placed on the same bus line at the same time. (a) [T]   (b) [F]

10. LVT series is fabricated using BiCMOS technology. (a) [T]   (b) [F]

9   MSI LOGIC CIRCUITS

Objectives

Upon completion of this chapter, you will be able to:

- Analyze and use decoders and encoders in various types of circuit applications.

- Compare the advantages and disadvantages of LEDs and LCDs.

- Utilize the observation/analysis technique for troubleshooting digital circuits.

- Understand the operation of multiplexers and demultiplexers by analyzing several circuit applications.

- Compare two binary numbers by using the magnitude comparator circuit.

- Understand the function and operation of code converters.

- Cite the precautions that must be considered when connecting digital circuits using the data-bus concept.

- Use CUPLs truth table entry format to implement the equivalent of MSI logic circuits.

(b)   What would these output levels be if switches SW3 and SW8 were simultaneously depressed?

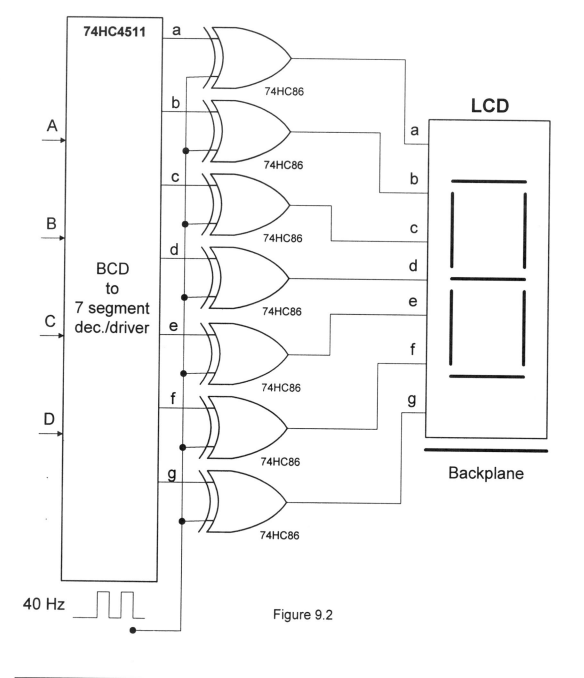

Figure 9.2

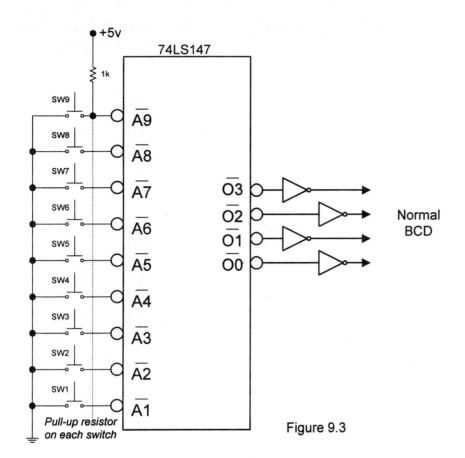

Figure 9.3

9.7 Explain the major difference between priority and non-priority encoders.

_____

_____

_____

_____

SECTION 9.5 *Troubleshooting.*

9.8 The circuit for a keyboard entry/display of a 2-digit number of Figure 9.4 is being tested. After the CLR switch is actuated, the tabulated results on page 171 are observed. Using the "Divide-and-Conquer" troubleshooting technique, determine the most probable cause for the circuit malfunction.

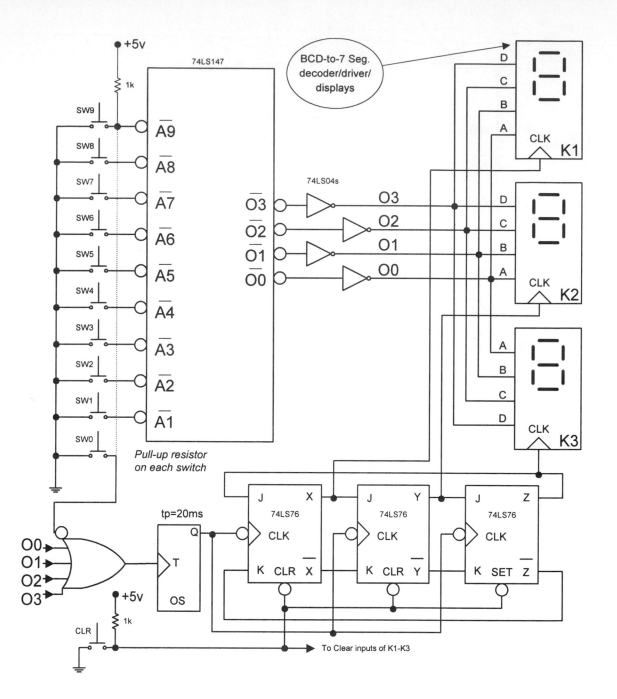

Figure 9.4

Switch Activation Sequence	BCD Display
SW8	800
SW6	806
SW4	846
SW5	546
SW2	542
SW7	572
SW3	372

_____

_____

_____

SECTIONS 9.6-9.9   *Multiplexers/Multiplexer Applications/Demultiplexers/More Troubleshooting.*

9.9 The Parallel-to-Serial converter circuit of Figure 9.5 (a) is built using CMOS integrated circuits and waveform Z of Figure 9.5 (b) is obtained. (*Assume that counter ABC is cleared before the first NGT of the CLK is applied.*)

(a) Determine the most probable cause for the circuit malfunction.

_____

_____

_____

(b) By analyzing waveform Z, determine what the contents of X_0-X_7 are most likely to be.

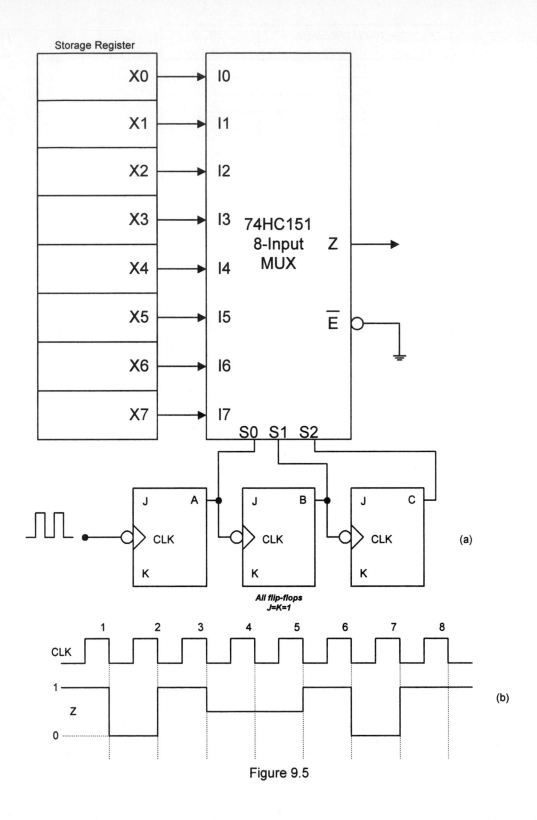

Figure 9.5

9.10 Implement the function $Z = \overline{C}\,\overline{B}A + C\overline{B}\,\overline{A} + CBA$ using a 74HC151 Multiplexer.

9.11 The Security Monitoring System circuit of Figure 9.6 was built and tested. During testing, the observations of the operating system were recorded below. Find the probable cause for the malfunction.

Condition	LEDs
All doors closed	All LEDs off
All doors open	All LEDs flashing
Door 0 open	LED 0 flashing
Door 1 open	LED 2 flashing
Door 2 open	LED 1 flashing
Door 3 open	LED 3 flashing
Door 4 open	LED 4 flashing
Door 5 open	LED 6 flashing
Door 6 open	LED 5 flashing
Door 7 open	LED 7 flashing

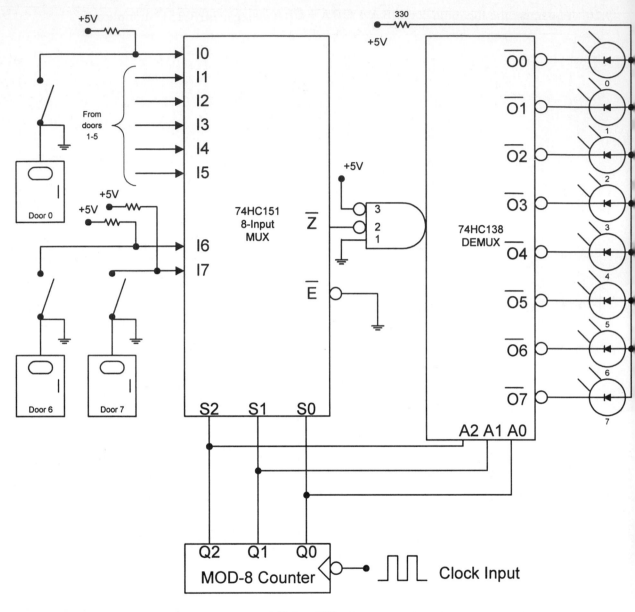

Figure 9.6

SECTIONS 9.10-9.14   *Magnitude Comparator/Code Converters/Data Busing/The 74ALS173-HC173 Tristate Register/Data Bus Operation*

9.12 Refer to Figure 9.7. It shows two 74HC85s cascaded in order to perform an 8-bit comparison. If the binary #A=11001101_2 and #B=11001110_2, what are the logic levels at the inputs $I_{A>B}$, $I_{A<B}$, $I_{A=B}$ of comparator Z2?

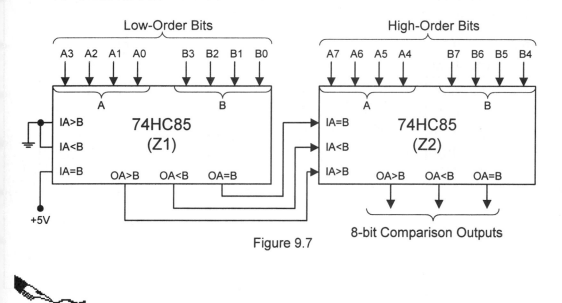

Figure 9.7

9.13 Show how to combine 74HC85s Comparator ICs in order to compare two 9-bit binary numbers

9.14 The table below shows a 4-bit code called *gray* code ($G_3G_2G_1G_0$) and its binary equivalencies ($B_3B_2B_1B_0$).

(a) Design a 4-bit Binary-to-Gray code converter.

Binary $B3B2B1B0$	Gray $G3G2G1G0$
0 0 0 0	0 0 0 0
0 0 0 1	0 0 0 1
0 0 1 0	0 0 1 1
0 0 1 1	0 0 1 0
0 1 0 0	0 1 1 0
0 1 0 1	0 1 1 1
0 1 1 0	0 1 0 1
0 1 1 1	0 1 0 0
1 0 0 0	1 1 0 0
1 0 0 1	1 1 0 1
1 0 1 0	1 1 1 1
1 0 1 1	1 1 1 0
1 1 0 0	1 0 1 0
1 1 0 1	1 0 1 1
1 1 1 0	1 0 0 1
1 1 1 1	1 0 0 0

(b) Design a 4-bit Gray-to-Binary code converter.

Binary	Gray
B3B2B1B0	G3G2G1G0
0 0 0 0	0 0 0 0
0 0 0 1	0 0 0 1
0 0 1 0	0 0 1 1
0 0 1 1	0 0 1 0
0 1 0 0	0 1 1 0
0 1 0 1	0 1 1 1
0 1 1 0	0 1 0 1
0 1 1 1	0 1 0 0
1 0 0 0	1 1 0 0
1 0 0 1	1 1 0 1
1 0 1 0	1 1 1 1
1 0 1 1	1 1 1 0
1 1 0 0	1 0 1 0
1 1 0 1	1 0 1 1
1 1 1 0	1 0 0 1
1 1 1 1	1 0 0 0

9.15 (a) What happens to the circuit's operation of Figure 9.8 if $\overline{\text{IE}}_B$ is always LOW?

_____

_____

(b) What happens to the circuit's operation of Figure 9.8 if $\overline{\text{OE}}_B$ is always LOW?

_____

_____

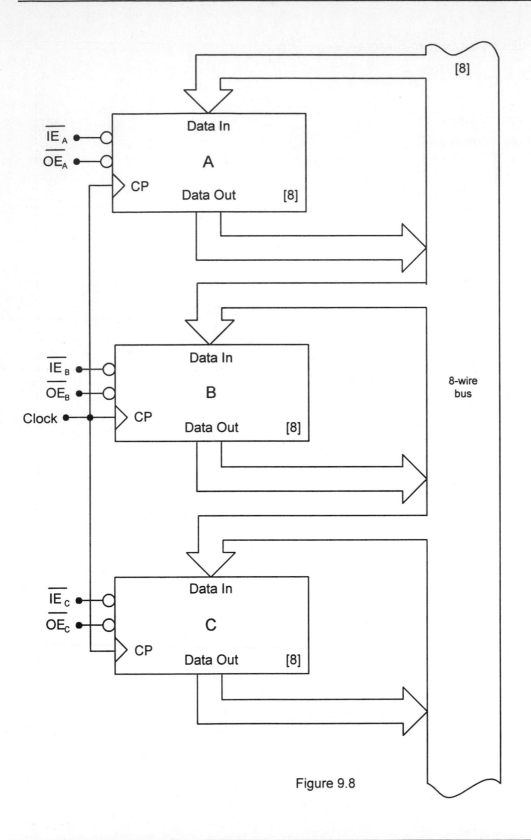

Figure 9.8

9.16 Redraw the circuit of Figure 9.8 using the Bundle method.

SECTION 9.15 *PLDs and Truth Table Entry*

9.17 Show three different ways (*set format, binary set values, decimal set values*) to enter an AND truth table in CUPL.

9.18 The IC depicted in Figure 9.9 is a 2 line-to-4 line decoder. Write the CUPL source file needed to implement this decoder on a GAL16V8.

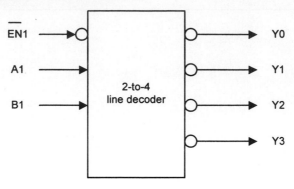

Figure 9.9

TEST 9

1. A 32-input multiplexer is to be used to perform parallel-to-serial data conversion. Which of the following counters would be required to provide the data select inputs?

    (a) MOD 4   (b) MOD 8   (c) MOD 16   (d) MOD 32

2. If two or more signals are active and are applied to the same point at the same time, it may result in what is called:

    (a) The Backplane effect   (b) Time-share   (c) Bus contention   (d) A bidirectional data line

3. Another term used to describe a demultiplexer is:

    (a) Data selector   (b) Data distributor   (c) Encoder   (d) Code converter

4. This device may have only one input line active and may have more than one output line active at any given time.

    (a) Demultiplexer   (b) Multiplexer   (c) Encoder   (d) Decoder

5. A 3-line-8-line decoder is often referred to as a:

    (a) Binary-to-octal decoder   (b) BCD-to-decimal decoder   (c) BCD-to-7-segment decoder   (d) None of the above

6. In an active matrix TFT LCD the active component is called

    (a) Thin film transistor   (b) Backplane   (c) Pixel   (d) Super twisted nematic

7. A 74HC85 magnitude comparator is used to:

    (a) Compare two input voltage levels and generate outputs to indicate which voltage has the greatest magnitude.
    (b) Compare two input binary quantities and generate outputs to indicate which quantity has the greatest magnitude.
    (c) Logically AND two binary quantities and generate outputs only if they are equal in magnitude.
    (d) Logically exclusive-OR two binary quantities and generate outputs indicating whether the two binary numbers are equal to or different from each other.

8. When different sets of data are appearing on the same output line at different times, the data is:

    (a) Frequency-shifted Demultiplexer   (b) Frequency-shifted multiplexed
    (c) Time-division-Demultiplexer   (d) Time-division-multiplexed

9. The Backplane is a connection common to all segments of a LED.

    (a) [TRUE] (b) [FALSE]

10. Reflective LCDs use ambient light for their operation.

    (a) [TRUE] (b) [FALSE]

10 INTERFACING WITH THE ANALOG WORLD

Objectives

Upon completion of this chapter, you will be able to:

- Understand the theory of operation and circuit limitations of several types of digital-to-analog converters (DACs).

- Read and understand the various DAC manufacturer specifications.

- Use different test procedures to troubleshoot DAC circuits.

- Compare the advantages and disadvantages among the digital-ramp analog-to-digital converter (ADC), successive-approximation ADC, and flash ADC.

- Analyze the process by which a computer in conjunction with an ADC digitizes an analog signal and then reconstructs that analog signal from the digital data.

- Describe the basic operation of a digital voltmeter.

- Understand the need for using sample-and-hold circuits in conjunction with ADCs.

- Describe the operation of an analog multiplexing system.

- Understand the features and basic operation of a digital storage oscilloscope.

- Understand the basic concepts of digital signal processing.

Glossary of key terms covered in this chapter:

- *Acquisition Time:* The amount of time needed for the hold capacitor C_h of a sample-and-hold circuit to charge to the current value of the analog input voltage. The acquisition time depends on the value of C_h and the characteristics of the sample-and-hold circuit. *[sec.10.15]*

- *Actuator:* Electrically controlled device that controls a physical variable. *[sec.10.1]*

- *Aliasing:* A phenomenon where a signal alias is produced by sampling the signal at a rate less than the minimum rate identified by Nyquist (twice the highest incoming frequency). *[sec.10.10]*

- *Analog-to-Digital Converter (ADC):* Circuit that converts an analog input to a corresponding digital output. *[sec.10.1]*

- *Bipolar DAC:* Digital-to-Analog Converter that accepts signed binary numbers as input and produces the corresponding positive or negative output value. *[sec.10.2]*

- *Conversion Time (t_c):* The interval between the end of the START pulse and the activation of the $\overline{EOC}$ output of an ADC. *[sec.10.9]*

- *Data Acquisition:* Process by which a computer acquires digitized analog data. *[sec.10.10]*

- *Digital-Ramp ADC:* Type of Analog-to-Decimal Converter in which an internal staircase waveform is generated and utilized for the purpose of accomplishing the conversion. The conversion time for this type of Analog-to-Decimal Converter varies depending on the value of the input analog signal. *[sec.10.9]*

- *Digital Signal Processing (DSP).* A very specialized form of a microprocessor that has been optimized to perform repetitive calculations on streams of digitized data fed from an A/D converter. *[sec.10.18]*

- *Digital Storage Oscilloscope (DSO):* Oscilloscope that uses both DACs and ADCs to acquire, digitize, store, and display analog waveforms. *[sec.10.17]*

- *Digital-to-Analog Converter (DAC):* Circuit that converts a digital input to a corresponding analog output. *[sec.10.1]*

- *Digitize:* Process by which analog data is converted to digital data. *[sec.10.6/10.10]*

- *Dual-Slope ADC:* Type of analog-to-digital converter that linearly changes a capacitor from a current proportional to V_A for a fixed time interval, and then increments a counter as the capacitor is linearly discharged to zero. *[sec.10.13]*

- *Flash ADC:* Type of Analog-to-Decimal Converter that has the highest operating speed available. *[sec.10.12]*

- *Full-Scale Error:* Term used by some Digital-to-Analog Converter manufacturers to specify the accuracy of a Digital-to-Analog Converter. It's defined as the maximum deviation of a Digital-to-Analog Converter's output from its expected ideal value. *[sec.10.4]*

- *Full-Scale Output:* The maximum possible output value of a Digital-to-Analog Converter. *[sec.10.2]*

- *Linearity Error:* Term used by some Digital-to-Analog Converter manufacturers to specify the devic accuracy. It's defined as the maximum deviation in step-size from the ideal step-size. *[sec.10.4]*

- *MAC:* Multiply and Accumulate. *[sec.10.18]*

- *Monotonicity:* A Digital-to-Analog Converter is said to be monotonic when its output either increases o stays the same as the input is increased. *[sec.10.4]*

- *Offset Error:* Under ideal conditions the output of a Digital-to-Analog Converter should be zero vo when the input is all 0s. In reality, there is a very small output voltage for this situation. This deviati from the ideal zero volts is called the offset error. *[sec.10.4]*

- *Percentage Resolution:* The ratio of the step-size to the full-scale value of a Digital-to-Analog Convert Percentage Resolution can also be defined as the reciprocal of the maximum number of steps of a Digit to-Analog Converter. *[sec.10.2]*

- *Quantization Error:* This is an inherent error of an A/D device. It is defined as the difference between t actual (analog) quantity and the digital value assigned to it. *[sec.10.9]*

- *R/2R Ladder DAC:* Type of Digital-to-Analog Converter where its internal resistance values only span range of 2 to 1. *[sec.10.3]*

- *Resolution:* The change that occurs in the analog output of a Digital-to-Analog Converter as a result of the change in the LSB of its digital input. *[sec.10.2/10.4]*

- *Sample-And-Hold Circuit:* Type of circuit which utilizes an unity-gain buffer amplifier in conjunction with a capacitor to accomplish a more stable analog-to-digital conversion process. *[sec.10.15]*

- *Sampling:* The process of acquiring a single data point's value of an analog signal. *[sec.10.10]*

- *Settling Time:* The amount of time that takes the output of a Digital-to-Analog Converter to go from ze to its full-scale value as the input is changed from all 0s to all 1s. Settling time is sometimes referred to the time needed for the DAC to settle within ± 1/2 step-size of its final value. *[sec.10.4]*

- *Sigma/Delta ADC:* An ADC that oversamples the analog information more often than the minimu sample rate. The oversampling provides interpolated data points in between those that would be taken the minimum sample rate. *[sec.10.13]*

- *Staircase Test:* Process by which a Digital-to-Analog Converter's digital input is incremented and output monitored to determine whether or not it exhibits a staircase format. The staircase wavefo should be without any missing steps or any downward steps until it reaches its full-scale value. *[sec.10.7]*

- *Staircase Waveform:* Type of waveform generated at the output of a Digital-to-Analog Converter as its digital input signal is incrementally changed. *[sec.10.2]*

- *Static Accuracy Test:* When a fixed binary value is applied to the input of a Digital-to-Analog Converte and the analog output is accurately measured. The measured result should fall within the expected range specified by the Digital-to-Analog Converter's manufacturer. *[sec.10.7]*

- *Step-Size:* See Resolution. *[sec.10.2]*

- *Successive-Approximation ADC (SAC):* Type of Analog-to-Decimal Converter in which an internal parallel register and complex control logic are used to perform the conversion. The conversion time for this type of Analog-to-Decimal Converter is always the same regardless of the value of the input analog signal. *[sec.10.11]*

- *Tracking ADC:* See Up/Down Digital-Ramp ADC. *[sec.10.13]*

- *Transducer:* Device that converts a physical variable to an electrical variable. *[sec.10.1]*

- *Up/Down Digital-Ramp ADC:* Type of analog-to-digital converter that uses an up/down counter to step up or step down the voltage from a digital-to-analog converter until it intersects the analog input. *[sec.10.13]*

- *Voltage-Controlled Oscillator (VCO):* Circuit that produces an output signal with a frequency proportional to the voltage applied to its input. *[sec.10.13]*

- *Voltage-to-Frequency ADC:* Type of analog-to-digital converter that employs a voltage-controlled oscillator (VCO) to convert an analog voltage to a pulse frequency that is then counted to produce a digital output. *[sec.10.13]*

- *Weighted Average:* This means that some of the data points during digital filtering are considered more important than others. *[sec.10.18]*

Problems

SECTIONS 10.1-10.2 *Interfacing With the Analog World/Digital-to-Analog conversion*

10.1   A 10-bit D/A converter has a F.S. value of 15V. What will be the output value if the binary input is 1010110111_2?

10.2   Determine the % Resolution for the DAC of problem 10.1.

$\oplus$**10.3**   Assume that the DAC used to control the motor of Figure 10.1(a) is a 4-bit DAC. The output signa of the DAC is shown in Figure 10.1(b).

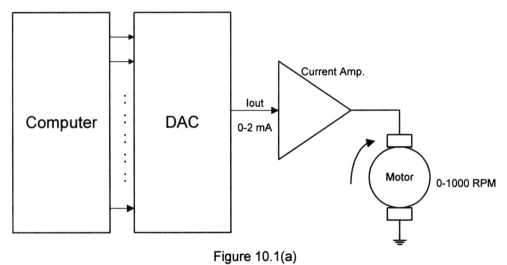

Figure 10.1(a)

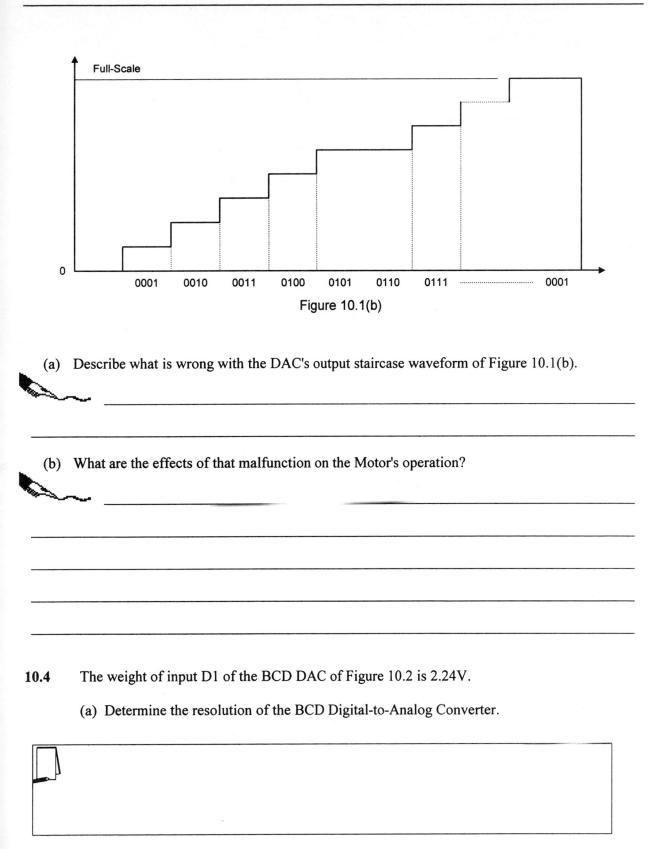

Figure 10.1(b)

(a) Describe what is wrong with the DAC's output staircase waveform of Figure 10.1(b).

_____

_____

(b) What are the effects of that malfunction on the Motor's operation?

_____

_____

_____

_____

_____

10.4 The weight of input D1 of the BCD DAC of Figure 10.2 is 2.24V.

(a) Determine the resolution of the BCD Digital-to-Analog Converter.

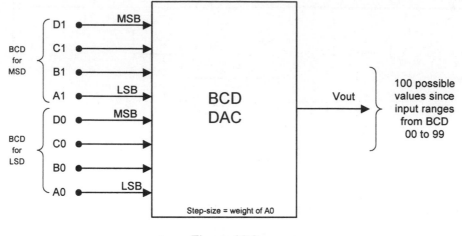

Figure 10.2

(b) Determine the % Resolution of the BCD Digital-to-Analog Converter.

(c) Determine the BCD input code when V_{out} is 2.156V.

SECTIONS 10.3,10.4,10.6 *D/A-Converter Circuitry/DAC Specifications/DAC Applications*

10.5 Change the DAC circuit of Figure 10.3 so that its step-size is equal to -78.13mV.

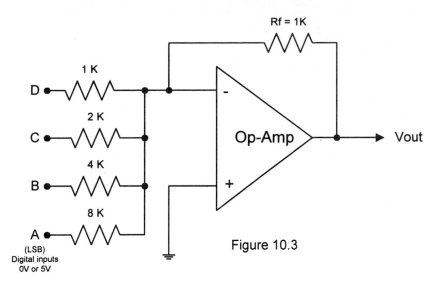

Figure 10.3

10.6 A 10-bit DAC has a full-scale output value of 1.590V and has an accuracy of ± 0.25% full-scale. When the binary input is 11001101102, the output is equal to 1.283V. Determine whether or not this output value is within the DAC's specified accuracy?

10.7 The input of a certain DAC is changed from all 0s to all 1s simultaneously. The output response was recorded on a storage oscilloscope and is shown in Figure 10.4. Determine the approximate *Settling time* for the DAC.

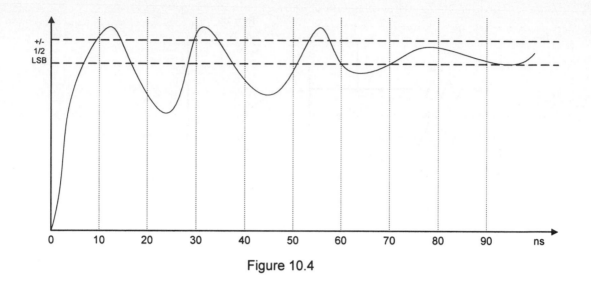

Figure 10.4

SECTIONS 10.7-10.9   *Troubleshooting DACs/Analog-to-Digital Conversion/Digital-Ramp ADC*

For the following five problems, refer to the digital ramp ADC of Figure 10.5.

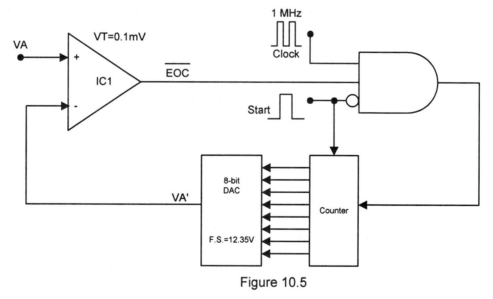

Figure 10.5

10.8   What is the *maximum*, *minimum* and *average* conversion time of this ADC?

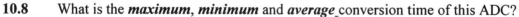

10.9 What is the value of $V_{A'}$ when the counter output is binary 10110001_2?

10.10 If input $V_A = 8.572V$, what is the DAC's input binary data at the end-of-conversion time?

10.11 While testing the ADC of Figure 10.5, a technician finds that the counter never stops counting, regardless of the value of V_A. State *one* possible cause for the malfunction.

10.12 For each of the following circuit changes determine whether or not a decrease in the *conversion time* would occur.

(a) Increase the clock frequency.

(b) Replace the existing DAC with a 10-bit DAC.

(c) Use op-amps that have faster slew-rates.

(d) Replace the existing DAC with a 4-bit DAC.

<u>**SECTIONS 10.10-10.12**</u>   *Data Acquisition/Successive-Approximation ADC/Flash ADCs.*

10.13   A sampled data acquisition system is being used to digitize an audio signal. Assume that the samp
frequency Fs is 25 kHz. Determine the output frequency that will be reproduced for each of t
following input frequencies.

   (a)   Input Signal = 5 kHz
   (b)   Input Signal = 10.1 kHz
   (c)   Input Signal = 12.3 kHz
   (d)   Input Signal = 18.7 kHz
   (e)   Input Signal = 22 kHz
   (f)   Input Signal = 24.6 kHz

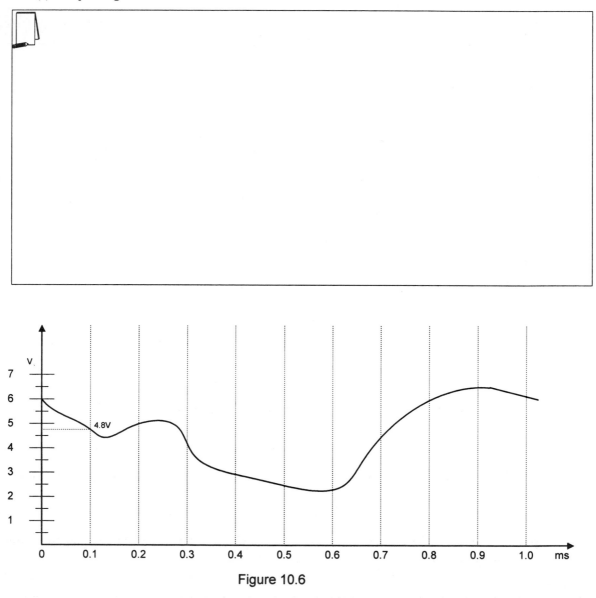

Figure 10.6

10.14 (a) Assume that the analog signal of Figure 10.6 is to be digitized by the ADC of Figure 10.5. Superimpose on Figure 10.6 the reconstructed signal using the data obtained during the digitalization process.

    (b) If a highly accurate reproduction of the digitized analog signal of Figure 10.6 is desired, what type of ADC should be used?

_____

_____

_____

10.15 On the triangle waveform of Figure 10.7, mark the points where a flash A/D converter takes samples at intervals of 75 µs (starting at the origin).

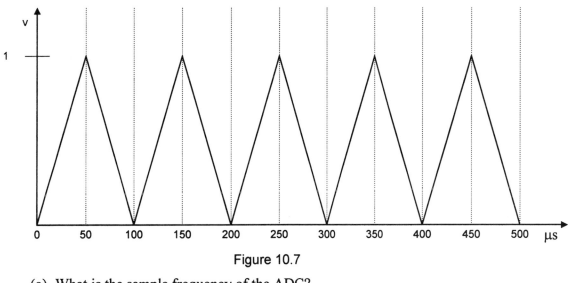

Figure 10.7

    (a) What is the sample frequency of the ADC?

_____

    (b) What is the frequency of the triangle signal being converted by the ADC?

_____

    (c) What is the difference between the sample frequency and the frequency of the triangle signal?

_____

    (d) Compare the frequency of the **reconstructed** waveform with the frequency of the original triangle waveform.

_____

10.16

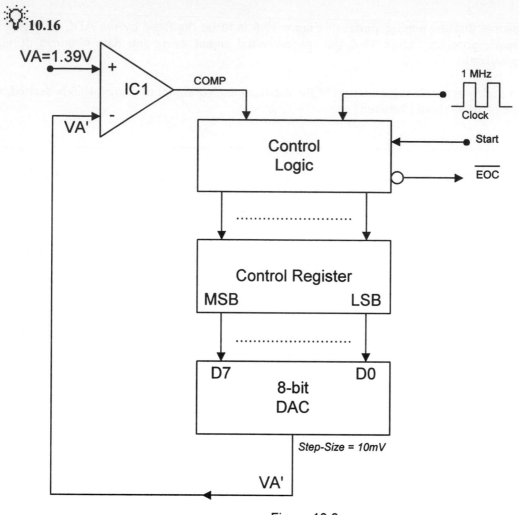

Figure 10.8

Complete the timing diagrams in the next two pages for the digital inputs D_0-D_7 and analog output $V_{A'}$ of the successive approximation ADC of Figure 10.8

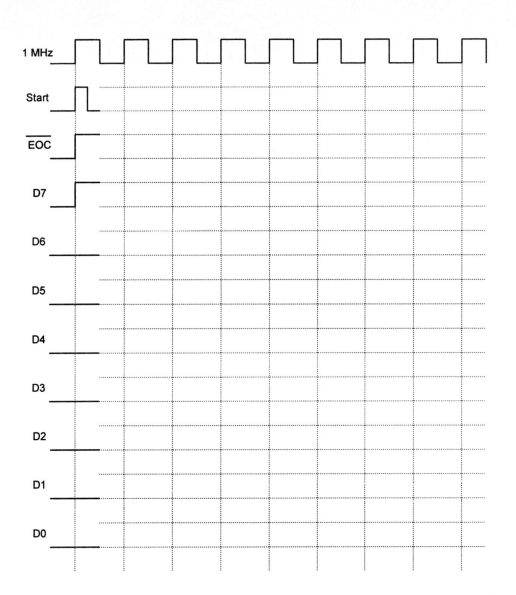

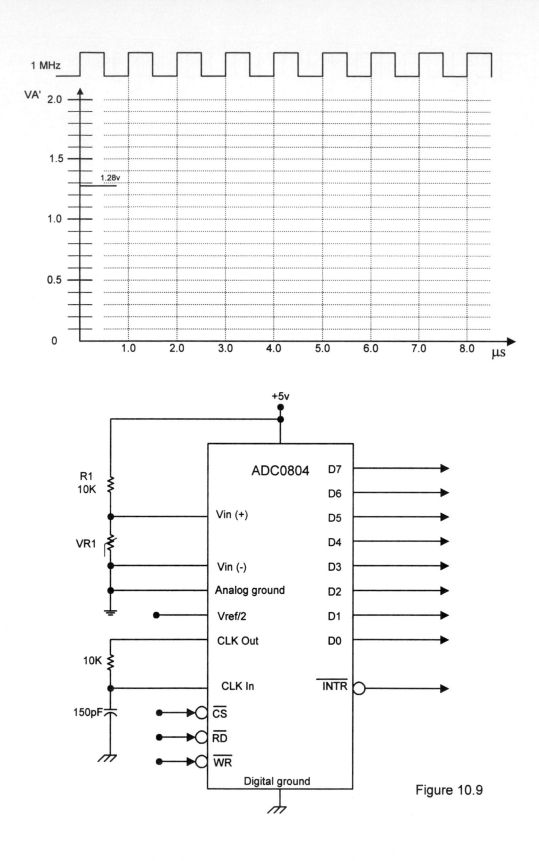

Figure 10.9

10.17 The circuit of Figure 10.9 is an 8-bit successive approximation ADC and is being used to convert the ambient temperature, as sensed by the thermistor VR1, to an equivalent binary value D_7-D_0. The thermistor will detect a range of temperatures from 0°- 60°C. When the temperature is 60°C, $V_{in}(+)$=5.0V.

(a)   What is the binary number D_7-D_0 when the temperature is 60°C?

(b)   What is the resolution in °C?

(c)   What is the resolution in volts?

(d)   After the circuit of Figure 10.9 is designed it is determined that 30°C is the actual maximum ambient temperature. When the temperature is 30°C, $V_{in}(+)$=3.0V. How would you modify the circuit of Figure 10.9 in order for the maximum output binary number to be representative of the maximum ambient temperature?

<u>**SECTIONS 10.13-10.18**</u>   *Other A/D Conversion Methods/Digital Voltmeter/Sample-and-Hold Circuits/ Multiplexing/Digital Storage Oscilloscope/Digital Signal Processing (DSP)*

10.18 Indicate which *Analog-to-Digital Conversion Method* is being described in each of the following statements:

(a)   The basic operation of this converter involves the linear charging and discharging of a capacitor using constant currents.

_____

(b)   It produces an output frequency that is proportional to its input voltage.

_____

(c)   When a new conversion is to begin, the counter is not reset to zero, but begins counting up or down from its last value.

_____

(d)   Because of its slow conversion times, it is not used in any data acquisition applications.

_____

(e)   To represent the positive portions of a waveform, a stream of bits with a high density of ones is generated.

_____

10.19   The circuit of Figure 10.10 is a *Continuous-conversion DVM* that uses a digital-ramp ADC. The DVM circuit is tested and the results are recorded in the accompanying table of Figure 10.10. Determine a possible cause for the discrepancy in the readings.

_____

_____

_____

_____

_____

_____

_____

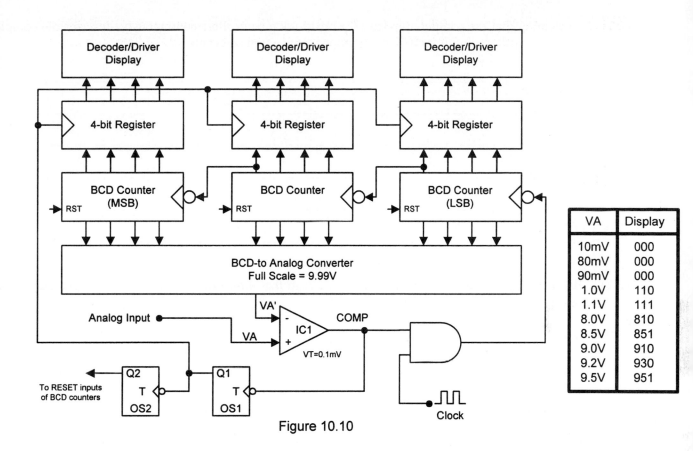

VA	Display
10mV	000
80mV	000
90mV	000
1.0V	110
1.1V	111
8.0V	810
8.5V	851
9.0V	910
9.2V	930
9.5V	951

Figure 10.10

The circuit of Figure 10.11 uses a computer to input data to a DAC and to control which one of the three transmission gates (IC1A-IC1C) becomes active. The output of each sample-and-hold circuit (A,B,C) is connected to the input of a positioning controller. The circuit of Figure 10.11 saves two DACs by using this multiplexing technique.

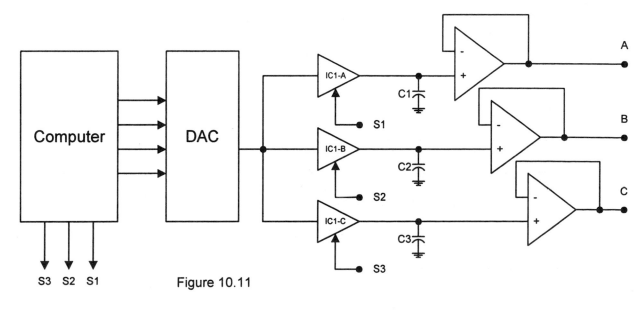

Figure 10.11

10.20 Assuming that the computer updates the positioning controllers continuously, describe the complete operation of the circuit including the proper sequencing of events.

_____

_____

_____

_____

_____

_____

10.21 What are the *two* major components in this circuit that limit the maximum speed at which data can be sent to each of the positioning controllers?

1. _____

_____

2. _____

_____

10.22 Cite the major advantage and disadvantage of using three DACs instead of multiplexing one DAC as in the circuit of Figure 10.11?

*Advantage:*_____

_____

Disadvantage: _____

_____

10.23 Cite the basic *sequence of operations* performed in a Digital Storage Oscilloscope (DSO).

_____

10.24 Give an example of a major application for Digital Signal Processing (DSP)?

_____

10.25 An A/D converter is sampling a signal and the input samples are listed in the table below. Calculate the simple average of the 5 most recent data points, starting with Out[5] and proceeding through Out[12].

Sample calculations: $Out[n] = \dfrac{In[n-4] + In[n-3] + In[n-2] + In[n-1] + In[n]}{5}$

Sample n	1	2	3	4	5	6	7	8	9	10	11	12
In[n] (v)	0	0	0	0	4	6	8	10	12	14	14	14
Out[n] (v)	0	0	0	0								

10.26 Redo problem 10.25 but this time calculate the simple average of the 4 most recent data points, starting with Out[5] and proceeding through Out[12]

Sample n	1	2	3	4	5	6	7	8	9	10	11	12
In[n] (v)	0	0	0	0	4	6	8	10	12	14	14	14
Out[n] (v)	0	0	0	0								

TEST 10

1. A certain 8-bit digital-to-analog converter has a full-scale output of 3mA and a full-scale error of $\pm$ 0.5% F.S. What is the range of possible outputs for an input of 10000001_2?

    (a) 1503-1533μA (b) 1518-1533μA (c) 994-1014μA (d) 1500-1530μA

2. A DAC has a 10-bit input and a 10.23V F.S. output. What is the DAC's step-size?

    (a) 100mV (b) 10mV (c) 10% (d) 9.9mV

3. A 12-bit DAC has a step-size of 10mV. Determine the % resolution.

    (a) $\approx$ 0.0244% (b) $\approx$ 0.1% (c) $\approx$ 1.0% (d) $\approx$ 2.5%

4. A Digital-to-Analog Converter is said to be monotonic when its output:

    (a) either increases or stays the same as the input is increased   (b) either decreases or stays the same as the input is increased (c) either increases or stays the same as the input is decreased   (d) either decreases or stays the same as the input is decreased.

5. The amount of time that takes the output of a DAC to go from zero to its full-scale value as the input is changed from all 0s to all 1s is called:

    (a) Settling time (b) Acquisition time (c) Conversion time (d) Staircase time.

6. An ADC that employs a VCO to convert an analog voltage to a pulse frequency that is then counted to produce a digital output is called:

    (a) Voltage-to-frequency ADC (b) Dual-slope ADC (c) Sigma/Delta ADC (d) Tracking ADC

7. The resolution of the ADC0804 successive approximation ADC can be increased by:

    (a) Increasing the voltage into the $V_{REF}/2$ input (b) Decreasing the voltage into the $V_{REF}/2$ input.
    (c) Increasing the clock frequency   (d) Leaving the $V_{REF}/2$ input open.

8. In a sample-and-hold circuit the acquisition time depends on:

    (a) The value of C_h and the characteristics of the S/H circuit   (b) The characteristics of the S/H circuit only   (c) The value of C_h only   (d) The gain of the amplifier used by the S/H circuit.

9. The weight of the LSB of a DAC is called the step-size   (a) [TRUE]   (b) [FALSE]

10. The conversion time of a digital-ramp ADC is fixed regardless of the analog voltage V_A, while in a successive approximation ADC the conversion time increases as the analog voltage V_A increases.

    (a) [TRUE]   (b) [FALSE]

11 MEMORY DEVICES

Objectives

Upon completion of this chapter, you will be able to:

• Understand and correctly use the terminology associated with memory systems.

• Describe the difference between read/write memory and read-only memory.

• Discuss the difference between volatile and nonvolatile memory.

• Determine the capacity of a memory device from its inputs and outputs.

• Outline the steps that occur when the CPU reads from or writes to memory.

• Distinguish among the various types of ROMs and cite some common applications.

•   Understand and describe the organization and operation of static and dynamic RAMs.

• Compare the relative advantages and disadvantages of EPROM, EEPROM, and flash memory.

• Combine memory ICs to form memory modules with larger word size and/or capacity.

• Use the test results on a RAM or ROM system to determine possible faults in the memory system.

Glossary of key terms covered in this chapter:

- *Access Time:* The time between the memory receiving a new input address and the output data becoming available in a read operation. *[sec.11.1/11.6]*

- *Address:* A number that uniquely identifies the location of a word in memory. *[sec.11.1]*

- *Address Bus:* A unidirectional bus that carries address bits from CPU to memory. *[sec.11.3]*

- *Address Decoders:* Part of the internal ROM architecture that determines which register in the array will be enabled to place its 8-bit data word onto the bus. *[sec.11.5]*

- *Address Multiplexing:* Used in dynamic RAMs to save IC pins, it involves latching the two halves of a complete address into the IC in separate steps. *[sec.11.14]*

- *Address Pointer Register:* Register that keeps track of where data are to be written and from where they are to be read during a FIFO operation. *[sec.11.19]*

- *Auxiliary Memory:* Nonvolatile memory used to store massive amounts of information external to the internal memory. *[sec.11.1]*

- *Bootstrap Program:* The program, stored in ROM, that a computer executes on power-up. *[sec.11.9]*

- *Bulk Erase:* Flash memory operation in which all cells on the chip are erased simultaneously. *[sec.11.8]*

- *Burning:* The process of entering data into a ROM. *[sec.11.4]*

- *Burst Refresh:* When the normal memory operation is suspended, and each row of the DRAM is refreshed in succession until all rows have been refreshed. *[sec.11.16]*

- *Byte:* An 8-bit word. *[sec.11.1]*

- *Cache Memory:* Block memory that communicates directly with the CPU at high speed in order to achieve maximum system operation. *[sec.11.19]*

- *Capacity:* Amount of storage space in a memory expressed as number of bits or number of words. *[sec.11.1]*

- $\overline{\text{CAS}}$-*before-*$\overline{\text{RAS}}$ *Refresh:* A common method for refreshing a DRAM. In this method the $\overline{\text{CAS}}$ signal is driven LOW and held there as $\overline{\text{RAS}}$ is pulsed LOW. *[sec.11.16]*

- *CD ROM:* Type of read only memory whereby data is written by a laser beam one bit at a time by burning or not burning a light-diffracting pit into the reflective coating of the disk. *[sec.11.8]*

- *Checksum:* A special data word stored in last ROM location. It is derived from the addition of all other data words in the ROM, and is used for error-checking purposes. *[sec.11.21]*

- **Chip Select:** An enable input that enables or disables a ROM/RAM outputs. *[sec.11.4]*

- **Circular Buffer:** This type of buffer differs from that of linear buffers in that, each time a new value is written to a circular buffer, it overwrites the oldest value. *[sec.11.20]*

- **Column Address Strobe (CAS):** Signal used to latch the column address into a DRAM chip. *[sec.11.14]*

- **Control Bus:** A bus carrying control signals from CPU to memory. *[sec.11.3]*

- **Data Bus:** A Bidirectional bus that carries data between CPU and memory. *[sec.11.3]*

- **Data Rate Buffer:** An application of FIFOs where sequential data are written into the FIFO at one rate, and read out at a different rate. *[sec.11.19]*

- **DDRSDRAM:** Double Data Rate SDRAM.-in-line memory module. *[sec.11.17]*

- **Density:** Another term for "Capacity". *[sec.11.1]*

- **DIMM:** Dual-in-line memory module. This is a circuit card with 84 functionally equivalent contacts on both sides of the card. *[sec.11.17]*

- **Distributed Refresh:** When the row refreshing of the DRAM is interspersed with the normal operations of the memory. *[sec.11.16]*

- **Downloading:** When the data to be burned into a PROM is obtained from a keyboard, from a disk drive, or transferred from a computer. *[sec.11.7]*

- **DRDRAM:** Direct Rambus DRAM. *[sec.11.17]*

- **Dynamic Memory Devices:** Semiconductor memory devices in which the stored data will not remain permanently stored even with power applied. *[sec.11.1]*

- **Dynamic RAM (DRAM):** Type of semiconductor memory that stores data as capacitor charges that need to be refreshed periodically. *[sec.11.13]*

- **DRAM Controller:** IC used to handle refresh and address multiplexing operations needed by DRAM systems. *[sec.11.16]*

- **EDO DRAM:** Extended Data Output DRAM. It offers a minor improvement to FPM DRAMs. For accesses on a given page, the data at the current memory location is sensed and latched onto the output pins. *[sec.11.17]*

- **Electrical Erasable Programmable ROM (EEPROM):** A ROM that can be electrically programmed, erased, and reprogrammed. *[sec.11.7]*

- **Erasable Programmable ROM (EPROM):** A ROM that can be electrically programmed by the user. It can be erased (usually with ultraviolet light) and reprogrammed as often as desired. *[sec.11.7]*

- *Fetch:* Another term for "Read operation." *[sec.11.1]*

- *Firmware:* Computer programs stored in ROM. *[sec.11.9]*

- *First-In First-Out Memory (FIFO):* A semiconductor sequential access memory in which data words are read out in the same order that they were written in. *[sec.11.19]*

- *Flash Memory:* A nonvolatile memory with the EEPROM's in-circuit electrically erasability, but with densities and costs much closer to EPROMs, while retaining the high-speed read access of both. *[sec.11.8]*

- *FPM DRAM:* Fast Page Mode DRAM. It allows quicker access to random memory locations within the current "page". *[sec.11.17]*

- *Fusible-link:* Fuse links that make up a PROM. The user burns these fuse links to produce the desired stored memory data. *[sec.11.7]*

- *JEDEC:* Joint Electronic Device Engineering Council. *[sec.11.12]*

- *Latency:* Term used to describe the time required to perform certain memory operations before data that is stored in a DRAM can actually appear on the outputs. *[sec.11.14]*

- *Linear Buffer:* Type of buffer where as soon as all the locations in the buffer are full, no more entries are made until the buffer is emptied. *[sec.11.20]*

- *Main Memory:* Semiconductor memory that stores instructions and data the CPU is currently working on. *[sec.11.1]*

- *Mask-Programmed ROM (MROM):* A ROM that is programmed by the manufacturer according to the customer's specifications. It cannot be erased or reprogrammed. *[sec.11.7]*

- *Mass Storage:* Another term used for "Auxiliary Memory." *[sec.11.1]*

- *Memory Cell:* A device that stores a single bit. *[sec.11.1]*

- *Memory Foldback:* It refers to areas in memory that are redundantly occupied by a device due to incomplete address decoding. *[sec.11.18]*

- *Memory Word:* A group of bits in memory that represents instructions or data of some type. *[sec.11.1]*

- *Nonvolatile Memory:* Memory that will keep storing its information without the need for electrical power. *[sec 11.4]*

- *Output Buffers:* Part of the internal ROM architecture through which data passes onto the data bus. *[sec.11.5]*

- *Power-Down Storage:* A special memory function that allows data to be saved in a nonvolatile memory when the system power is shut down. *[sec.11.19]*

- **Power-Up Self-Test:** A program stored in ROM and executed by the CPU on power-up to test RAM and/or ROM portions of the computer circuitry. *[sec.11.20]*

- **Programmable ROM (PROM):** A ROM that can be electrically programmed by the user. It cannot be erased and reprogrammed. *[sec.11.7]*

- **Programming:** The process of entering data into a ROM. *[sec.11.4]*

- **Random-Access Memory (RAM):** Memory in which the access time is the same for any location. *[sec.11.1]*

- $\overline{RAS}$ **-Only Refresh:** A common method for refreshing a DRAM. A row address is strobed with $\overline{RAS}$ while $\overline{CAS}$ and R/ $\overline{W}$ remain HIGH. *[sec.11.16]*

- **Read-Only Memory (ROM):** Memory devices that are designed for applications where the ratio of read operations to write operations is very high. *[sec.11.1]*

- **Read Operation:** A word in a specific memory location is sensed and possibly transferred to another device. *[sec.11.1]*

- **Read/Write Input:** Input that controls which memory operation is to take place - read (R) or write (W). *[sec.11.2]*

- **Read/Write Memory (RWM):** Any memory that can be read from and written into with equal ease. *[sec.11.1]*

- **Refresh Counter:** During the refresh cycle of a DRAM, this counter supplies row addresses to the DRAM address inputs. *[sec.11.16]*

- **Refreshing:** The process of recharging the cells of a dynamic memory. *[sec.11.13]*

- **Register Array:** Part of the internal ROM architecture that stores the data that have that have been programmed into the ROM. *[sec.11.5]*

- **RIMM:** Rambus In-line Memory Module. *[sec.11.17]*

- **Row Address Strobe (RAS):** Signal used to latch row address into dynamic RAM chip. *[sec.11.14]*

- **SDRAM:** Synchronous DRAM. The data is clocked out by the system clock (instead of the $\overline{CAS}$ control line) in bursts of memory locations within the same page. *[sec.11.17]*

- **Sector Erase:** Flash memory operation in which specific sectors of the memory array are erased at one time. *[sec.11.8]*

- **Sequential-Access Memory (SAM):** Memory in which the access time will vary depending on where the data is stored. *[sec.11.1]*

- **SIMM:** Single memory module. This is a circuit card with 72 functionally equivalent contacts on both sides of the card. *[sec.11.17]*

- **SLDRAM**: Synchronous-link DRAM. *[sec.11.17]*

- **SODIMM**: Small outline dual-in-line memory module. A SODIMM is especially designed for compact applications, such as lap-top computers. *[sec.11.17]*

- **Static Memory Devices**: Semiconductor memory devices in which the stored data will remain permanently stored as long as power is applied. *[sec.11.1]*

- **Static RAM (SRAM)**: Semiconductor RAM that stores information in flip-flop cells that do not have to be periodically refreshed. *[sec.11.12]*

- **Store**: Another term for "Write operation." *[sec.11.1]*

- **Volatile Memory**: Requires electrical power to keep information stored. *[sec.11.1]*

- **Working Memory**: Another term for "Main Memory." *[sec.11.1]*

- **Write Operation**: A new word is placed into a specific memory location. *[sec.11.1]*

Problems

SECTIONS 11.1-11.2   *Memory Terminology/General Memory Operation.*

11.1   Complete each of the following statements by filling in the blank:

   a) The _____ of a certain memory device is 1Kx8.

   b) The term used to describe an 8-bit word is a _____ .

   c) Any device that is capable of storing a single bit can be called a _____ _____ .

   d) A _____ memory is a memory that requires the application of electrical power in order to store information.

   e) The amount of time required to perform a read operation is called the _____ time.

   f) A _____ memory is a semiconductor memory in which the stored data will remain permanently stored as long as power is applied. Data stored in a _____ memory, on the other hand, does not remain stored even with power applied, unless it is periodically refreshed.

   g) _____ memory stores instructions and data the CPU is currently working on.

   h) In a _____ the access time is the same for any address in memory.

   i) Any memory that can be read from or written into with equal ease is called a _____

11.2   Describe the step-by-step procedure necessary to read the contents of memory location 11001_2 of Figure 11.1.

_____

_____

_____

_____

_____

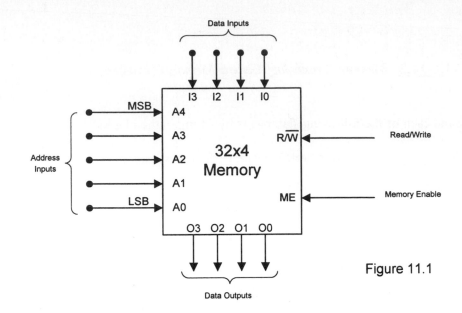

Figure 11.1

11.3 A certain memory device has 10 address lines. How many memory locations does it have?

SECTION 11.3   *CPU-Memory Connections*

11.4   The following statements are all false. Rewrite each of them in order to make them true.

a) The bus that carries data between the CPU and the memory ICs is unidirectional.

b) During a WRITE operation data may flow from a memory IC into the CPU via the Data bus.

c) During a READ operation data flows out of the CPU via the Data bus.

SECTIONS 11.4-11.6   *Read-Only Memories/ROM Architecture/ROM Timing.*

11.5 Consider the following signal conditions: $A_0=1$, $A_1=1$, $A_2=1$, $A_3=0$, CS=1. Which of the 16x8 ROM registers of Figure 11.2 is sending data to the Output buffers?

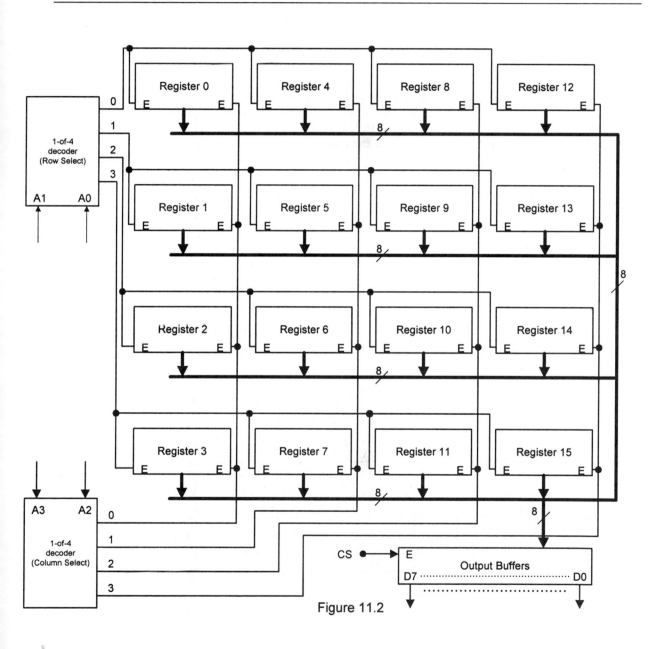

Figure 11.2

11.6 The 16x8 ROM circuit of Figure 11.2 is tested and the technician finds that everything works as expected except that the contents of Register 14 cannot be accessed. Determine what malfunction could cause the circuit to behave this way.

_____

_____

_____

_____

11.7   a) Determine the capacity of the memory of Figure 11.3.

     b) Is this a ROM or a RAM? Why?

_____

_____

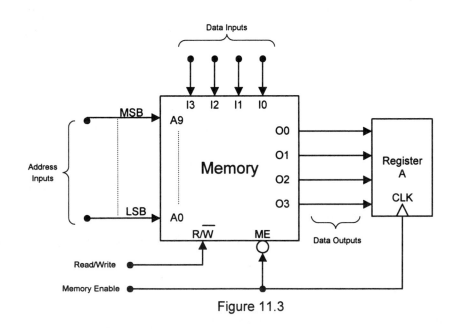

Figure 11.3

11.8   The memory system of Figure 11.3 has a t_{OE} requirement of 150ns. In this circuit, memory location 1111100000_2 is loaded with data 1111_2. While the signals on the address bus are kept stable at 1111100000_2, the Enable signal goes LOW for 100ns. Predict what data would be clocked into Register A.

_____

_____

_____

_____

SECTIONS 11.7-11.9   *Types of ROMs/Flash Memory/ROM Applications*

11.9   True or False:

a)   EPROMs are examples of volatile memories. [   ]

b)   EEPROMs and Flash memories can be easily erased and/or programmed without removing them from the circuit. [   ]

c)   MROMs should be used in circuit designs where few units are required to be built. [   ]

d)   Fusible-link PROMs operate in the same manner as MROMs. [   ]

e)   The most popular PROMs available in the market today use CMOS technology. [   ]

f)   Data is stored on a CD-ROM by burning or not burning a pit into the reflective coating on the disk. [   ]

The following two problems refer to the 28F256A flash memory.

11.10   *Complete* each statement by filling in the blank.

(a)   The code _____ must be loaded into the 28F256A's command register in order to perform a READ operation.

(b)   The code _____ is loaded twice into the 28F256A's command register in order to erase the entire contents of the memory.

(c) To verify that all memory cells have been erased, code _____ is loaded into the 28F256A's command register followed by a READ operation on the address to be verified.

(d) Data can be written into a desired address by writing code _____ into the 28F256A's command register.

(e) Code $C0_{16}$ is loaded into the 28F256A's command register whenever the _____ _____ operation is to be executed.

11.11   A technician executes the following operational steps to a 28F256A CMOS flash memory:

I)   Writes the code 20_{16} to the command register.
II) Again, he writes the code 20_{16} to the command register.

a) How was the flash memory affected by the two-step procedure?

_____

b) What data would you expect to find in memory location 0300_{16} after the two step procedure?

_____

11.12   Below are the SCK and SID signals that are applied to the ML2035 Programmable Sine Wave Generator of *(Figure 11.18 in your textbook).* Assuming that the LSB is shifted in first, what 16-bit hex value will be loaded into the 16-bit Latch that will produce the desired frequency?

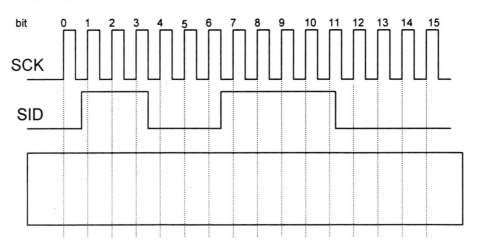

11.13   The circuit of Figure 11.4 utilizes a MOD-16 counter and a 16x1 PROM to generate a 1.25 kHz, 37.5% duty-cycle waveform at output X. Show the PROM programming table necessary to achieve the desired output waveform.

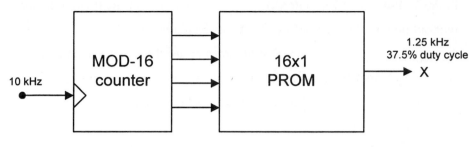

Figure 11.4

SECTIONS 11.12-11.16   *Static RAM (SRAM)/Dynamic RAM (DRAM)/Dynamic RAM Structure and Operation/DRAM Read/Write Cycles/DRAM Refreshing*

11.14   Fill in the missing word/s in order to make the statement true:

a)   SRAM memory cells are essentially _____ that will stay in a given state indefinitely, provided that power to the circuit is not interrupted.

b)   If the t_{RC} of a SRAM is 50ns, the CPU can read _____ million words per second.

c)   Dynamic RAMs require periodic recharging of the memory cells; this is called _____ the memory.

d)   In order to reduce the number of pins on high-capacity DRAM chips, manufacturers utilize address _____.

e)   During a read cycle the $\overline{\text{RAS}}$ signal is activated _____ the $\overline{\text{CAS}}$ signal.

---

f) $\overline{RAS}$ -only refresh method is performed by strobing in a row address with _____ while _____ and _____ remain HIGH.

g)   In the TMS44100 4Mx1 DRAM, _____ is the longest time that the memory can be without being refreshed before it loses its contents.

h)   A _____ _____ is a chip that may be used to perform address multiplexing and refresh count sequence generation.

i)   The term _____ is often used to describe the time required to perform certain DRAM timing operations.

SECTION 11.17 *DRAM Technology*

11.15   Fill in the missing term or terms:

a)   A _____ is a memory card with 72 functionally equivalent contacts on both sides of the card.

b)   In a _____ the data is clocked out by the bus system clock in bursts of memory locations within the same page.

c)   A _____ is a memory card with 84 functionally unique contacts on each side of the card.

d)   A _____ is a memory card used for compact applications, such as lap-top computers.

e)   RIMM stands for _____ ___-_____ _____ _____ .

f)   In a ____ _____, the data on a given page and at a current memory location is sensed and latched onto the output pins.

g)   ____ _____ allows quicker access to random memory locations within the current page.

h)   _____ technology allows for transfers of data on the rising and falling edges of the system clock, effectively doubling the potential rate of data transfer.

i)   _____ can operate at bus speeds up to 200 MHz and clocks of data synchronously on the rising and falling edges of the system clock

<u>**SECTIONS 11.18-11.19**</u>   *Expanding Word Size and Capacity/Special Memory Functions*

11.16 Design a 4Kx8 memory module using 1Kx4 RAM chips.

11.17 How many 2125A RAM ICs would be necessary to build the 4Kx8 memory module of
problem 11.16?

_____

_____

_____

11.18 While testing the 8Kx8 memory circuit of Figure 11.5, the technician finds that regardless
of the address on the Address bus, the data on the Data Bus are always in the Hi-Z state.
Determine a possible cause for the malfunction.

_____

_____

_____

_____

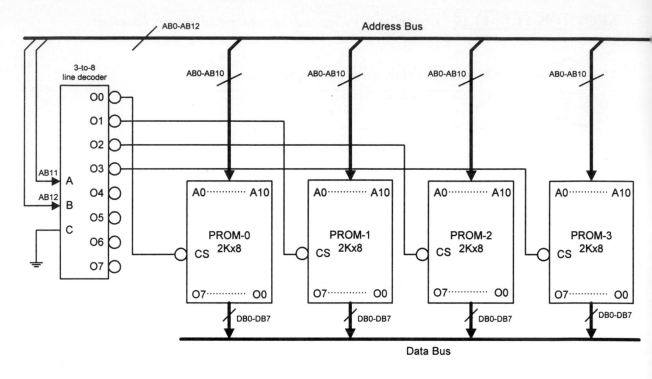

Figure 11.5

11.19 Give three different ways to prevent the loss of memory data during a system power failure.

_____

_____

_____

_____

_____

_____

_____

_____

_____

_____

11.20 A certain memory system is specified as 7-2-2-2. What do the numbers 7-2-2-2 represent?

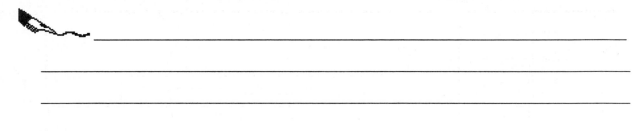

_____

_____

_____

SECTIONS 11.20-11.21   *Troubleshooting RAM Systems/Testing ROM.*

11.21   Modify the 4Kx8 RAM memory circuit of Figure 11.6 as follows:

1) Disconnect A15 from the OR gate and E3 from Vcc.
2) Connect A15 to E3 and the unused input of the OR gate to Ground.

Determine the complete new range of addresses for each RAM module?

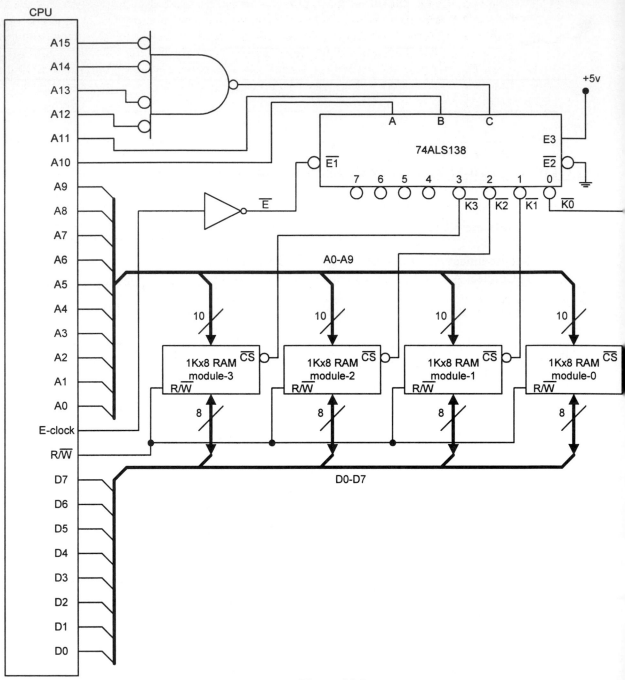

Figure 11.6

⊕ **11.22** The operation of the circuit of Figure 11.6 is checked and it is determined that the CPU is placing **valid** data on the data bus to be written into memory. After data are written into a certain memory location, the technician is able to verify the data by reading them back from that memory location. However, the contents of other memory locations have been changed with completely *different* and *unpredictable* data. Determine what could cause the malfunction and how you would troubleshoot the circuit in order to verify your prediction.

_____

_____

_____

_____

11.23 The table below represents the contents of a 16x8 ROM. Determine the checksum word that should be stored in memory location 1111_2.

Address	Data
0 0 0 0	0 0 1 1 0 1 1 0
0 0 0 1	1 1 0 0 1 1 0 0
0 0 1 0	1 1 0 0 0 0 0 1
0 0 1 1	0 0 1 1 1 0 0 1
0 1 0 0	1 1 1 1 1 1 1 1
0 1 0 1	0 0 0 0 0 0 0 0
0 1 1 0	0 1 1 1 0 0 1 1
0 1 1 1	1 0 0 1 1 0 0 1
1 0 0 0	0 0 0 1 0 0 0 1
1 0 0 1	0 1 0 1 1 1 1 1
1 0 1 0	1 1 0 0 0 0 1 1
1 0 1 1	1 0 0 1 0 0 1 0
1 1 0 0	0 0 1 1 1 1 0 1
1 1 0 1	1 1 1 0 0 0 0 0
1 1 1 0	1 0 0 0 0 0 0 0
1 1 1 1	[ ]

TEST 11

1. How many address lines would be required for a 2Kx8 memory?

    (a) 9   (b) 10   (c) 11   (d) 12

2. This kind of memory is an in-circuit, electrically erasable, byte-by-byte memory.

    (a) EPROM   (b) MROM   (c) FLASH   (d) EEPROM

3. How many bits of data can be stored in a memory with a capacity of 128K?

    (a) 131,072   (b) 262,144   (c) 1,048,576   (d) 128,000

4. A ROM that stores programming instructions is often referred to as:

    (a) hardware   (b) software   (c) firmware   (d) None of the above

5. _____ describes the time required to perform the memory operations before the data that is stored in a DRAM can actually appear on the outputs. (*fill-in the blank*)

    (a) Refreshing   (b) Latency   (c) Multiplexing   (d) Row address strobe

6. Which type of memory is associated with the "Command Register"?

    (a) PROM   (b) EPROM   (c) EEPROM   (d) FLASH

7. This type of memory can store data as long as power is applied to the chip.

    (a) DRAM   (b) EEPROM   (c) FLASH   (d) CD ROM

8. How many 1Kx4 memory chips are needed to build an 8Kx16 memory module?

    (a) 64   (b) 32   (c) 16   (d) 8

9. The most universal method for refreshing a DRAM is the "$\overline{CAS}$ - before - $\overline{RAS}$."

    (a) $\overline{CAS}$ – before – $\overline{RAS}$ (b) $\overline{RAS}$ – only refresh   (c) $\overline{RAS}$ – before – $\overline{CAS}$
    (c) Distributed refresh

10.   SIMMs are often used in compact applications, such as lap-top computers.

    (a) [TRUE]   (b) [FALSE]

12 PROGRAMMABLE LOGIC DEVICES: HARDWARE AND APPLICATIONS

Objectives

Upon completion of this chapter, you will be able to:

- Understand the differences in architecture of various PLDs.

- Read and understand data books that describe PLDs.

- Identify features and limitations of various modes of operation for GAL devices.

- Make wise decisions in selecting input and output pins when using GAL devices.

- Use CUPL to take full advantage of a PLD's architecture.

Glossary of key terms covered in this chapter:

- *Anti-fuse:* A one-time programmable connection that is originally an open circuit until it is programmed to cause a short. *[sec.12.8]*

- *Complex Mode:* A mode of operation used by the GAL 16V8A. This mode is used to implement SOP combinational logic with tri-state outputs that are enabled by an AND product expression. *[sec.12.3]*

- *Complex PLDs (CPLDs):* Also referred to as multi-level arrays, are devices that combine a number of PAL type circuits on the same chip. The logic blocks are programmable AND, fixed OR, with fewer product terms than most PAL devices. *[sec.12.8]*

- *CPLDs:* see Complex PLDs

- *CUPL (Universal Compiler for Programmable Logic:* One of the most popular high-level compilers available today for the development of PLDs. *[sec.12.5]*

- *Feedback Multiplexer (FMUX):* A multiplexer within an Output Logic Macro Cell (OLMC) that selects the logic signal that is fed back to the input matrix of a GAL16V8A. *[sec.12.3]*

- *Field Programmable Gate Arrays (FPGAs):* FPGAs offer a number of configurable logic blocks that contain programmable combinational logic and registers for sequential circuits. All of the configurable logic blocks and input/output blocks can be programmably interconnected to implement virtually any logic circuit. *[sec.12.8]*

- *Field Programmable Logic Array (FPLA):* A more flexible PLA that combines the characteristics of the PROM and the PAL by providing both a programmable OR array and a programmable AND array. *[sec.12.2]*

- *FMUX: see Feedback Multiplexer*

- *FPGAs:* see Field Programmable Gate Arrays

- *FPLA:* see Field Programmable Logic Array

- *Fuse Plot:* A file that is like a map that shows which fuses in a programmable device are to be fused open and which ones are to remain intact. *[sec.12.4]*

- *GAL 16V8A:* A generic array logic manufactured by Lattice Semiconductor. The GAL 16V8A uses an EEPROM array. *[sec.12.3]*

- *Gate Arrays:* ULSI circuits that offer hundreds of thousands of gates. They are often referred to as MPGA (mask programmed gate arrays. *[sec.12.8]*

- *ISP:* In-System Programmable. *[sec.12.8]*

- *JEDEC File:* A standardized file which is loaded into any JEDEC-compatible PLD programmer that is capable of programming the desired type of PLD. *[sec.12.4]*

- *JEDEC:* Joint Electronic Device Engineering Council. *[sec.12.4]*

- *Mask Programmed Gate Array:* see Gate Arrays.

- *MPGA: (Mask programmed gate array):* see Gate Arrays.

- *OLMC: see Output Logic Macro Cells*

- *OMUX: see Output Multiplexer*

- *Output Logic Macro Cells (OLMC):* Vital output logic circuitry of a GAL16V8 device. Products (outputs of AND gates) are applied as inputs to the OLMC and then these products are ORed together within the OLMC to generate the sum-of-products. *[sec.12.3]*

- *Output Multiplexer (OMUX):* Two input multiplexer within an Output Logic Macro Cell (OLMC). *[sec.12.3]*

- *PAL:* see Programmable Array Logic

- *PLD:* see Programmable Logic Device

- *Product Term Multiplexer (PTMUX):* Multiplexer within an Output Logic Macro Cell (OLMC). *[sec.12.3]*

- *Programmable Array Logic (PAL):* A type of Programmable Logic Device that contains an array of AND gates and OR gates as with PROMs, but in the PAL the inputs to the AND gates are programmable while the inputs to the OR gates are hard-wired. *[sec.12.2]*

- *Programmable Logic Device (PLD):* An IC that contains a large number of interconnected logic functions. The user can program the IC for a specific function by selectively breaking the appropriate interconnections. *[sec.12.1]*

- *Programmable ROM (PROM):* A ROM that can be electrically programmed by the user. It cannot be erased and reprogrammed. *[sec.12.2]*

- *PROP:* see Programmable ROM

- *PTMUX: see Product Term Multiplexer*

- *Registered Mode:* A mode of operation used by the GAL 16V8. This mode allows individual OLMCs to operate in combinational configuration with tri-state outputs or in a synchronous mode with clocked D FFs synchronized to a common clock signal. *[sec.12.3]*

- *Simple Mode:* A mode of operation used by the GAL16V8. This mode is used to implement simple SOP combinational without tri-state outputs. *[sec.12.3]*

- *SOP (Sum-of-Products):* In a GAL16V8, an OLMC will OR together eight different products in order to generate the SOP. *[sec.12.3]*

- **TSMUX (Tri-State Multiplexer):** Four input tri-state multiplexer within an Output Logic Macro Cell (OLMC). *[sec.12.3]*

- **VHDL:** VHSIC Hardware Description Language.*[sec.12.8]*

- **VHSIC:** Very High-Speed Integrated Circuit.*[sec.12.8]*

Problems

SECTIONS 12.1-12.2   *Fundamentals of PLD Circuitry/PLD Architecture*

12.1 Program the fusible links in the circuit of Figure 12.1 so that the following Sum-of-product outputs are obtained:

(Note: A blown OR input acts as a logic 0)

$$O1 = 1$$
$$O2 = 0$$
$$O3 = AB$$
$$O4 = \overline{A}\,\overline{B} + \overline{A}\,B$$

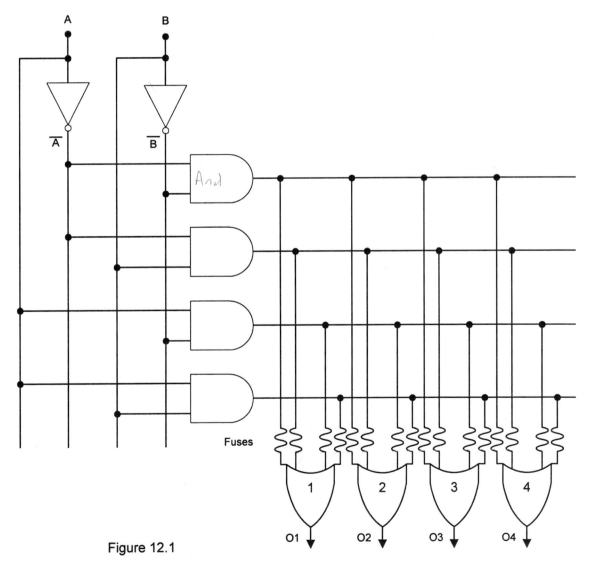

Figure 12.1

12.2 Determine the Boolean expression for the programmed output functions (O0-O3) of the PROM shown in Figure 12.2. Simplify the final expressions using Karnaugh maps.

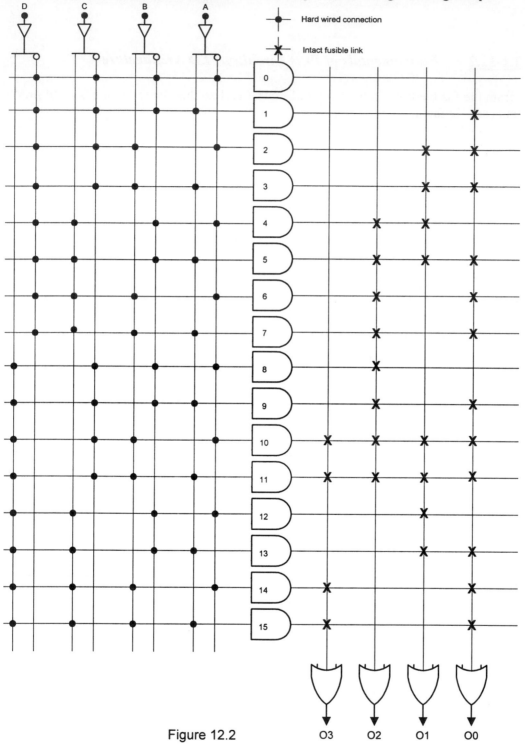

Figure 12.2

12.3 Program the unprogrammed PAL of Figure 12.3 by removing the appropriate Xs, so that its output logic functions are equivalent to those of the PROM of Figure 12.3.

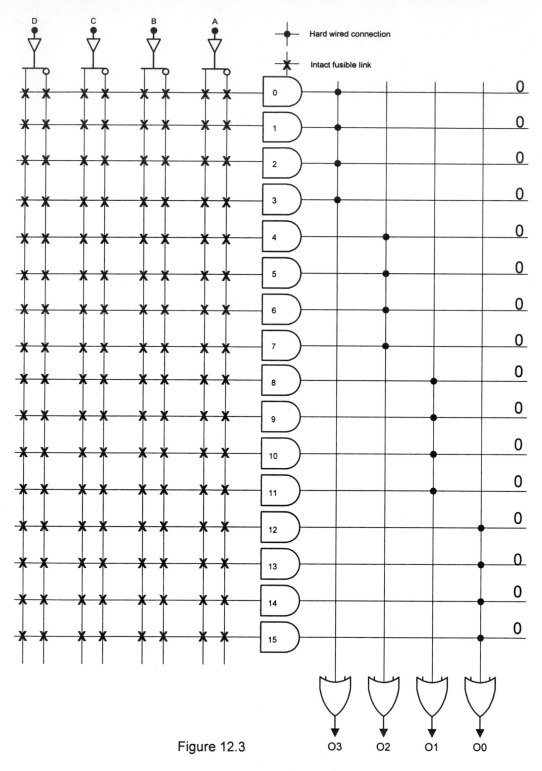

Figure 12.3

12.4   (a)   How will the operation of the PAL of Figure 12.3 be affected if the output of AND gate 0 is shorted to ground?

      (b)   Repeat (a) but with the output of AND gate 0 shorted to Vcc.

SECTIONS 12.3-12.4 *The GAL16V8/Relating CUPL Fuse Plots to GAL16V8 Architecture*

12.5   Complete the following statements by filling in the blank spaces.

      (a)   The major components of the GAL16V8 devices are the input term _____, the _____ gates,

          and the _____ _____ _____ _____ (OLMC)

      (b)   Within each OLMC the products are _____ together to generate the SOP.

      (c)   The GAL16V8 has three different modes of operation. They are the _____ mode, the

          _____ mode, and the _____ mode.

12.6   What must be the conditions of signals SYN, AC0, and AC1 in order to program the GAL16V8 in *complex mode*?

12.7   Refer to the Simple Combinational Logic Implementation of Figure 12.4. Determine the SOP expression present at output Z of the OLMC 19.

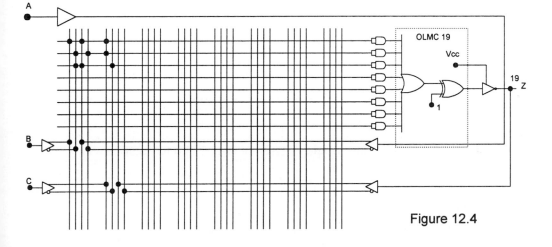

Figure 12.4

12.8   Complete the table below by determining the proper logic levels for the signals *SYN*, *AC0* and *ACI*.

Mode	Configuration	SYN	AC0	AC1
Simple mode	IN			
	OUT			
Complex mode				
Registered mode	Registered			
	Combinational			

SECTION 12.5   *Design Problems*

12.9   A compiler generates a documentation file that shows the reduced expression:
X = !A # !C & D # A $ B # !B & D. Express the simplified expression using the conventional logic format.

12.10   On the next page, write the source file that would program a GAL16V8 to function as a 1-of-4 decoder.

Source File

12.11 Write the equations in CUPL format that will implement the synchronous counter stated in problem 7.14(a) of this study guide.

Source File

SECTION 12.6   *The GAL 22V10*

12.12   Complete the following statements:

    (a)   The GAL 22V10 has _____ output pins.

    (b)   Each OR gate in the GAL 22V10 does not combine the same number of _____ _____

    (c)   In the GAL 22V10, the AR input stands for _____ _____.

    (d)   In the GAL 22V10, the SP input stands for _____ _____.

    (e)   In the GAL 22V10, the number of product terms range from ____ to ____.

SECTION 12.8   *Advanced PLD Development*

12.13   (a)   What is the major advantage that the ISPGAL22V10 has over the GAL22V10?

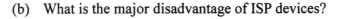

    _____

    _____

    _____

    _____

    (b)   What is the major disadvantage of ISP devices?

    _____

12.14   Complete the following statements:

    (a)   _____ are devices that combine an array of PAL-type devices on the same chip.

    (b)   _____ offer a number of configurable logic blocks that contain programmable combinational logic and registers for sequential circuits.

    (c)   _____ _____are ULSI circuits that offer hundreds of thousands of gates.

    (d)   VHDL stands for _____ _____ _____ _____.

    (e)   A one-time programmable connection that is originally an open circuit until it is programmed to cause a short is often referred to as an _____.

TEST 12

1. Which configuration of the GAL16V8 is capable of getting eight product terms into a SOP expression to generate a combinational output.

    (a) Simple mode/dedicated input.   (b) Simple mode/dedicated combinational output.
    (c) Complex mode   (d) Registered output.

2. A certain design uses some basic gates, a D latch, and has a tri-state output. Which mode of operation should the GAL16V8 be programmed for?

    (a)   Simple   (b)   Complex   (c)   Registered   (d)   Any of the above

3. The ! sign is used by the CUPL in order to denote which operation?

    (a) XOR   (b) OR   (c) NOT   (d) AND

4. The XOR gates present at the output of some of the OLMCs are used:

    (a)   as a SYN signal.   (b)   to program the output polarity.
    (c)   to allow the I/O pin to be used a an input.   (d)   as a feedback signal to the input matrix.

5. The following equation when expressed in words means: *The D input of the QA flip-flop is connected to the complement of the QA output.*

    (a) QA\$D = $\overline{QA}$ (b) QA#D = !QA   (c) QA.D = $\overline{QA}$ (d) QA.D = !QA

6. The following are used to enclose any comments that might make the input file more understandable:

    (a) "/!" and "!/"   (b) "/*" and "*/"   (c) "/#" and "#/"   (d) "/\$" and "\$/"

7. In the GAL22V10 the input labeled AR allows the user to:

    (a) Reset all of the FFs (b) Preset all of the FFs
    (c) Recall the status of all FFs. (d) None of the above

8. ISP devices are available only in:

    (a)   SSI packages   (b)   MSI packages   (c)   GAL22V120s   (d)   PLCC packages

9. The GAL16V8 has JK flip-flops in some of the OLMCs.

    (a) True   (b) False

10. CPLDs are devices that combine an array of PAL-type devices on the same chip.

    (a) True   (b) False

1   INTRODUCTORY CONCEPTS

SECTION 1.1 Numerical Representations

1.1   (a)   ANALOG is the continuous representation of a quantity, while DIGITAL is the discrete representation of a quantity.

       (b)   Systems in which both analog and digital quantities are manipulated are called HYBRID.

SECTION 1.2 Digital and Analog Systems

1.2   1. Digital systems are generally easier to design
       2. Information storage is easy
       3. Accuracy and precision are greater
       4. Operation can be programmed
       5. Digital circuits are less affected by noise
       6. More digital circuitry can be fabricated in IC chips

SECTION 1.3 Digital Number Systems

1.3   (a) $10110_2 = (\underline{1} \times 2^4) + (\underline{0} \times 2^3) + (\underline{1} \times 2^2) + (\underline{1} \times 2^1) + (\underline{0} \times 2^0) = \mathbf{22_{10}}$

       (b) $11101_2 = (\underline{1} \times 2^4) + (\underline{1} \times 2^3) + (\underline{1} \times 2^2) + (\underline{0} \times 2^1) + (\underline{1} \times 2^0) = \mathbf{29_{10}}$

       (c) $11011110110010_2 = (\underline{1} \times 2^{13}) + (\underline{1} \times 2^{12}) + (\underline{0} \times 2^{11}) + (\underline{1} \times 2^{10}) +$
         $+ (\underline{1} \times 2^9) + (\underline{1} \times 2^8) + (\underline{1} \times 2^7) + (\underline{0} \times 2^6) + (\underline{1} \times 2^5) + (\underline{1} \times 2^4) +$
         $+ (\underline{0} \times 2^3) + (\underline{0} \times 2^2) + (\underline{1} \times 2^1) + (\underline{0} \times 2^0) = \mathbf{14258_{10}}$

       (d) $1101.1101_2 = (\underline{1} \times 2^3) + (\underline{1} \times 2^2) + (\underline{0} \times 2^1) + (\underline{1} \times 2^0) + (\underline{1} \times 2^{-4}) +$
         $+ (\underline{1} \times 2^{-3}) + (\underline{0} \times 2^{-2}) + (\underline{1} \times 2^{-1}) = \mathbf{13.8125_{10}}$

       (e) $0.1110111101_2 = (\underline{1} \times 2^{-1}) + (\underline{1} \times 2^{-2}) + (\underline{1} \times 2^{-3}) + (\underline{0} \times 2^{-4}) + (\underline{1} \times 2^{-5}) + (\underline{1} \times 2^{-6}) + (\underline{1} \times 2^{-7})$
         $+ (\underline{0} \times 2^{-8}) + (\underline{1} \times 2^{-9}) = \mathbf{0.93164_{10}}$

1.4 $(2^N - 1) = (2^{12} - 1) = \mathbf{4095_{10}} = 111111111111_2$

1.5 $2^9 = 512_{10}$ and $2^{10} = 1024_{10}$. Therefore, we need **10** binary bits.

1.6   Counts $\mathbf{0100_2}$, $\mathbf{1010_2}$ and $\mathbf{1110_2}$ are missing from the expected descending sequence.

SECTION 1.6 *Parallel and Serial Transmission*

1.7 10110110_2

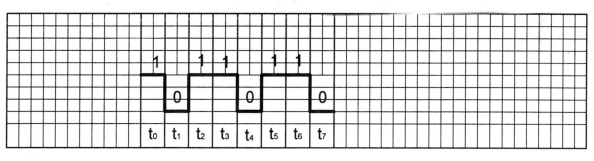

   In this example the LSB (t_0) is the first bit to be transmitted.

1.8   Since 8 bits have to be transmitted and each bit takes 10 μs to transmit, the complete serial transmission will take 80 μs.

1.9   In the circuit of Figure 1.1(b) all eight bits are transmitted simultaneously (***parallel*** transmission), compared with one bit at a time for the circuit of Figure 1.1(a) (***serial*** transmission). Thus, the circuit of Figure 1.1(b) is eight times faster than the circuit of Figure 1.1(a).

1.10 10110110_2

   In this example the MSB (t_0) is the first bit to be transmitted.

1.11 In parallel transmissions all bits are transmitted at once. Therefore, the number of lines required between the transmitter and the receiver must be equal to the number of bits being transmitted. Thus, ***ten*** lines are necessary to transmit 1100011010_2 using the parallel transmission method.

SECTION 1.8 *Digital Computers*

1.12   1 - *Input Unit* 2 - *Memory Unit* 3 - *Arithmetic Logic Unit* 4 - *Output Unit* 5 - *Control Unit*

1.13 The CPU contains all of the circuitry for fetching and interpreting instructions, and controlling and performing the various operations called by the instructions.

1.14 A microprocessor is a chip that contains the control unit and the arithmetic logic unit (ALU). microcontroller is a chip that contains a microprocessor as well as input/output devices and memory

2   NUMBER SYSTEMS AND CODES

SECTION 2.1 *Binary-to-Decimal Conversions*

2.1   Recall that the Binary number system is a *positional-value system*.

(a) $1101_2 = (\underline{1} \times 2^3) + (\underline{1} \times 2^2) + (\underline{0} \times 2^1) + (\underline{1} \times 2^0) = \mathbf{13}_{10}$

(b) $1010_2 = (\underline{1} \times 2^3) + (\underline{0} \times 2^2) + (\underline{1} \times 2^1) + (\underline{0} \times 2^0) = \mathbf{10}_{10}$

(c) $1100011010_2 = (\underline{1} \times 2^9) + (\underline{1} \times 2^8) + (\underline{0} \times 2^7) + (\underline{0} \times 2^6) + (\underline{0} \times 2^5) + (\underline{1} \times 2^4) + (\underline{1} \times 2^3) +$
        $+ (\underline{0} \times 2^2) + (\underline{1} \times 2^1) + (\underline{0} \times 2^0) = \mathbf{794}_{10}$

(d) $1000001101_2 = (\underline{1} \times 2^9) + (\underline{0} \times 2^8) + (\underline{0} \times 2^7) + (\underline{0} \times 2^6) + (\underline{0} \times 2^5) + (\underline{0} \times 2^4) + (\underline{1} \times 2^3) +$
        $+ (\underline{1} \times 2^2) + (\underline{0} \times 2^1) + (\underline{1} \times 2^0) = \mathbf{525}_{10}$

(e) $11101_2 = (\underline{1} \times 2^4) + (\underline{1} \times 2^3) + (\underline{1} \times 2^2) + (\underline{0} \times 2^1) + (\underline{1} \times 2^0) = \mathbf{29}_{10}$

SECTION 2.2 *Decimal-to-Binary Conversions*

Converting decimal numbers to their binary equivalent can be done by using two different methods:

One way

By adding together the *weights* of the various positions in the binary number which contain a 1.

2.2   (a) $51_{10} = 32+16+0+0+2+1$
                    $= (1 \times 2^5) + (1 \times 2^4) + (0 \times 2^3) + (0 \times 2^2) + (1 \times 2^1) + (1 \times 2^0) = 110011_2$

            Thus, $51_{10} = \mathbf{110011}_2$

            (b) $13_{10} = 8+4+0+1$
                    $= (1 \times 2^3) + (1 \times 2^2) + (0 \times 2^1) + (1 \times 2^0) = 1101_2$

            Thus, $13_{10} = \mathbf{1101}_2$

Another way

By using the <u>Repeated Division</u> method.

(c) $137/2$ = 68_{10} + remainder of 1 (LSB)
    $68/2$ = 34_{10} + remainder of 0
    $34/2$ = 17_{10} + remainder of 0
    $17/2$ = 8_{10} + remainder of 1
     $8/2$ = 4_{10} + remainder of 0
     $4/2$ = 2_{10} + remainder of 0
     $2/2$ = 1_{10} + remainder of 0
     $1/2$ = 0_{10} + remainder of 1 (MSB)

Thus, 137_{10} = 10001001_2

(d) $567/2$ = 283_{10} + remainder of 1 (LSB)
  $283/2$ = 141_{10} + remainder of 1
  $141/2$ = 70_{10} + remainder of 1
   $70/2$ = 35_{10} + remainder of 0
   $35/2$ = 17_{10} + remainder of 1
   $17/2$ = 8_{10} + remainder of 1
    $8/2$ = 4_{10} + remainder of 0
    $4/2$ = 2_{10} + remainder of 0
    $2/2$ = 1_{10} + remainder of 0
    $1/2$ = 0_{10} + remainder of 1 (MSB)

Thus, 567_{10} = 1000110111_2

(e) $777/2$ = 388_{10} + remainder of 1 (LSB)
  $388/2$ = 194_{10} + remainder of 0
  $194/2$ = 97_{10} + remainder of 0
   $97/2$ = 48_{10} + remainder of 1
   $48/2$ = 24_{10} + remainder of 0
   $24/2$ = 12_{10} + remainder of 0
   $12/2$ = 6_{10} + remainder of 0
    $6/2$ = 3_{10} + remainder of 0
    $3/2$ = 1_{10} + remainder of 1
    $1/2$ = 0_{10} + remainder of 1 (MSB)

Thus, 777_{10} = 1100001001_2

(f) $1000/2$ = 500_{10} + remainder of 0 (LSB)

        $500/2$ = 250_{10} + remainder of 0

        $250/2$ = 125_{10} + remainder of 0

        $125/2$ = 62_{10} + remainder of 1

        $62/2$ = 31_{10} + remainder of 0

        $31/2$ = 15_{10} + remainder of 1

        $15/2$ = 7_{10} + remainder of 1

        $7/2$ = 3_{10} + remainder of 1

        $3/2$ = 1_{10} + remainder of 1

        $1/2$ = 0_{10} + remainder of 1 (MSB)

Thus, $1000_{10} = \boldsymbol{1111101000_2}$

2.3 $(2^N - 1) = 1023_{10}$; $N = 10$. Therefore, we need **10 binary bits**.

2.4   The highest decimal number that can be represented by a 16-bit number is:
$(2^N - 1) = (2^{16} - 1) = (65,536 - 1) = \boldsymbol{65,535_{10}}$

SECTION 2.3 Octal Number System

2.5   Recall that the Octal number system is a *positional-value system*.

(a) $217_8 = (2 \times 8^2)+(1 \times 8^1)+(7 \times 8^0) = \boldsymbol{143_{10}}$

(b) $55_8 = (5 \times 8^1)+(5 \times 8^0) = \boldsymbol{45_{10}}$

(c) $5076_8 = (5 \times 8^3)+(0 \times 8^2)+(7 \times 8^1)+(6 \times 8^0) = \boldsymbol{2622_{10}}$

(d) $511_8 = (5 \times 8^2)+(1 \times 8^1)+(1 \times 8^0) = \boldsymbol{329_{10}}$

(e) $100_8 = (1 \times 8^2)+(0 \times 8^1)+(0 \times 8^0) = \boldsymbol{64_{10}}$

(f) $898_8 = $ Illegal octal number. Octal numbers *cannot* have digits greater than 7_{10}.

2.6   (a) $323/8$ =   40   + remainder of 3 (LSD)

             $40/8$ =   5   + remainder of 0

             $5/8$ =   0   + remainder of 5 (MSD)

        Thus, $323_{10} = \boldsymbol{503_8}$

(b) $123/8$ =   15   + remainder of 3 (LSD)

             $15/8$ =   1   + remainder of 7

             $1/8$ =   0   + remainder of 1 (MSD)

Thus, $123_{10} = \boldsymbol{173_8}$

(c) $\begin{array}{rcl} 898/8 &=& 112 \\ 112/8 &=& 14 \\ 14/8 &=& 1 \\ 1/8 &=& 0 \end{array}$ + remainder of 2 (LSD)
+ remainder of 0
+ remainder of 6
+ remainder of 1 (MSD)

Thus, $898_{10} = 1602_8$

(d) $\begin{array}{rcl} 32536/8 &=& 4067 \\ 4067/8 &=& 508 \\ 508/8 &=& 63 \\ 63/8 &=& 7 \\ 7/8 &=& 0 \end{array}$ + remainder of 0 (LSD)
+ remainder of 3
+ remainder of 4
+ remainder of 7
+ remainder of 7 (MSD)

Thus, $32536_{10} = 77430_8$

(e) $\begin{array}{rcl} 245/8 &=& 30 \\ 30/8 &=& 3 \\ 3/8 &=& 0 \end{array}$ + remainder of 5 (LSD)
+ remainder of 6
+ remainder of 3 (MSD)

Thus, $245_{10} = 365_8$

(f) $\begin{array}{rcl} 2000/8 &=& 250 \\ 250/8 &=& 31 \\ 31/8 &=& 3 \\ 3/8 &=& 0 \end{array}$ + remainder of 0 (LSD)
+ remainder of 2
+ remainder of 7
+ remainder of 3 (MSD)

Thus, $2000_{10} = 3720_8$

2.7   It requires three binary bits to represent any single octal digit.

(a) $217_8 = 010\ 001\ 111$

   Thus, $217_8 = 010001111_2$

(b) $55_8 = 101\ 101$

   Thus, $55_8 = 101101_2$

(c) $5076_8 = 101\ 000\ 111\ 110$

   Thus, $5076_8 = 101000111110_2$

(d) $511_8 = 101\ 001\ 001$

   Thus, $511_8 = 101001001_2$

(e) $100_8 = 001\ 000\ 000$

   Thus, $100_8 = 001000000_2$

(f) $898_8 = 1000\ 1001\ 1000$

898 is an illegal octal number. Only three binary bits can be used to represent any octal digit. Clearly, this limits the range of octal digits from 0_8 to 7_8. Therefore, any octal number which may contain digits greater than 7_8 (111_2) is an illegal octal number.

2.8   To convert a binary number to its octal equivalent, the bits that make the binary number must be grouped into groups of three, starting with the LSB and moving towards the MSB.

   (a) $1101_2 = 001\ 101 = 15_8$

   (b) $1010_2 = 001\ 010 = 12_8$

   (c) $1100011010_2 = 001\ 100\ 011\ 010 = 1432_8$

   (d) $1000001101_2 = 001\ 000\ 001\ 101 = 1015_8$

   (e) $11101_2 = 011\ 101 = 35_8$

SECTION 2.4 *Hexadecimal Number System*

2.9   Recall that the Hexadecimal number system is a *positional-value system*.

   (a) $FF_{16} = (15 \times 16^1) + (15 \times 16^0) = 255_{10}$

   (b) $AD3_{16} = (10 \times 16^2) + (13 \times 16^1) + (3 \times 16^0) = 2771_{10}$

   (c) $589_{16} = (5 \times 16^2) + (8 \times 16^1) + (9 \times 16^0) = 1417_{10}$

   (d) $3AFD_{16} = (3 \times 16^3) + (10 \times 16^2) + (15 \times 16^1) + (13 \times 16^0) = 15101_{10}$

   (e) $FEED_{16} = (15 \times 16^3) + (14 \times 16^2) + (14 \times 16^1) + (13 \times 16^0 = 65261_{10}$

   (f) $00FA_{16} = (0 \times 16^3) + (0 \times 16^2) + (15 \times 16^1) + (10 \times 16^0) = 250_{10}$

2.10   (a) $323/16 = 20$ + remainder of 3 (LSD)
                $20/16 = 1$ + remainder of 4
                $1/16 = 0$ + remainder of 1 (MSD)

   Thus, $323_{10} = 143_{16}$

   (b) $123/16 = 7$ + remainder of 11 (LSD)
          $7/16 = 0$ + remainder of 7 (MSD)

   Thus, $123_{10} = 7B_{16}$

(c)   898/16 =   56   + remainder of 2 (LSD)
        56/16 =   3   + remainder of 8
         3/16 =   0   + remainder of 3 (MSD)

Thus, $898_{10} = 382_{16}$

(d)   32536/16 =   2033   + remainder of 8 (LSD)
        2033/16 =   127   + remainder of 1
         127/16 =   7   + remainder of 15
           7/16 =   0   + remainder of 7 (MSD)

Thus, $32536_{10} = 7F18_{16}$

(e)   245/16 =   15   + remainder of 5 (LSD)
        15/16 =   0   + remainder of 15 (MSD)

Thus, $245_{10} = F5_{16}$

(f)   2000/16 =   125   + remainder of 0 (LSD)
        125/16 =   7   + remainder of 13
          7/16 =   0   + remainder of 7

Thus, $2000_{10} = 7D0_{16}$

2.11   It requires four binary bits to represent any hexadecimal digit.

(a) $FF_{16} = 1111\ 1111$

Thus, $FF_{16} = 11111111_2$

(b) $AD3_{16} = 1010\ 1101\ 0011$

Thus, $AD3_{16} = 101011010011_2$

(c) $589_{16} = 0101\ 1000\ 1001$

Thus, $589_{16} = 010110001001_2$

(d) $3AFD_{16} = 0011\ 1010\ 1111\ 1101$

Thus, $3AFD_{16} = 0011101011111101_2$

(e) $FEED_{16} = 1111\ 1110\ 1110\ 1101$

Thus, $FEED_{16} = 1111111011101101_2$

(f) $00FA_{16} = 0000\ 0000\ 1111\ 1010$

Thus, $00FA_{16} = 0000000011111010_2$

2.12   To convert a binary number to its hexadecimal equivalent, we must divide the binary number into groups of four bits, starting with the LSB and moving towards the MSB.

   (a) $1101_2 = D_{16}$

   (b) $1010_2 = A_{16}$

   (c) $110001 1010_2 = 0011\ 0001\ 1010_2 = 31A_{16}$

   When binary zeros are added to the left of the MSB, the binary number is not affected.

   (d) $1000001101_2 = 0010\ 0000\ 1101_2 = 20D_{16}$

   (e) $11101_2 = 0001\ 1101_2 = 1D_{16}$

2.13   (a) $1230_5 = (1 \times 5^3) + (2 \times 5^2) + (3 \times 5^1) + (0 \times 5^0) = 190_{10}$

   (b)
$$
\begin{array}{lll}
777/5 & = & 155 \quad + \quad \text{remainder of 2 (LSD)} \\
155/5 & = & 31 \quad + \quad \text{remainder of 0} \\
31/5 & = & 6 \quad + \quad \text{remainder of 1} \\
6/5 & = & 1 \quad + \quad \text{remainder of 1} \\
1/5 & = & 0 \quad + \quad \text{remainder of 1 (MSD)}
\end{array}
$$

   Thus, $777_{10} = 11102_5$

2.14   (a) $333_4 = (3 \times 4^2) + (3 \times 4^1) + (3 \times 4^0) = 63_{10}$

   (b)
$$
\begin{array}{lll}
777/4 & = & 194 \quad + \quad \text{remainder of 1 (LSD)} \\
194/4 & = & 48 \quad + \quad \text{remainder of 2} \\
48/4 & = & 12 \quad + \quad \text{remainder of 0} \\
12/4 & = & 3 \quad + \quad \text{remainder of 0} \\
3/4 & = & 0 \quad + \quad \text{remainder of 3 (MSD)}
\end{array}
$$

   Thus, $777_{10} = 30021_4$

2.15   (a) $96_{16}, 97_{16}, 98_{16}, 99_{16}, 9A_{16}, 9B_{16}, 9C_{16}, 9D_{16}, 9E_{16}, 9F_{16}, A0_{16}, A1_{16}, A2_{16}, A3_{16}, A4_{16}, A5_{16}, A6_{16}, A7_{16}, A8_{16}, A9_{16}, AA_{16}, AB_{16}, AC_{16}, AD_{16}, AE_{16}, AF_{16}.$

2.16   A hex digit requires 4 bits to represent. Consequently, 32 bits are needed to express an eight digit hex number. The highest decimal number that can be expressed with 32 bits is $(2^N - 1) = (2^{32} - 1) = 4,294,967,295$. Therefore, the range of decimal numbers that can be represented with an eight digit hex number is from 0 to 4,294,967,295.

SECTION 2.5 BCD Code

2.17   (a) 63_{10} =   *0110 0011*$_{BCD}$

(b) 105_{10} =   *0001 0000 0101*$_{BCD}$

(c) 757_{10} =   *0111 0101 0111*$_{BCD}$

(d) 999_{10} =   *1001 1001 1001*$_{BCD}$

(e) 36543_{10} =   *0011 0110 0101 0100 0011*$_{BCD}$

(f) 777_{10} =   *0111 0111 0111*$_{BCD}$

2.18   (a)   0111 0100 0010 1001$_{BCD}$ = *7429*$_{10}$

(b)   **1010** 0010 0111$_{BCD}$ = *?27*$_{10}$

|___|

|_____ Illegal BCD code

☝ *1010*$_2$, *1011*$_2$, *1100*$_2$, *1101*$_2$, *1110*$_2$, and *1111*$_2$ are illegal BCD codes.

(c) 0101 0011 1001$_{BCD}$ = *539*$_{10}$

SECTION 2.6 Putting it All Together

2.19   First we must convert the decimal number 1000_{10} to binary. We can use the repeated divis method.

1000/2	=	500	+ remainder of 0 (LSB)
500/2	=	250	+ remainder of 0
250/2	=	125	+ remainder of 0
125/2	=	62	+ remainder of 1
62/2	=	31	+ remainder of 0
31/2	=	15	+ remainder of 1
15/2	=	7	+ remainder of 1
7/2	=	3	+ remainder of 1
3/2	=	1	+ remainder of 1
1/2	=	0	+ remainder of 1 (MSB)

Thus, 1000_{10} = *1111101000*$_2$

Now, in order to convert from binary to octal the binary number has to be divided into groups of three bits, starting with the LSB. Thus, $1111101000_2 = 1\ 111\ 101\ 000_2$. Next, each individual group of three bits is evaluated. Hence, $1\ 111\ 101\ 000_2 = 1750_8$.

In order to convert from binary to hexadecimal the binary number has to be divided into groups of four bits, starting with the LSB. Thus, $1111101000_2 = 11\ 1110\ 1000_2$. Next, each individual group of four bits is evaluated. Hence, $11\ 1110\ 1000_2 = 3E8_{16}$.

Finally, in order to convert from decimal to BCD each individual decimal digit has to be expressed by using four binary bits. Thus, $1000_{10} = 0001\ 0000\ 0000\ 0000_{BCD}$.

SECTION 2.7 The Byte

2.20   Four bits are needed to represent a hex digit. Therefore, *two* bytes (16 bits) are needed to represent a four hex digit number.

2.21   There are 24 binary bits in three bytes of data (8-bits/byte). It requires three binary bits to represent an octal digit. Consequently, the largest octal value that can be represented by three bytes is 77777777_8 ($111\ 111\ 111\ 111\ 111\ 111\ 111\ 111_2$).

SECTION 2.8 Alphanumerical Codes

2.22   Take each character in the message, look up its ASCII code, and attach an even parity bit as the leftmost bit.

FLOPPY A - OK	7-bit ASCII code with an even parity bit
F	1100 0110
L	1100 1100
O	1100 1111
P	0101 0000
P	0101 0000
Y	0101 1001
(blank)	1010 0000
A	0100 0001
(blank)	1010 0000
-	0010 1101
(blank)	1010 0000
O	1100 1111
K	0100 1011

2.23   *Refer to the Partial Listing of ASCII Codes in Chapter 2 of your textbook.*

Note that padding was performed by adding a $\underline{0}$ to the leftmost bit of each ASCII code.

$$H \;=\; \underline{0}100 \;\; 1000 \;=\; 48_{16}$$
$$E \;=\; \underline{0}100 \;\; 0101 \;=\; 45_{16}$$
$$L \;=\; \underline{0}100 \;\; 1100 \;=\; 4C_{16}$$
$$L \;=\; \underline{0}100 \;\; 1100 \;=\; 4C_{16}$$
$$O \;=\; \underline{0}100 \;\; 1111 \;=\; 4F_{16}$$

Thus, the five hex numbers stored in memory representing the word HELLO are: 48_{16}, 45_{16}, $4C_{16}$, $4C_{16}$, and $4F_{16}$.

SECTION 2.9 Parity Method For Error Detection

2.24   (a) $\underline{1}00110001_2$
         |_____ Even parity bit.

        (b) $\underline{0}100001_2$
         |_____ Even parity bit.

        (c) $\underline{0}10011001_2$
         |_____ Even parity bit.

        (d) $\underline{0}11111111_2$
         |_____ Even parity bit.

2.25   Since the receiver will be checking for odd parity the transmitter must be sending data that have been coded with an odd parity bit. The transmitted data would have to be changed as follows:

        (a) $\underline{0}00110001_2$
         |_____ Odd parity bit.

        (b) $\underline{1}100001_2$
         |_____ Odd parity bit.

        (c) $\underline{1}10011001_2$
         |_____ Odd parity bit.

        (d) $\underline{1}11111111_2$
         |_____ Odd parity bit.

2.26   *Refer to the Partial Listing of ASCII Codes in Chapter 2 of your textbook.*

FLIP-FLOP	**Message Transmitted**		**Message Stored**	
F	0100 0110 =	46_{16}	1100 0110 =	$C6_{16}$
L	0100 1100 =	$4C_{16}$	1100 1100 =	CC_{16}
I	0100 1001 =	49_{16}	1100 1001 =	$C9_{16}$
P	1101 0000 =	$D0_{16}$	0101 0000 =	50_{16}
-	1010 1101 =	AD_{16}	0010 1101 =	$2D_{16}$
F	0100 0110 =	46_{16}	1100 0110 =	$C6_{16}$
L	0100 1100 =	$4C_{16}$	1100 1100 =	CC_{16}
O	0100 1111 =	$4F_{16}$	1100 1111 =	CF_{16}
P	1101 0000 =	$D0_{16}$	0101 0000 =	50_{16}

By comparing the "Message Transmitted" with the "Message Stored" in the computer's memory, it can be observed that the codes received have the wrong parity bit. In fact, all of the codes received have had an <u>even</u> parity bit rather than an odd parity bit added to the original 7-bit ASCII code. Thus, it appears that the transmitter added an even parity bit instead of an odd parity bit to each and all of the ASCII codes transmitted.

In cases such as this, the parity checker (special circuit) in the receiver, which in this case would have been checking for odd parity, detected an error for each ASCII code received. Therefore, in this particular example a problem exists with the parity generator (special circuit) in the transmitter. It may be malfunctioning or simply programmed for even rather than odd parity generation.

SECTION 2.10 Applications

2.27   A byte is 8 bits, and Mega is 2^{20}. A CD-ROM that can hold 650-Megabytes of data can store 5,452,595,200 bits of data (650 x 2^{20} x 8). Since the ASCII code is a 7-bit code, this CD-ROM can store 778,942,171 (5,452,595,200 /7) ASCII codes.

2.28   (a)   Since this microcontroller has a 16-bit address bus, each addressable memory location will be identified with a 16-bit binary number. It requires 4 bits to represent a single hexadecimal digit. Hence, it requires four hexadecimal digits (16 bits/4 bits) to represent each memory location.

         (b)   With a 16-bit address bus, this microcontroller can address 2^{16} or 65,536 memory locations.

3 LOGIC GATES AND BOOLEAN ALGEBRA

SECTION 3.1 *Boolean Constants and Variables*

3.1   (a) Logical addition, can also be referred to as **_OR_** operation.

(b) Inversion or logical complementation is often called the **_NOT_** operation.

(c) The **_AND_** operation can also be referred to as the logical multiplication.

SECTIONS 3.2-3.5   *Truth Tables/OR Operation With OR Gates/ AND Operation With AND Gates/NOT Operation*

3.2   The output of an OR gate is LOW only when <u>all</u> of its inputs are LOW. If one or more inputs is HIGH, then the output is HIGH (Figure P3.2).

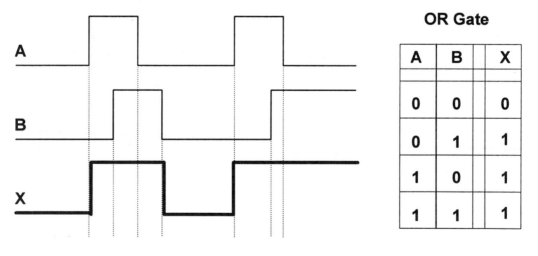

OR Gate

A	B	X
0	0	0
0	1	1
1	0	1
1	1	1

Figure P3.2

3.3

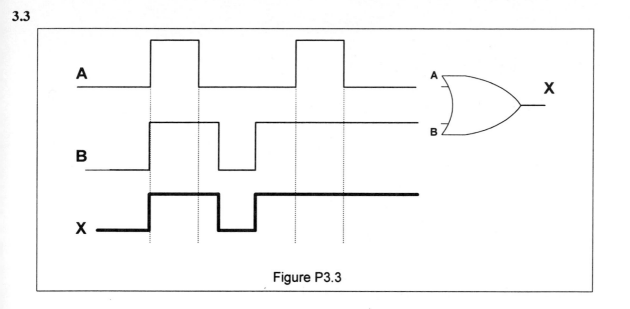

Figure P3.3

3.4 The output of a 2-input AND gate is HIGH only when <u>both</u> of its inputs are HIGH. If either or both inputs are LOW, then the output is LOW (see Figure P3.4).

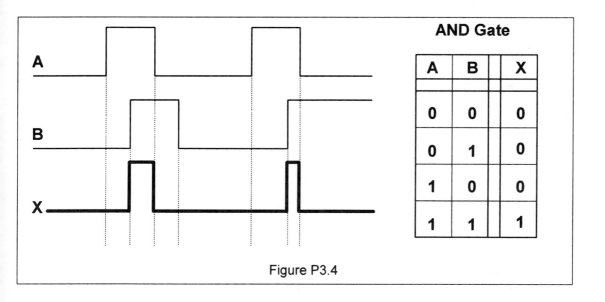

Figure P3.4

3.5

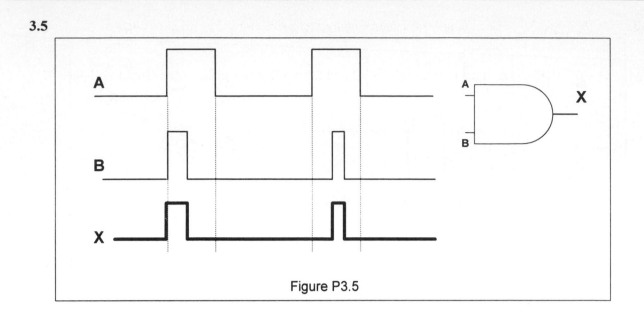

Figure P3.5

3.6   There are four possible input combinations in this circuit. The condition of X can be determined by evaluating the Boolean expression for each of the four combinations of A and B.

A	B	X = $\overline{A}$+B
0	0	1 = (1 + 0)
0	1	1 = (1 + 1)
1	0	0 = (0 + 0)
1	1	1 = (0 + 1)

3.7   (a) *False*. The output of a 3-input AND gate is HIGH *only when all* of its inputs are <u>HIGH</u>.

(b) *False*. The output of a 3-input OR gate is LOW *only when all* of its inputs are <u>LOW</u>.

(c) True.

3.8   (a) $X = A + B + C$

(b) $X = A \bullet B \bullet C$

SECTIONS 3.6-3.7 *Describing Logic Circuits Algebraically/Evaluating Logic-Circuit Outputs*

3.9 INVERTERS added to the outputs of the OR and the AND gates result in the circuit of Figure P3.9.

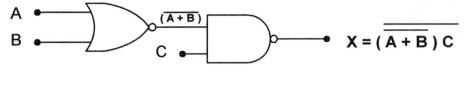

Figure P3.9

3.10 A, B, C and D are the four variables in the expression. Therefore, there are 16 (2^4) combinations.

A	B	C	D	$Y = \overline{(\overline{ABC}) + D}$
0	0	0	0	$1 = \overline{(\overline{000}) + 0}$
0	0	0	1	$0 = \overline{(\overline{000}) + 1}$
0	0	1	0	$1 = \overline{(\overline{001}) + 0}$
0	0	1	1	$0 = \overline{(\overline{001}) + 1}$
0	1	0	0	$1 = \overline{(\overline{010}) + 0}$
0	1	0	1	$0 = \overline{(\overline{010}) + 1}$
0	1	1	0	$1 = \overline{(\overline{011}) + 0}$
0	1	1	1	$0 = \overline{(\overline{011}) + 1}$
1	0	0	0	$1 = \overline{(\overline{100}) + 0}$
1	0	0	1	$0 = \overline{(\overline{100}) + 1}$
1	0	1	0	$1 = \overline{(\overline{101}) + 0}$
1	0	1	1	$0 = \overline{(\overline{101}) + 1}$
1	1	0	0	$1 = \overline{(\overline{110}) + 0}$
1	1	0	1	$0 = \overline{(\overline{110}) + 1}$
1	1	1	0	$0 = \overline{(\overline{111}) + 0}$
1	1	1	1	$0 = \overline{(\overline{111}) + 1}$

3.11 (Conditions: A=0, B=1 and C=1)

$$Y = A\,B + C\,\overline{B} + \overline{A}\,B\,C$$
$$Y = 0\,1 + 1\,\overline{1} + \overline{0}\,1\,1$$
$$Y = 0\,1 + 1\,0 + 1\,1\,1$$
$$Y = 0 + 0 + 1$$
$$Y = 1$$

SECTIONS 3.8-3.9   *Implementing Circuits From Boolean Expressions/NOR gates and NAND Gates*

3.12   (a) $X = \overline{\overline{A}\,B\,\overline{C}} + E\,F$

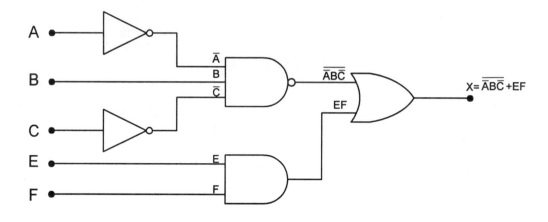

Figure P3.12a

(b) $X = \overline{\overline{A + B + \overline{C + D}}}$

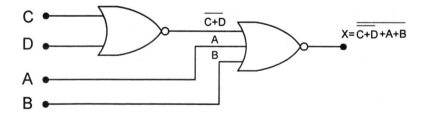

Figure P3.12b

(c) $X = \overline{(\overline{A + B})\,(\overline{B}C)}$

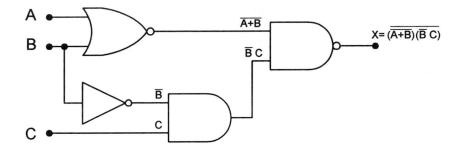

Figure P3.12c

(d) $X = \overline{(\overline{ABC})\,(A + D)}$

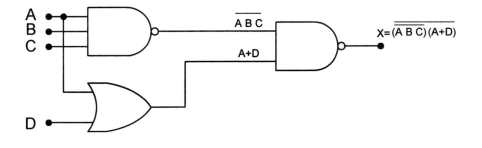

Figure P3.12d

SECTIONS 3.10 *Boolean Theorems*

3.13   (a) $X = (\overline{A} + B)(A + \overline{B})$

                                   }----> Boolean Theorem #13b

        $X = (\overline{A}\,A + \overline{A}\,\overline{B} + B\,A + B\,\overline{B})$

                                     }----> Boolean Theorem #4

        $X = (\overline{A}\,\overline{B} + A\,B)$

(b) $Y = A B C + A B \overline{C} + A \overline{B} C$

                         }----> Boolean Theorem #13a

$Y = A B (C + \overline{C}) + A \overline{B} C$

                         }----> Boolean Theorem #8

$Y = A B (1) + A \overline{B} C$

                         }----> Boolean Theorem #13a

$Y = A (B + \overline{B} C)$

                         }----> Boolean Theorem #15a

$Y = A (B + C)$

                         }----> Boolean Theorem #13a

$Y = A B + A C$

(c) $Z = \overline{A}\,\overline{B}\overline{C} + \overline{B}\overline{C}C$

                         }----> Boolean Theorem #3

$Z = \overline{A}\,\overline{B}\overline{C} + \overline{B}\overline{C}$

                         }----> Boolean Theorem #13a

$Z = \overline{B}\overline{C} (\overline{A} + 1)$

                         }----> Boolean Theorem #6

$Z = \overline{B}\overline{C}(1)$

                         }----> Boolean Theorem #2

$Z = \overline{B}\overline{C}$

(d) $W = \overline{A}BC + A\overline{B}C + \overline{A}\overline{B}C$

                         }----> Boolean Theorem #13a

$W = \overline{B}C(A + \overline{A}) + \overline{A}BC$

                         }----> Boolean Theorem #8

$W = \overline{B}C(1) + \overline{A}BC$

                         }----> Boolean Theorem #2

$W = \overline{B}C + \overline{A}BC$

                         }----> Boolean Theorem #13a

$W = C(\overline{B} + \overline{A}B)$

                         }----> Boolean Theorem #15b

$W = C(\overline{B} + \overline{A})$

                         }----> Boolean Theorem #13a

$W = C\overline{B} + C\overline{A}$

(e) $Q = A\,C\,D + \overline{A}\,B\,C\,D$

$\qquad\qquad\qquad\qquad\qquad$ }----> *Boolean Theorem #13a*

$\qquad Q = C\,D\,(A + \overline{A}\,B)$

$\qquad\qquad\qquad\qquad\qquad$ }----> *Boolean Theorem #15a*

$\qquad Q = C\,D\,(A + B)$

$\qquad\qquad\qquad\qquad\qquad$ }----> *Boolean Theorem #13a*

$\qquad Q = C\,D\,A + C\,D\,B$

(f) $L = A\,\overline{B}\,C + \overline{A}\,\overline{B}\,\overline{C} + A\,C$

$\qquad\qquad\qquad\qquad\qquad$ }----> *Boolean Theorem #13a*

$\qquad L = A\,C\,(\overline{B} + 1) + \overline{A}\,\overline{B}\,\overline{C}$

$\qquad\qquad\qquad\qquad\qquad$ }----> *Boolean Theorem #6*

$\qquad L = A\,C\,(1) + \overline{A}\,\overline{B}\,\overline{C}$

$\qquad\qquad\qquad\qquad\qquad$ }----> *Boolean Theorem #2*

$\qquad L = A\,C + \overline{A}\,\overline{B}\,\overline{C}$

(g) $K = A\,B + C\,(A + C)$

$\qquad\qquad\qquad\qquad\qquad$ }----> *Boolean Theorem #13a*

$\qquad K = A\,B + C\,A + C\,C$

$\qquad\qquad\qquad\qquad\qquad$ }----> *Boolean Theorem #3*

$\qquad K = A\,B + C\,A + C$

$\qquad\qquad\qquad\qquad\qquad$ }----> *Boolean Theorem #13a*

$\qquad K = C\,(A + 1) + A\,B$

$\qquad\qquad\qquad\qquad\qquad$ }----> *Boolean Theorem #6*

$\qquad K = C\,(1) + A\,B$

$\qquad\qquad\qquad\qquad\qquad$ }----> *Boolean Theorem #2*

$\qquad K = C + A\,B$

SECTIONS 3.11 *DeMorgan's Theorems*

3.14   (a) $X = \overline{(A + B)\,(C + D)}$

$\qquad\qquad\qquad\qquad\qquad$ }----> *DeMorgan's Theorem #17*

$\qquad X = \overline{(A + B)} + \overline{(C + D)}$

$\qquad\qquad\qquad\qquad\qquad$ }----> *DeMorgan's Theorem #16*

$\qquad X = \overline{\overline{(A + B)}}\ \overline{\overline{(C + D)}}$

$\qquad\qquad\qquad\qquad\qquad$ }----> *Double inversion signs cancel out*

$\qquad X = (A + B)\,(C + D)$

$\qquad\qquad\qquad\qquad\qquad$ }----> *Boolean Theorem #13b*

$\qquad X = A\,C + A\,D + B\,C + B\,D$

(b) $Y = \overline{\overline{(A\ B)} + \overline{(C\ D)}}$

$}\text{----> }$ *DeMorgan's Theorem #16*

$Y = \overline{\overline{(A\ B)}}\ \overline{\overline{(C\ D)}}$

$}\text{----> }$ *DeMorgan's Theorem #17*

$Y = \overline{\overline{(A\ B)}} + \overline{\overline{(C\ D)}}$

$}\text{----> }$ *Double inversion signs cancel out*

$Y = A\ B + C\ D$

(c) $Z = \overline{(A + 0) + (A + B + C + D + 1)}$

$}\text{----> }$ *DeMorgan's Theorem #16*

$Z = \overline{(A + 0)}\ \overline{(A + B + C + D + 1)}$

$}\text{----> }$ *Boolean Theorem #5*

$Z = \overline{(A)}\ \overline{(A + B + C + D + 1)}$

$}\text{----> }$ *Boolean Theorem #6*

$Z = \overline{(A)}\ \overline{(1)}$

$Z = \overline{(A)}\ (0)$

$}\text{----> }$ *Boolean Theorem #1*

$Z = 0$

(d) $W = \overline{\overline{A\ B\ \overline{C}}}$

$}\text{----> }$ *DeMorgan's Theorem #17*

$W = \overline{\overline{A}} + \overline{B} + \overline{\overline{C}}$

$}\text{----> }$ *Double inversion signs cancel out*

$W = A + \overline{B} + C$

(e) $Q = \overline{K\ L\ \overline{(M + N)}\ K\ L}$

$}\text{----> }$ *DeMorgan's Theorem #17*

$Q = \overline{K\ L} + \overline{\overline{(M + N)}} + \overline{K\ L}$

$}\text{----> }$ *Double inversion signs cancel out*

$Q = \overline{K\ L} + (M + N) + \overline{K\ L}$

$}\text{----> }$ *DeMorgan's Theorem #17*

$Q = \overline{K} + \overline{L} + (M + N) + \overline{K} + \overline{L}$

$}\text{----> }$ *Boolean Theorem #7*

$Q = \overline{K} + \overline{L} + M + N$

(f)　$L = \overline{\overline{A\,B}\,(A+B)}$

　　　　　　　　　　　　　　　　}----> *DeMorgan's Theorem #17*

$L = \overline{\overline{A\,B}} + \overline{(A+B)}$

　　　　　　　　　　　　　　　　}----> *DeMorgan's Theorem #16*

$L = \overline{\overline{A\,B}} + (\overline{A}\,\overline{B})$

　　　　　　　　　　　　　　　　}----> *Double inversion signs cancel out*

$L = A\,B + \overline{A}\,\overline{B}$

(g)　$K = \overline{A\,B\,\overline{C\,D}}$

　　　　　　　　　　　　　　　　}----> *DeMorgan's Theorem #17*

$K = \overline{A} + \overline{B} + \overline{\overline{C\,D}}$

　　　　　　　　　　　　　　　　}----> *Double inversion signs cancel out*

$K = \overline{A} + \overline{B} + C\,D$

SECTION 3.12 *Universality of NAND Gates and NOR Gates*

3.15　The circuit of Figure P3.15 shows how the circuit of Figure 3.7 is converted to a circuit that uses only NAND gates. Note the following:

(a)　The ***INVERTER*** was replaced with NAND <u>gate 1</u> (with the inputs tied together).
(b)　The ***2-inpt AND*** gate was replaced with the combination of NAND gates 2 <u>and 3</u>.
(c)　The ***2-inpt OR*** gate was replaced with the combination of NAND <u>gates 4, 5, and 6</u>.

We can simplify the circuit by eliminating NAND gates 3 and 4, since they create a double inversion.

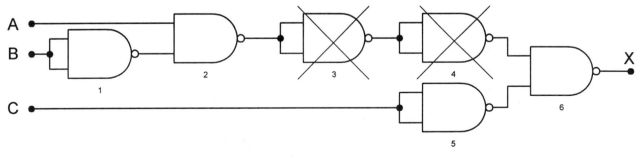

Figure P3.15

3.16 The circuit that implements X = (A + B)(C + D) uses one 2-input AND gate and two 2-input OR gates. It requires two NOR gates to make an OR gate, and three NOR gates to make an AND gate After the double inversions are cancelled, the final circuit will have a total of three 2-input NOR gates as shown in Figure P3.16.

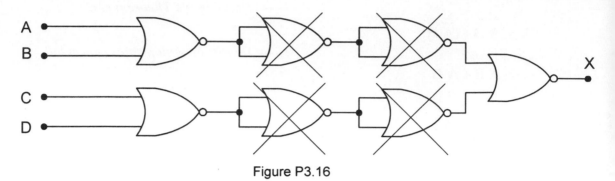

Figure P3.16

3.17 First, the expression $X = ((A + \overline{B})\ (B + C)\ B)$ should be simplified as much as possible.

$$X = ((A + \overline{B})\ (B + C)\ B)$$

}----> Boolean Theorem #13b

$$X = (A\ B + A\ C + \overline{B}\ B + \overline{B}\ C)\ B$$

}----> Boolean Theorem #13a

$$X = A\ B\ B + A\ C\ B + \overline{B}\ B\ B + \overline{B}\ C\ B$$

}----> Boolean Theorem #4

$$X = A\ B\ B + A\ C\ B$$

}----> Boolean Theorem #3

$$X = A\ B + A\ C\ B$$

}----> Boolean Theorem #13a

$$X = A\ B\ (1 + C)$$

}----> Boolean Theorem #6

$$X = A\ B$$

The 7400 IC is a quad 2-input NAND package. Thus, it requires two 2-input NAND gates, as shown in Figure P3.17, to implement the expression X = AB.

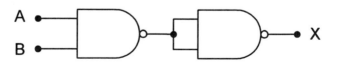

Figure P3.17

3.18

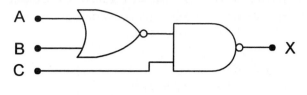

Figure P3.18

SECTIONS 3.13-3.15   *Alternate Logic-Gate Representation/Which Gate Representation to Use/New IEEE Standard Logic Symbols.*

3.19

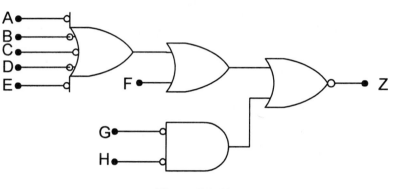

Figure P3.19

3.20

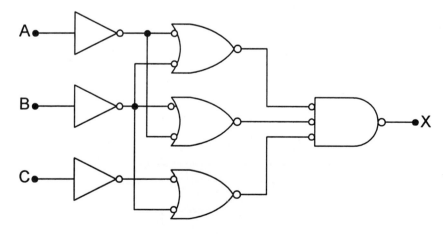

Figure P3.20

3.21   The term ***unasserted*** means Not-Active. For the circuit of Figure 3.10 the LED turns ON when the output of gate 3 (2-input NOR gate) is LOW. Therefore, we must determine the necessary state conditions at the inputs A and B that will cause the output of gate 3 to be HIGH (***unasserted***). Hence, there are two conditions under which the output signal "$\overline{\text{LIGHT}}$" will be HIGH. When A=0 and B=1, or when A=1 and B=0.

3.22

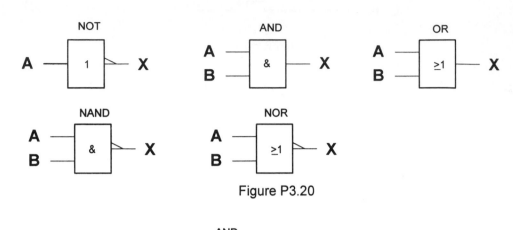

Figure P3.20

3.23

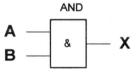

Figure P3.23

3.24

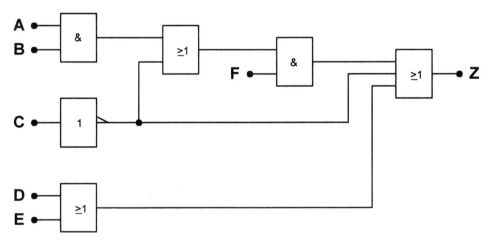

Figure P3.24

4 COMBINATIONAL LOGIC CIRCUITS

SECTIONS 4.1-4.3 *Sum-of-Products Form/Simplifying Logic Circuits/Algebraic Simplification*

4.1 (a) $X = A\,\overline{B}\,\overline{C} + \overline{A}\,\overline{B}\,\overline{C}$

$X = \overline{B}\,\overline{C}\,(A + \overline{A})$

$X = \overline{B}\,\overline{C}$

(b) $X = A\,B + A\,\overline{B} + B\,C + \overline{B}\,\overline{C}$

$X = A\,(B + \overline{B}) + B\,C + \overline{B}\,\overline{C}$

$X = A + B\,C + \overline{B}\,\overline{C}$

(c) $X = A\,\overline{B}\,\overline{C} + \overline{A}\,\overline{B}\,\overline{C} + \overline{A}\,\overline{B}\,C$ $\qquad \overline{B}\left(A\overline{C} + \overline{A}\overline{C} + \overline{A}C\right)$

$X = \overline{B}\,\overline{C}\,(\overline{A} + A) + \overline{A}\,\overline{B}\,C$

$X = \overline{B}\,\overline{C} + \overline{A}\,\overline{B}\,C$

$X = \overline{B}\,(\overline{C} + \overline{A}\,C)$

$X = \overline{B}\,(\overline{C} + \overline{A})$

$X = \overline{B}\,\overline{C} + \overline{A}\,\overline{B}$

(d) $X = A\,B\,C + A\,\overline{B}\,C + \overline{A}\,B\,C + \overline{(A + B)}\,C$ $\quad AC(B + \overline{B}) +$

$X = A\,B\,C + A\,\overline{B}\,C + \overline{A}\,B\,C + (\overline{A}\,\overline{B})\,C$ $\qquad\qquad\qquad BC + \overline{B}C$

$X = A\,B\,C + A\,\overline{B}\,C + \overline{A}\,B\,C + \overline{A}\,\overline{B}\,C$

$AC(B + \overline{B}) + \overline{A}C(B + \overline{B}) \qquad BC(A + \overline{A}) + \overline{B}C(A + \overline{A})$

$$X = A C (B + \overline{B}) + \overline{A} C (B + \overline{B})$$

$$X = A C + \overline{A} C$$

$$X = C (A + \overline{A})$$

$$X = C$$

(e) $K = \overline{X} \ \overline{Y} \ Z + \overline{X} \ Y \ Z + X \ \overline{Y} \ \overline{Z} + X \ \overline{Y} \ Z + (\overline{\overline{X} + \overline{Y} + \overline{Z}})$

$$K = \overline{X} \ \overline{Y} \ Z + \overline{X} \ Y \ Z + X \ \overline{Y} \ \overline{Z} + X \ \overline{Y} \ Z + X \ Y \ Z$$

$$K = \overline{X} \ Z \ (\overline{Y} + Y) + X \ \overline{Y} \ (\overline{Z} + Z) + X \ Y \ Z$$

$$K = \overline{X} \ Z + X \ \overline{Y} + X \ Y \ Z$$

$$K = X \ (\overline{Y} + Y \ Z) + \overline{X} \ Z$$

$$K = X \ (\overline{Y} + Z) + \overline{X} \ Z$$

$$K = X \ \overline{Y} + X \ Z + \overline{X} \ Z$$

$$K = Z \ (X + \overline{X}) + X \ \overline{Y}$$

$$K = Z + X \ \overline{Y}$$

(f) $W = (K + N + M)(K + \overline{N} + M) + (\overline{K} + N + M)(\overline{K} + \overline{N} + M)$

$$W = (KK + K\overline{N} + KM + NK + N\overline{N} + NM + MK + M\overline{N} + MM) +$$

$$(\overline{K}\overline{K} + \overline{K}\overline{N} + \overline{K}M + N\overline{K} + N\overline{N} + NM + M\overline{K} + M\overline{N} + MM)$$

$$W = (K + K\overline{N} + KM + NK + NM + MK + M\overline{N} + M) +$$

$$(\overline{K} + \overline{K}\overline{N} + \overline{K}M + N\overline{K} + NM + M\overline{K} + M\overline{N} + M)$$

$$W = (K(1 + \overline{N} + M + N + M) + NM + M\overline{N} + M) + (\overline{K}(1 + \overline{N} + M + N + M) + NM + M\overline{N} + M)$$

$$W = (K + NM + M\overline{N} + M) + (\overline{K} + NM + M\overline{N} + M)$$

$$W = M (1 + \overline{N} + N) + K + M (1 + \overline{N} + N) + \overline{K}$$

$$W = M + K + M + \overline{K}$$

$$W = M + K + \overline{K}$$

$$W = M + 1$$

$$W = 1$$

4.2   (a)   DRIV=A; $\overline{BELTP} = \overline{BELTD}$ = B; PASS=C; IGN=E; $\overline{ALARM}$ = X

$$X = \overline{(A\overline{\overline{B}} + \overline{\overline{B}}C)} E$$

   (b) $X = \overline{\overline{A}\overline{\overline{B}}} \cdot \overline{\overline{B}\overline{\overline{C}}} + \overline{E}$

$$X = \overline{(A\overline{B})} \, \overline{(\overline{B}C)} + \overline{E}$$

$$X = (\overline{A} + B)(B + \overline{C}) + \overline{E}$$

$$X = \overline{A}B + \overline{A}\,\overline{C} + BB + B\overline{C} + \overline{E}$$

$$X = B(\overline{A} + 1 + \overline{C}) + \overline{A}\,\overline{C} + \overline{E}$$

$$X = B + \overline{A}\,\overline{C} + \overline{E}$$

   (c)

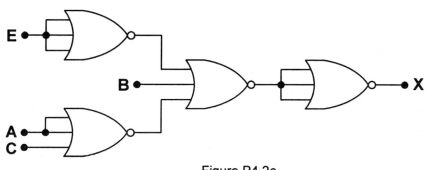

Figure P4.2c

SECTION 4.4 *Designing Combinational Logic Circuits*

4.3   *Step #1*: Set up the truth table for the problem.

A	B	C	D	X
0	0	0	0	1
0	0	0	1	1
0	0	1	0	1
0	0	1	1	1
0	1	0	0	0
0	1	0	1	0
0	1	1	0	0
0	1	1	1	1
1	0	0	0	0
1	0	0	1	0
1	0	1	0	0
1	0	1	1	1
1	1	0	0	0
1	1	0	1	0
1	1	1	0	0
1	1	1	1	1

Step #2: Write the AND term for each case where output X=1.

A	B	C	D	X	AND terms
0	0	0	0	1	$\overline{A}\,\overline{B}\,\overline{C}\,\overline{D}$
0	0	0	1	1	$\overline{A}\,\overline{B}\,\overline{C}\,D$
0	0	1	0	1	$\overline{A}\,\overline{B}\,C\,\overline{D}$
0	0	1	1	1	$\overline{A}\,\overline{B}\,C\,D$
0	1	1	1	1	$\overline{A}\,B\,C\,D$
1	0	1	1	1	$A\,\overline{B}\,C\,D$
1	1	1	1	1	$A\,B\,C\,D$

Step #3: Write the SOP expression for all the cases where output X = 1.

$$X = \overline{A}\,\overline{B}\,\overline{C}\,\overline{D} + \overline{A}\,\overline{B}\,\overline{C}\,D + \overline{A}\,\overline{B}\,C\,\overline{D} + \overline{A}\,\overline{B}\,C\,D + \overline{A}\,B\,C\,D + A\,\overline{B}\,C\,D + A\,B\,C\,D$$

Step #4: Simplify the SOP expression as much as possible using Boolean algebra.

$$X = \overline{A}\,\overline{B}\,\overline{C}\,(\overline{D} + D) + \overline{A}\,\overline{B}\,C\,(\overline{D} + D) + A\,C\,D\,(\overline{B} + B) + \overline{A}\,B\,C\,D$$

$$X = \overline{A}\,\overline{B}\,\overline{C} + \overline{A}\,\overline{B}\,C + A\,C\,D + \overline{A}\,B\,C\,D + [\overline{A}\,\overline{B}\,C\,D]\,*$$

*   *This term can be added since it already exists in the original Boolean expression. This technique is often used in order make the simplification process easier.*

$$X = \overline{A}\,\overline{B}\,\overline{C} + \overline{A}\,\overline{B}\,C + A\,C\,D + \overline{A}\,C\,D\,(\overline{B} + B)$$

$$X = \overline{A}\,\overline{B}\,\overline{C} + \overline{A}\,\overline{B}\,C + A\,C\,D + \overline{A}\,C\,D$$

$$X = \overline{A}\,\overline{B}\,(\overline{C} + C) + C\,D\,(\overline{A} + A)$$

$$X = \overline{A}\,\overline{B} + C\,D$$

Step #5: Implement the simplified expression using logic gates (either circuit (a) or (b) of Figure P4.3 is acceptable).

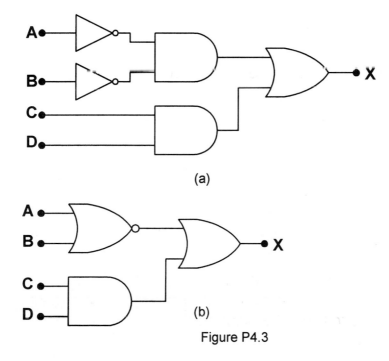

Figure P4.3

4.4   In this problem we have two different sources of signals. First, we have a 3-bit binary number com
from the external fuel tanks, which monitors the fuel pressure. Second, we have a 3-bit binary num
coming from the computer, which represents the desired pressure in the fuel tanks. Consequently,
have to design a logic circuit that compares the two sets of 3-bit binary numbers and determines w
they are equal. Once the circuit determines the equality of the two binary numbers, a green LEI
turned ON. Let's follow the procedure step-by-step of the previous problem. However, before we
that, let's call $X_2 X_1 X_0$ the binary number coming from the transducer, and $Y_2 Y_1 Y_0$ the bir
number from the on board computer, and finally Z the green LED.

Since we are only concerned with those situations when the two numbers are equal, only eight (8)
combinations of $Y_2 Y_1 Y_0 X_2 X_1 X_0$ have to be considered:

Step #1: Set up the truth table for the problem.

Y_2	Y_1	Y_0	X_2	X_1	X_0	Z	
0	0	0	0	0	0	*1*	both numbers equal to 0_{10}
0	0	1	0	0	1	*1*	both numbers equal to 1_{10}
0	1	0	0	1	0	*1*	both numbers equal to 2_{10}
0	1	1	0	1	1	*1*	both numbers equal to 3_{10}
1	0	0	1	0	0	*1*	both numbers equal to 4_{10}
1	0	1	1	0	1	*1*	both numbers equal to 5_{10}
1	1	0	1	1	0	*1*	both numbers equal to 6_{10}
1	1	1	1	1	1	*1*	both numbers equal to 7_{10}

Step #2: Write the AND term for each case where output Z=1.

Y_2	Y_1	Y_0	X_2	X_1	X_0	Z	*AND terms*
0	0	0	0	0	0	*1*	$\overline{Y2}\,\overline{Y1}\,\overline{Y0}\,\overline{X2}\,\overline{X1}\,\overline{X0}$
0	0	1	0	0	1	*1*	$\overline{Y2}\,\overline{Y1}\,Y0\,\overline{X2}\,\overline{X1}\,X0$
0	1	0	0	1	0	*1*	$\overline{Y2}\,Y1\,\overline{Y0}\,\overline{X2}\,X1\,\overline{X0}$
0	1	1	0	1	1	*1*	$\overline{Y2}\,Y1\,Y0\,\overline{X2}\,X1\,X0$
1	0	0	1	0	0	*1*	$Y2\,\overline{Y1}\,\overline{Y0}\,X2\,\overline{X1}\,\overline{X0}$
1	0	1	1	0	1	*1*	$Y2\,\overline{Y1}\,Y0\,X2\,\overline{X1}\,X0$
1	1	0	1	1	0	*1*	$Y2\,Y1\,\overline{Y0}\,X2\,X1\,\overline{X0}$
1	1	1	1	1	1	*1*	$Y2\,Y1\,Y0\,X2\,X1\,X0$

Step #3: Write the Sum-of-Products expression for all the cases where output Z=1.

$$Z = \overline{Y2}\,\overline{Y1}\,\overline{Y0}\,\overline{X2}\,\overline{X1}\,\overline{X0} + \overline{Y2}\,\overline{Y1}\,Y0\,\overline{X2}\,\overline{X1}\,X0 + \overline{Y2}\,Y1\,\overline{Y0}\,\overline{X2}\,X1\,\overline{X0} + \overline{Y2}\,Y1\,Y0\,\overline{X2}\,X1\,X0 +$$
$$+\, Y2\,\overline{Y1}\,\overline{Y0}\,X2\,\overline{X1}\,\overline{X0} + Y2\,\overline{Y1}\,Y0\,X2\,\overline{X1}\,X0 + Y2\,Y1\,\overline{Y0}\,X2\,X1\,\overline{X0} + Y2\,Y1\,Y0\,X2\,X1\,X0$$

Step #4: Simplify the SOP expression as much as possible using Boolean algebra.

$$Z = \overline{X0}\,\overline{Y0}\,(\overline{X1}\,\overline{Y1}\,\overline{X2}\,\overline{Y2} + X1\,Y1\,\overline{X2}\,\overline{Y2} + \overline{X1}\,\overline{Y1}\,X2\,Y2 + X1\,Y1\,X2\,Y2) +$$
$$+\, X0\,Y0\,(\overline{X1}\,\overline{Y1}\,\overline{X2}\,\overline{Y2} + X1\,Y1\,\overline{X2}\,\overline{Y2} + \overline{X1}\,\overline{Y1}\,X2\,Y2 + X1\,Y1\,X2\,Y2)$$

$$Z = \overline{X0}\,\overline{Y0}\,(\overline{X2}\,\overline{Y2}\,(\overline{X1}\,\overline{Y1} + X1\,Y1) + X2\,Y2\,(\overline{X1}\,\overline{Y1} + X1\,Y1)) +$$
$$+\, X0\,Y0\,(\overline{X2}\,\overline{Y2}\,(\overline{X1}\,\overline{Y1} + X1\,Y1) + X2\,Y2\,(\overline{X1}\,\overline{Y1} + X1\,Y1))$$

Let $K = (\overline{X1}\,\overline{Y1} + X1\,Y1) = \overline{(X1 \oplus Y1)}$

$$Z = \overline{X0}\,\overline{Y0}\,(\overline{X2}\,\overline{Y2}\,(K) + X2\,Y2\,(K)) + X0\,Y0\,(\overline{X2}\,\overline{Y2}\,(K) + X2\,Y2\,(K))$$

$$Z = \overline{X0}\,\overline{Y0}\,K\,(\overline{X2}\,\overline{Y2} + X2\,Y2) + X0\,Y0\,K\,(\overline{X2}\,\overline{Y2} + X2\,Y2)$$

Let $Q = (\overline{X2}\,\overline{Y2} + X2\,Y2) = \overline{(X2 \oplus Y2)}$

$$Z = \overline{X0}\,\overline{Y0}\,K\,Q + X0\,Y0\,K\,Q$$

$$Z = K\,Q\,(\overline{X0}\,\overline{Y0} + X0\,Y0)$$

$$Z = \overline{(X1 \oplus Y1)}\,\overline{(X2 \oplus Y2)}\,\overline{(X0 \oplus Y0)}$$

Step #5: Implement the circuit for the final expression.

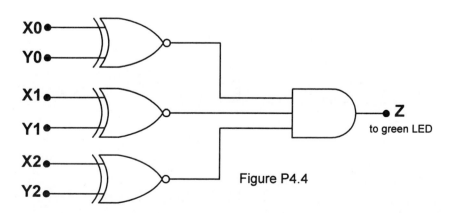

Figure P4.4

4.5 The LSB represents 100 p.s.i.. When the pressure of 600 p.s.i. is reached inside of the tanks, the transducer should have its output $X_2 X_1 X_0$ equal to 110_2. Thus, a circuit has to be designed that detects when the binary number $X_2 X_1 X_0$ exceeds 110_2.

X_2	X_1	X_0	W	*AND terms*
0	0	0	0	
0	0	1	0	
0	1	0	0	
0	1	1	0	
1	0	0	0	
1	0	1	0	
1	1	0	0	
1	1	1	1	X2 X1 X0

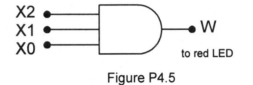

Figure P4.5

4.6 First set up the truth table, then write the SOP expression, then simplify it using Boolean algebra and finally implement the logic circuit.

A	B	C	X	*AND terms*
0	0	0	0	
0	0	1	0	
0	1	0	0	
0	1	1	0	
1	0	0	0	
1	0	1	0	
1	1	0	1	A B $\overline{C}$
1	1	1	0	

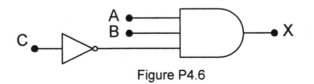

Figure P4.6

4.7 First set up the truth table, then write the SOP expression, then simplify it using Boolean algebra and finally implement the logic circuit.

A	B	C	D	Z	AND terms
0	0	0	0	0	
0	0	0	1	0	
0	0	1	0	0	
0	0	1	1	0	
0	1	0	0	1	$\overline{A}B\overline{C}\,\overline{D}$
0	1	0	1	0	
0	1	1	0	0	
0	1	1	1	0	
1	0	0	0	1	$A\overline{B}\,\overline{C}\,\overline{D}$
1	0	0	1	0	
1	0	1	0	0	
1	0	1	1	0	
1	1	0	0	1	$AB\overline{C}\,\overline{D}$
1	1	0	1	0	
1	1	1	0	0	
1	1	1	1	0	

$$Z = \overline{A}\,B\,\overline{C}\,\overline{D} + A\,\overline{B}\,\overline{C}\,\overline{D} + A\,B\,\overline{C}\,\overline{D}$$

$$Z = \overline{C}\,\overline{D}(\overline{A}\,B + A\,\overline{B} + A\,B)$$

$$Z = \overline{C}\,\overline{D}(\overline{A}\,B + A\,(\overline{B} + B))$$

$$Z = \overline{C}\,\overline{D}(\overline{A}\,B + A)$$

$$Z = \overline{C}\,\overline{D}(A + B)$$

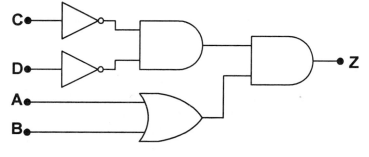

Figure P4.7

4.8   Let's first set up the truth table.

P	M	W	E	Z	AND terms
0	0	0	0	0	$\overline{P}\,\overline{M}\,\overline{W}\,\overline{E}$
0	0	0	1	1	
0	0	1	0	1	
0	0	1	1	1	
0	1	0	0	1	
0	1	0	1	1	
0	1	1	0	1	
0	1	1	1	1	
1	0	0	0	1	
1	0	0	1	1	
1	0	1	0	1	
1	0	1	1	1	
1	1	0	0	1	
1	1	0	1	1	
1	1	1	0	1	
1	1	1	1	1	

Note: In this truth table Z=1 for all cases except when P=M=W=E=0. There are two easy ways
simplify the SOP expression obtained from this truth table:

Method # 1: Use Karnaugh mapping for all the cases where Z = 1. (You may skip this method u
it's covered in section 4.5 of your textbook)

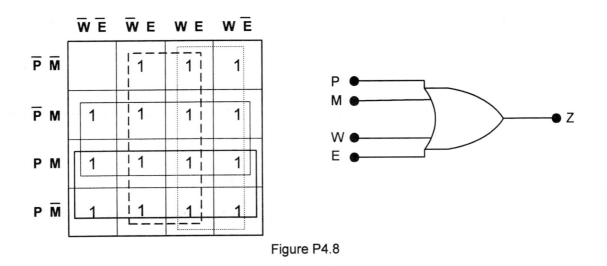

Figure P4.8

Therefore, by using *method #1*, from the Karnaugh map we get: Z = P+M+E+W.

Method # 2: By writing the SOP expression for $\overline{Z}$, and then inverting it.

The SOP expression for $\overline{Z} = \overline{P}\ \overline{M}\ \overline{W}\ \overline{E}$

After we invert $\overline{Z}$, and simplify the expression by using DeMorgan's theorems we have :

$$Z = \overline{\overline{P}\ \overline{M}\ \overline{W}\ \overline{E}} = P + M + W + E$$

Either method yields the same final circuit of Figure P4.8.

4.9 An 8-bit microcomputer has an 8-bit microprocessor with 16 address bus lines and 8 data bus lines. Since we are interested in decoding the two most significant hexadecimal digits of the address bus, we have to consider address lines A_8-A_{15}. Keep in mind that signals DCL, SBB, and ECS are active HIGH, while signal $\overline{\text{ION}}$ is active LOW.

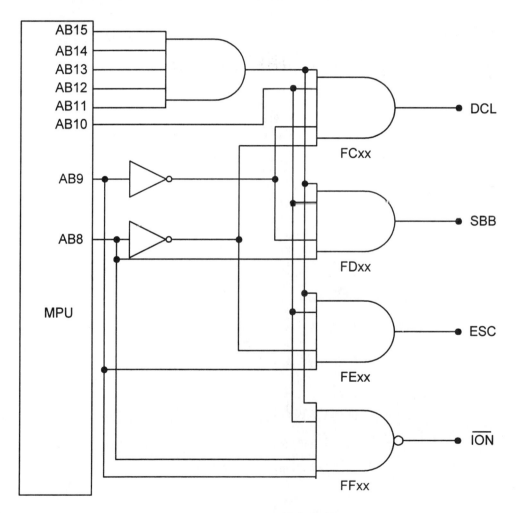

Figure P4.9

SECTIONS 4.5-4.6 *The Karnaugh map Method/Exclusive-OR and Exclusive-NOR Circuits*

4.10   (a) $X = \overline{A}\,\overline{B}\,\overline{C}\,\overline{D} + \overline{A}\,\overline{B}\,C\,\overline{D} + A\,\overline{B}\,C\,\overline{D} + \overline{A}\,B\,\overline{C}\,D + \overline{A}\,B\,C\,D + A\,\overline{B}\,\overline{C}\,\overline{D}$

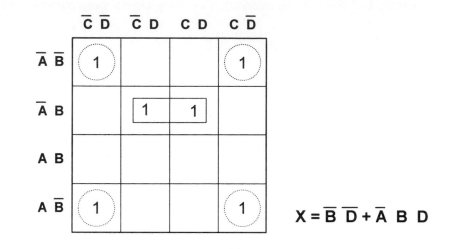

$$X = \overline{B}\,\overline{D} + \overline{A}\,B\,D$$

Figure P4.10a

(b) $Z = \overline{K}\,\overline{N}\,M + \overline{K}\,\overline{N}\,\overline{M} + \overline{K}\,N\,\overline{M}$

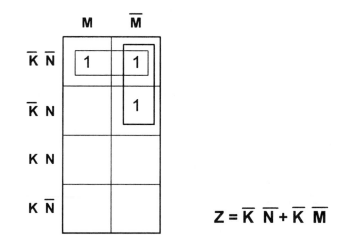

$$Z = \overline{K}\,\overline{N} + \overline{K}\,\overline{M}$$

Figure P4.10b

(c) $Y = \overline{P}Q\overline{R}S + \overline{P}QRS + PQ\overline{R}S + PQRS$

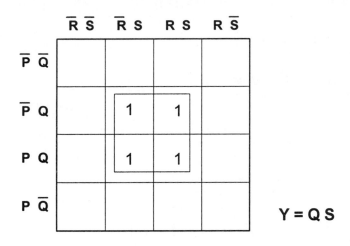

$Y = Q\,S$

Figure P4.10c

4.11   (a) *Steps 1 and 2:* Set up the truth table and write the AND term for each case where Z=1.

A	B	C	D	Z	*AND terms*
0	0	0	0	1	$\overline{A}\,\overline{B}\,\overline{C}\,\overline{D}$
0	0	0	1	1	$\overline{A}\,\overline{B}\,\overline{C}\,D$
0	0	1	0	1	$\overline{A}\,\overline{B}\,C\,\overline{D}$
0	0	1	1	1	$\overline{A}\,\overline{B}\,C\,D$
0	1	0	0	0	
0	1	0	1	0	
0	1	1	0	0	
0	1	1	1	1	$\overline{A}\,B\,C\,D$
1	0	0	0	0	
1	0	0	1	0	
1	0	1	0	0	
1	0	1	1	0	
1	1	0	0	0	
1	1	0	1	0	
1	1	1	0	0	
1	1	1	1	1	$A\,B\,C\,D$

Step 3: Write the SOP expression for output Z.

$$Z = \overline{A}\,\overline{B}\,\overline{C}\,\overline{D} + \overline{A}\,\overline{B}\,\overline{C}\,D + \overline{A}\,\overline{B}\,C\,\overline{D} + \overline{A}\,\overline{B}\,C\,D + \overline{A}\,B\,C\,D + A\,B\,C\,D$$

Steps 4 and 5: Simplify the SOP expression using the Karnaugh map and finally implement the Boolean expression $Z = \overline{A}\,\overline{B} + B\,C\,D$ (Figure P4.11a).

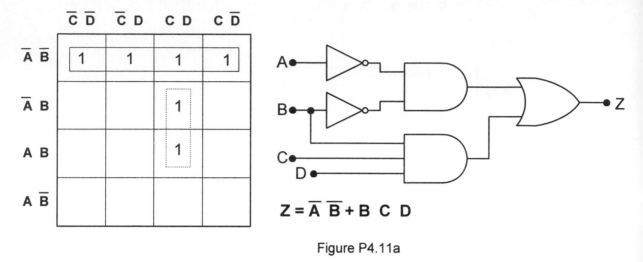

$$Z = \overline{A}\,\overline{B} + B\,C\,D$$

Figure P4.11a

(b)   Apply the same step-by-step procedure used in question (a).

Steps 1 and 2:

K	L	M	N	Z	*AND terms*
0	0	0	0	1	$\overline{K}\,\overline{L}\,\overline{M}\,\overline{N}$
0	0	0	1	1	$\overline{K}\,\overline{L}\,\overline{M}\,N$
0	0	1	0	0	
0	0	1	1	0	
0	1	0	0	1	$\overline{K}\,L\,\overline{M}\,\overline{N}$
0	1	0	1	1	$\overline{K}\,L\,\overline{M}\,N$
0	1	1	0	0	
0	1	1	1	0	
1	0	0	0	0	
1	0	0	1	0	
1	0	1	0	1	$K\,\overline{L}\,M\,\overline{N}$
1	0	1	1	1	$K\,\overline{L}\,M\,N$
1	1	0	0	0	
1	1	0	1	0	
1	1	1	0	1	$K\,L\,M\,\overline{N}$
1	1	1	1	1	$K\,L\,M\,N$

Step 3:

$$Z = \overline{K}\,\overline{L}\,\overline{M}\,\overline{N} + \overline{K}\,\overline{L}\,\overline{M}\,N + \overline{K}\,L\,\overline{M}\,\overline{N} + \overline{K}\,L\,\overline{M}\,N + K\,\overline{L}\,M\,\overline{N} + K\,\overline{L}\,M\,N + K\,L\,M\,\overline{N} + K\,L\,M\,N$$

Steps 4 and 5: Figure P4.11b

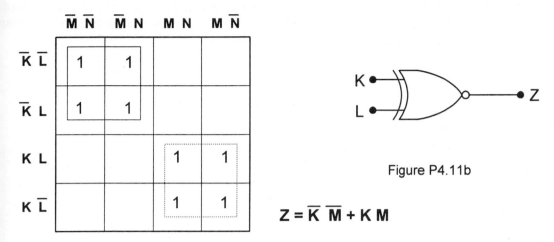

$$Z = \overline{K}\,\overline{M} + K\,M$$

Figure P4.11b

4.12 (a) Set up the truth table the same way we did in problem 4.11 (a). However, in this case we will assign an X to each "don't care" condition.

Steps 1 and 2: Set up the truth table and write the AND term for each case where Z=1.

A	B	C	D	Z	*AND terms*
0	0	0	0	1	$\overline{A}\,\overline{B}\,\overline{C}\,\overline{D}$
0	0	0	1	1	$\overline{A}\,\overline{B}\,\overline{C}\,D$
0	0	1	0	1	$\overline{A}\,\overline{B}\,C\,\overline{D}$
0	0	1	1	1	$\overline{A}\,\overline{B}\,C\,D$
0	1	0	0	X	
0	1	0	1	X	
0	1	1	0	X	
0	1	1	1	1	$\overline{A}\,B\,C\,D$
1	0	0	0	0	
1	0	0	1	0	
1	0	1	0	0	
1	0	1	1	0	
1	1	0	0	X	
1	1	0	1	X	
1	1	1	0	X	
1	1	1	1	1	$A\,B\,C\,D$

Step 3: Write the SOP expression for output Z.

$$Z = \overline{A}\,\overline{B}\,\overline{C}\,\overline{D} + \overline{A}\,\overline{B}\,\overline{C}\,D + \overline{A}\,\overline{B}\,C\,\overline{D} + \overline{A}\,\overline{B}\,C\,D + \overline{A}\,B\,C\,D + A\,B\,C\,D$$

Steps 4 and 5: Now that we have the SOP expression, we can use the Karnaugh Map to simplify Boolean expression Z taking into account the "don't care" conditions. By assigning 1s to each of "don't care" conditions we'll have a simplified Karnaugh map that yields two quads. Fina implement the Boolean expression $Z = \overline{A} + B$ (Figure P4.12a).

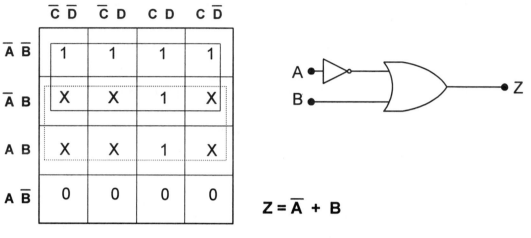

$$Z = \overline{A} + B$$

Figure P4.12a

(b) ***Step 1:*** Get the expression into SOP form if it is not already so.

$$X = A\,B\,(\overline{C}\,D + \overline{D}) + \overline{C}\,\overline{D} + \overline{A}\,B\,\overline{C} + A$$

$$X = A\,B\,\overline{C}\,D + A\,B\,\overline{D} + \overline{C}\,\overline{D} + \overline{A}\,B\,\overline{C} + A$$

$$X = A\,(B\,\overline{C}\,D + B\,\overline{D} + 1) + \overline{C}\,\overline{D} + \overline{A}\,B\,\overline{C}$$

$$X = A + \overline{C}\,\overline{D} + \overline{A}\,B\,\overline{C}$$

$$X = A + \overline{C}\,\overline{D} + B\,\overline{C}$$

Step 2: For each product term in the SOP expression, place a 1 in each K map square whose label contains the same combination of input variables. Place a 0 in all other squares (Figure P4.12b).

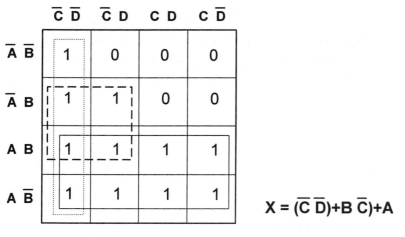

$$X = (\overline{C}\ \overline{D}) + B\ \overline{C} + A$$

Figure P4.12b

SECTIONS 4.6 *Exclusive-OR and Exclusive-NOR Circuits*

4.13 (a) and (b) Exclusive gates are often referred to as controlled INVERTERS. This is because an Exclusive gate can perform the same function as an INVERTER by simply controlling the logic state at one of its inputs. An XOR gate acts as an INVERTER when one of its inputs is permanently HIGH (Figure P4.13a). Conversely, an XNOR gate acts as an INVERTER when one of its inputs is permanently LOW (Figure P4.13b).

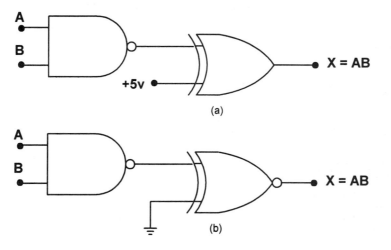

Figure P4.13

(c)

1. The output of an XOR gate is LOW when the inputs are *equal.*

2. The output of an XOR gate is HIGH when the inputs are *different.*

3. The output of an XNOR gate is *LOW* when the inputs are different.

4. The output of an XNOR gate is *HIGH* when the inputs are equal.

5. If *one* of the inputs of an XNOR gate is grounded, the XNOR gate behaves as an *INVERTER.*

6. One way to make an XOR gate behave like an INVERTER is to *tie* both inputs together.

SECTION 4.7 *Parity Generator and Checker*

4.14 The first step is to set up the truth table for the problem. Note that output Y will be the "ODD parity" output, while Z is the "EVEN parity" output. By looking at the truth table it is obvious that output Z is the complement of output Y. Therefore, we can design the circuit for the output Y and then add an INVERTER to the output of that circuit to obtain output Z.

C	B	A	Y	Z
0	0	0	1	0
0	0	1	0	1
0	1	0	0	1
0	1	1	1	0
1	0	0	0	1
1	0	1	1	0
1	1	0	1	0
1	1	1	0	1

$$Y = \overline{A}\,\overline{B}\,\overline{C} + A\,B\,\overline{C} + A\,\overline{B}\,C + \overline{A}\,B\,C$$

$$Y = \overline{C}\,(\overline{A}\,\overline{B} + A\,B) + C\,(A\,\overline{B} + \overline{A}\,B)$$

Let C=X and $W = A\overline{B} + \overline{A}B$

Hence, $Y = \overline{X}\,\overline{W} + X\,W$

$$Y = \overline{X \oplus W}$$

The expression $Y = \overline{X \oplus W}$ is implemented in Figure P4.14.

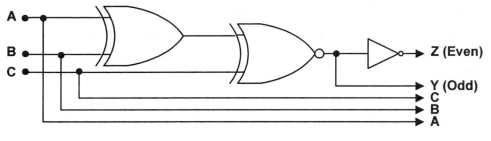

Figure P4.14

4.15 The output of the 3-bit Odd/Even Parity Checker (Figure P4.15) will be HIGH if there is an error in the data received from circuit of Figure P4.14.

Y	C	B	A	E	*AND terms*
0	0	0	0	1	$\overline{Y}\,\overline{C}\,\overline{B}\,\overline{A}$
0	0	0	1	0	
0	0	1	0	0	
0	0	1	1	1	$\overline{Y}\,\overline{C}\,B\,A$
0	1	0	0	0	
0	1	0	1	1	$\overline{Y}\,C\,\overline{B}\,A$
0	1	1	0	1	$\overline{Y}\,C\,B\,\overline{A}$
0	1	1	1	0	
1	0	0	0	0	
1	0	0	1	1	$Y\,\overline{C}\,\overline{B}\,A$
1	0	1	0	1	$Y\,\overline{C}\,B\,\overline{A}$
1	0	1	1	0	
1	1	0	0	1	$Y\,C\,\overline{B}\,\overline{A}$
1	1	0	1	0	
1	1	1	0	0	
1	1	1	1	1	$Y\,C\,B\,A$

$$E = \overline{Y}\,\overline{C}\,\overline{B}\,\overline{A} + \overline{Y}\,\overline{C}\,B\,A + \overline{Y}\,C\,\overline{B}\,A + \overline{Y}\,C\,B\,\overline{A} + Y\,\overline{C}\,\overline{B}\,A + Y\,\overline{C}\,B\,\overline{A} + Y\,C\,\overline{B}\,\overline{A} + Y\,C\,B\,A$$

$$E = \overline{Y}\,\overline{C}\,(\overline{A}\,\overline{B} + A\,B) + \overline{Y}\,C\,(\overline{A}\,B + A\,\overline{B}) + Y\,\overline{C}\,(\overline{A}\,B + A\,\overline{B}) + Y\,C\,(\overline{A}\,\overline{B} + A\,B)$$

Let X= $\overline{A}\,\overline{B} + A\,B$

$$E = \overline{Y}\,\overline{C}\,X + \overline{Y}\,C\,\overline{X} + Y\,\overline{C}\,\overline{X} + Y\,C\,X$$

$$E = X\,(\overline{Y}\,\overline{C} + Y\,C) + \overline{X}\,(\overline{Y}\,C + Y\,\overline{C})$$

$$E = \overline{(A \oplus B)}\ \overline{(Y \oplus C)} + (A \oplus B)\ (Y \oplus C)$$

Let $K = (Y \oplus C)$ and $Q = (A \oplus B)$

$$E = \overline{Q}\ \overline{K} + Q\ K = \overline{Q \oplus K}$$

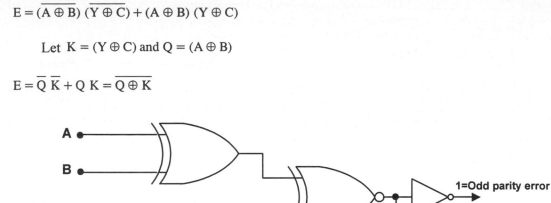

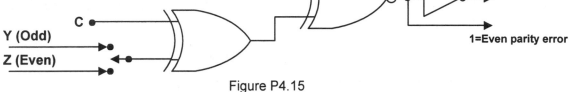

Figure P4.15

SECTION 4.9 *Basic Characteristics of Digital ICs*

4.16   (a) Bipolar transistors are used by the ***TTL*** logic family, while the ***CMOS*** logic family uses P-channel and N-channel MOSFETs.

      (b) If a TTL input is left unconnected, that input acts like a logic ***HIGH***.

      (c) If a ***CMOS*** input is left floating, the IC may become overheated and eventually destroy itself

      (d) If an IC has 50,000 gates built on its substrate, then it's considered ***Very Large Scale Integration***. However, if it has over 1,000,000 gates built on its substrate, then the IC falls in the category of ***Giga Scale*** Integration.

SECTION 4.10 *Troubleshooting Digital Systems*

4.17 The signal at Z1-6 and Z2-2 should be a logic HIGH. The logic probe indicates a logic LOW at both points. The following are the most probable causes of the malfunction:

    1.   An internal short to ground at Z2-2 (Bad Z2).
    2.   An internal short to ground at Z1-6 (Bad Z1).
    3.   An external short to ground between output Z1-6 and input Z2-2.

    Remote possibility:

    4.   By checking the specification sheet for a 74HC02, we see that Z1-7 is the ground connection for IC-Z1. It is possible that the technician made the connection from Z2-2 to Z1-7, thereby making the connection to the pin adjacent to pin 6.

4.18   Pin Z2-10 is a logic LOW, while Z2-2, which is the same electrical point, is a logic HIGH. This means that the most probable cause for the malfunction is an open at pin Z2-2. Since this is a TTL logic circuit, an open at input Z2-2 would have acted as a logic HIGH, however, the logic probe would have indicated "indeterminate."

4.19   Clearly, the signal at Z1-4 should be present at Z2-1. However, Z2-1 is indeterminate instead of pulsing. Since the technician used IC sockets, it is possible and very common, for one of the pins (pin 1) of the IC socket or IC Z2 itself to get bent during installation. As a result this may cause one of the IC pins or IC socket pins (pin 1) not to get connected to the rest of the circuit. In either case, an indeterminate state would have been recorded by the logic probe at Z2-1.

4.20   In cases such as this, it helps to know what the circuit looks like. To determine that, we must use the procedure discussed earlier in the chapter to set up the truth table, write the SOP expression, simplify and implement it.

1.   Truth table and simplification of the SOP expression.

D	C	B	A	X	*AND terms*
0	0	0	0	0	
0	0	0	1	0	
0	0	1	0	1	$\overline{D}\,\overline{C}\,B\,\overline{A}$
0	0	1	1	1	$\overline{D}\,\overline{C}\,B\,A$
0	1	0	0	0	
0	1	0	1	0	
0	1	1	0	0	
0	1	1	1	0	
1	0	0	0	0	
1	0	0	1	1	$D\,\overline{C}\,\overline{B}\,A$
1	0	1	0	X	Don't care condition[*]
1	0	1	1	X	Don't care condition[*]
1	1	0	0	X	Don't care condition[*]
1	1	0	1	X	Don't care condition[*]
1	1	1	0	X	Don't care condition[*]
1	1	1	1	X	Don't care condition[*]

[*] *These are don't care conditions since a BCD code cannot have binary numbers greater than 1001₂.*

$$X = \overline{D}\,\overline{C}\,B\,\overline{A} + \overline{D}\,\overline{C}\,B\,A + D\,\overline{C}\,\overline{B}\,A$$

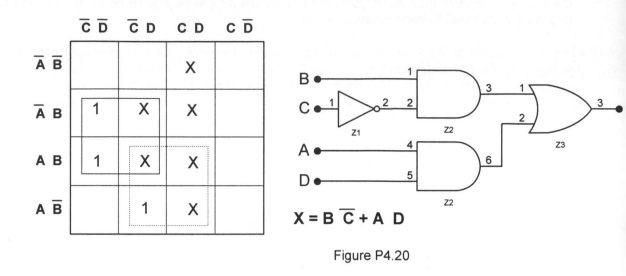

$$X = B\,\overline{C} + A\,D$$

Figure P4.20

Figure P4.20 shows the circuit implementation for the $X = B\,\overline{C} + A\,D$ expression. Remember that the technician noticed that output X was always HIGH. The following are 5 *possible* causes:

1. Output Z3-3 is open or shorted to Vcc.
2. Input Z3-1 is open or shorted to Vcc.
3. Input Z3-2 is open or shorted to Vcc.
4. Output Z2-6 is open or shorted to Vcc.
5. Output Z2-3 is open or shorted to Vcc.

4.21 The problem with this TTL circuit is that points Z2-6, and Z2-10 are indeterminate instead of logic HIGH. Likewise, points Z2-11 and Z2-9 are indeterminate instead of pulsing.

(a) No. This would cause input Z2-13 to float and thereby assume a logic HIGH. Under norm operating conditions, Z2-13 should be HIGH. Therefore, choice (a) could not cause t observed malfunction.

(b) No. This would make Z2-11 and Z2-9 assume a permanent logic HIGH. This does not explai the indeterminate logic levels at Z2-6 and Z2-10.

(c) No. This would cause Z2-9 to float, or assume a logic HIGH, and would not prevent Z2-11 from pulsing.

(d) Yes. If these two points were shorted together, then Z2-6/9/10 would try to follow the pulsi output of Z2-11. However, output Z2-6 under normal conditions is a constant HIGH. Th when Z2-11 goes LOW, an indeterminate logic level may occur at Z2-6. This particu problem occurs when a point in a circuit is forced to be LOW and HIGH at the same tin This condition is called *signal contention*.

(e) Yes. This would cause the observed indeterminate logic levels at the various outputs of Z2.

4.22 The technician needs three 2-input NAND gates, and she uses three 3-input NAND gates. To use these 3-input NAND gates in the circuit she must connect the unused input from each NAND gate to +5V (unused CMOS inputs must be connected to +5v or ground). If these CMOS inputs are left floating, then the results reported can, and most probably will occur.

SECTION 4.14 *Programmable Logic*

4.23 (a) Set up the truth table.

A	B	C	X	AND terms
0	0	0	0	
0	0	1	0	
0	1	0	0	
0	1	1	1	$\overline{A}\,B\,C$
1	0	0	0	
1	0	1	1	$A\,\overline{B}\,C$
1	1	0	1	$A\,B\,\overline{C}$
1	1	1	1	$A\,B\,C$

Write the SOP expression.

$$X = \overline{A}\,B\,C + A\,\overline{B}\,C + A\,B\,\overline{C} + A\,B\,C$$

Next we program the PLD by removing the unwanted links (Figure P4.23a).

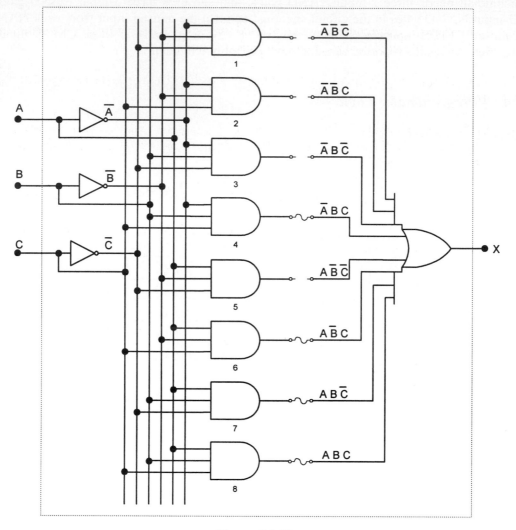

Figure P4.23a

(b) 1. X = A&B&C # C&D&E

2. X = !A&!B # !A&B # !B

3. X = !A&B # A&!B <u>*or*</u> A$B

(c)   /*   The SOP Expression   */

(d)

1. A *simulator* is a computer program that calculates the correct output logic states based on a description of the logic circuit and the current inputs.

2. A set of hypothetical inputs that will prove that the PLD works as expected are called *test vectors.*

3. An IC that contains a large number of logic gates whose interconnections can be programmed by the user to generate the desired logic relationship between inputs and outputs is called a *PLD* .

4. A *ZIF* socket allows you to drop the IC chip in and then clamp the contacts onto the pins.

5. The syntax used to describe a PLD's operation is often referred to as the *Hardware Description Language.*

5   FLIP-FLOPS AND RELATED DEVICES

SECTIONS 5.1-5.3 *NAND Gate Latch/NOR Gate Latch/Troubleshooting Case Study*

5.1   (a)   The output of a *NOR* gate latch is invalid, when the SET and the CLEAR inputs are HIGH.
  (b)   The Q output of a NAND gate latch is LOW, when the SET input is *HIGH* and the CLEAR input is *LOW*.
  (c)   The output of a *NAND* gate latch will not change, if both inputs are HIGH.

5.2   (a)

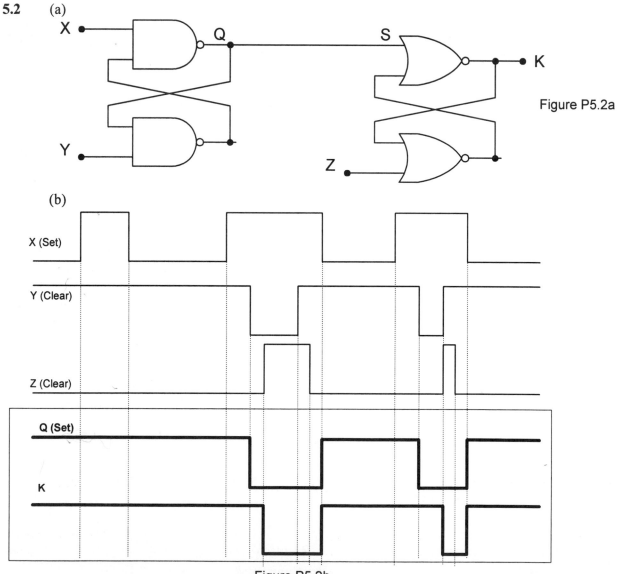

Figure P5.2a

  (b)

Figure P5.2b

5.3   There are two possibilities for the malfunction:

   (1) If the K output is permanently HIGH, then it can be said that the K latch is always Set. The conditions necessary for a NOR latch to set are: Clear=0, Set=1. Since FF K is a TTL NOR latch, if its Set input is open or shorted to Vcc (either case is a TTL HIGH), then the latch will always be Set. This condition in conjunction with waveform Z will cause, at certain times, FF K to have a logic HIGH at both the Set and Clear inputs. This is a violation of the truth table for the NOR latch and may cause erroneous flip-flop operation.
   (2) Output K is internally or externally connected to Vcc.

SECTIONS 5.4-5.5 *Clock Signals and Clocked Flip-Flops/Clocked S-C Flip-Flop*

5.4

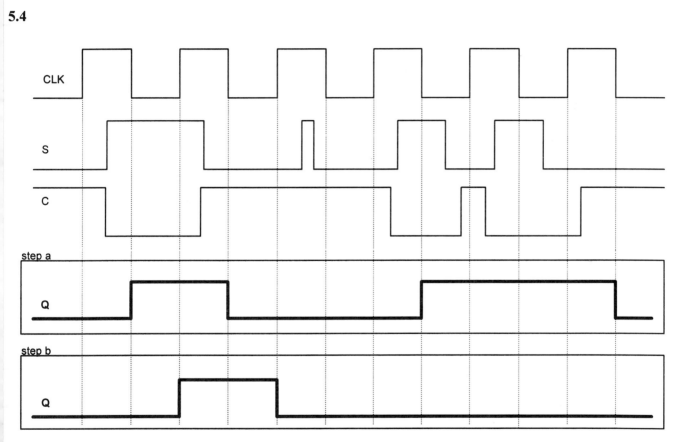

Figure P5.4

5.5 (a) In ***synchronous*** digital systems, the time during which the output of a circuit can change is determined by a signal called CLOCK.

   (b) The ***hold*** time requirement of a flip-flop is that time interval immediately following the active transition of the CLK signal during which the synchronous inputs have to be maintained at the proper level.

   (c) The internal circuitry of the edge-triggered S-C flip-flop consists of an edge-detector circuit, a pulse-steering circuit, and a basic ***NAND*** latch.

SECTIONS 5.9-5.10 *Asynchronous Inputs/IEEE-ANSI Symbols*

5.9   (a)

C	J	K	R	S	Q
NGT	1	1	1	0	*1*
NGT	1	0	1	1	*1*
NGT	0	0	0	1	*0*
NGT	1	1	1	1	*1*

Figure P5.9a

(b)

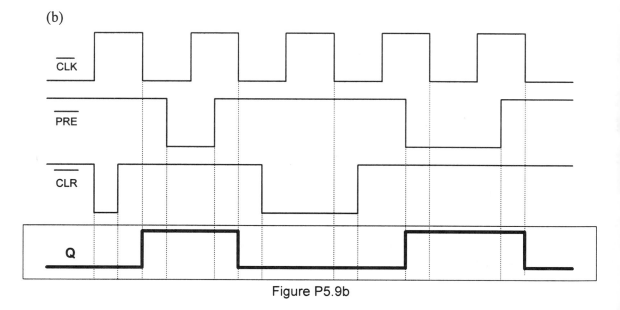

Figure P5.9b

SECTIONS 5.11-5.12 *Flip-Flop Timing Considerations/Potential Timing Problem in FF Circuits*

5.10 The input clock signal is 1-MHz, 7.5% D.C. Therefore, $T=1\mu s$ and $t_P=75ns$. Figure 5.6 shows t $t_{W(H)}=100ns$ for the 74C74 flip-flop. It is evident that the $t_{W(H)}$ requirement has been violated, consequently under this condition the manufacturer cannot guarantee the normal operation of the f flop.

5.11 The Z waveform cannot be properly sketched because the signal at the asynchronous input L changing at the same time as the clock (Positive-Going-Transitions a and b). This becomes a probl because the required hold-time for the 7474 flip-flop is 5ns and in this situation the allowed hold-ti is basically 0ns. Therefore, waveform Z can only be predicted with any degree of certainty up to shaded area. It is anyone's guess what happens during the shaded area. This problem does not exist output M, because the hold-time requirement for a 74C74 flip-flop is 0ns.

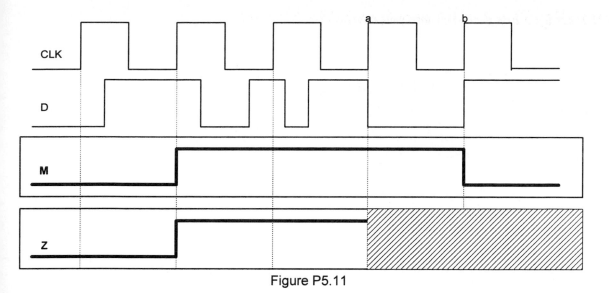

Figure P5.11

SECTION 5.13-5.14 *Master-Slave flip-flops/Flip-Flop Applications*

5.12 (a) Master/slave flip-flops have been replaced with a new master/slave version called a *Master Slave with data lockout.*

(b) A *sequential* circuit is one in which the outputs follow a predetermined *sequence* of states, with a new state occurring each time a clock pulse occurs.

SECTIONS 5.17-5.18 *Data Storage and Transfer/Serial Data Transfer: Shift Registers*

5.13 (a) D flip-flop Y_0 of the Y-Register should be Set after the fourth shift pulse. Instead, it stays at a logic LOW. Thus, one possible cause for the malfunction is that Y_0 output may be internally or externally shorted to ground. Another possible cause is an open CLK input to flip-flop Y_0.

(b)

X_3	X_2	X_1	X_0	Y_3	Y_2	Y_1	Y_0	
1	0	1	1	0	0	0	0	← Before pulses applied.
0	1	0	1	1	0	0	0	← After the first pulse.
0	0	1	0	1	1	0	0	← After the second pulse.
0	0	0	1	0	1	1	0	← After the third pulse.
0	0	0	0	1	0	1	1	← After the fourth pulse.

SECTION 5.19 *Frequency Division and Counting*

5.14

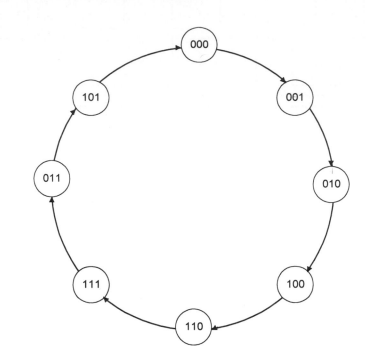

Figure P5.14

5.15 This counter is called a MOD-8 counter because it has 8 different states.

5.16 *Note that the sequence of counts for this counter is 0, 1, 2, 4, 6, 7, 3, 5, and then it recycles. In other words, this counter recycles every eight pulses (MOD-8 counter).*

(a) This counter starts at count 000_2. Let us determine how many times the counter recycles by dividing 16 pulses by the MOD number (16/8=2). In other words, the counter will be at count 000_2 after it recycles twice. Therefore, at the end of 16 pulses the counter will hold count 000_2.

(b) This counter starts at count 111_2. The counter recycles 105 times (842/8=105.25). In other words, the counter will be at count 111_2 after it recycles 105 times. However, 0.25 represents *two* more counts (0.25x8). Therefore, at the end of 842 pulses the counter will hold count 101_2.

(c) This counter starts at count 100_2. The counter recycles 44 times (358/8=44.75). This counter will be at count 100_2 after it recycles 44 times. However, 0.75 represents *six* more counts (0.75x8). Therefore, at the end of 358 pulses the counter will hold count 001_2.

(d) This counter starts at count 101_2. The counter recycles 459 times (3673/8=459.125). Consequently, the counter will be at count 101_2 after it recycles 459 times. However, 0.125 represents *one* more count (0.125 x 8). Therefore, at the end of 3673 pulses the counter will hold count 000_2.

5.17 (a) Let's look at the timing diagram of Figure P5.17a. This counter is a MOD-8 counter. The input frequency (100KHz, 10% D.C.) is divided by 2 at X_0, divided by 4 at X_1, and divided by 8 at X_2. Furthermore, the resulting signals are 50% Duty Cycle waveforms. Thus, squarewaves are present at X_0, X_1 and X_2 outputs and their frequencies are 50KHz, 25KHz and 12.5KHz respectively.

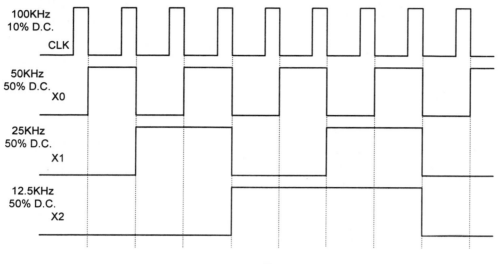

Figure P5.17a

(b) The total number of states is equal to 2^N, or 2^8, or 256. Thus, the counter can go through there a total of 256 different states (0_{10}-255_{10}).

(c) The maximum binary count that this counter can reach is 11111111_2.

SECTION 5.20 *Microcomputer Applications*

5.18 Let's look at the necessary logic levels on the Address bus lines A_0-A_{15}:

A15	A14	A13	A12	A11	A10	A9	A8	A7-A0	
0	0	0	0	1	1	1	1	X--------X	= $0Fxx_{16}$
0	0	0	0	1	1	1	0	X--------X	= $0Exx_{16}$
0	0	0	0	1	1	0	1	X--------X	= $0Dxx_{16}$
0	0	0	0	1	1	0	0	X--------X	= $0Cxx_{16}$

The circuit of Figure P5.18 shows one possible way of decoding the MPU's address bus for the design of the "Decoding Logic" circuitry.

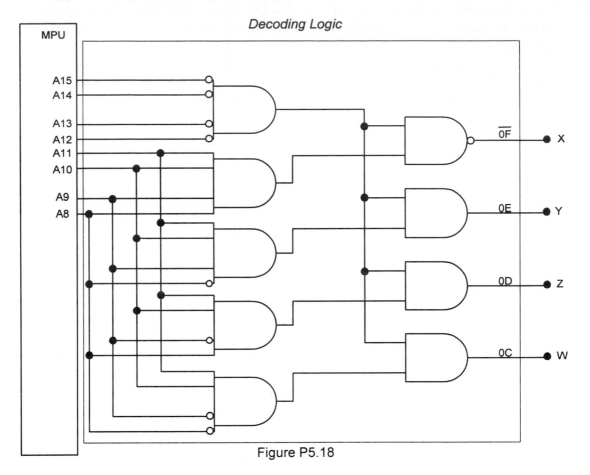

Figure P5.18

5.19 An external open on the address bus line A_9 has the same affect as a permanent TTL logic HIC input to the decoding logic circuit. Address line A_9 must be LOW for the decoding of addres 0Dxx$_{16}$ and 0Cxx$_{16}$. Therefore, if an external open exists on the Address Bus line A_9, outputs W a Z will always be LOW regardless of the logic levels on the address bus.

SECTION 5.22 *One-Shot*

5.20 (a) A *Retriggerable* One-shot can be triggered while it is in the Quasi-Stable state and as a result will begin a new t$_P$ interval. A *Nonretriggerable* One-Shot will not react to any signal on trigger input while it is in its Quasi-Stable state. A Nonretriggerable One-Shot must time-before it will react to another trigger pulse.

(b)

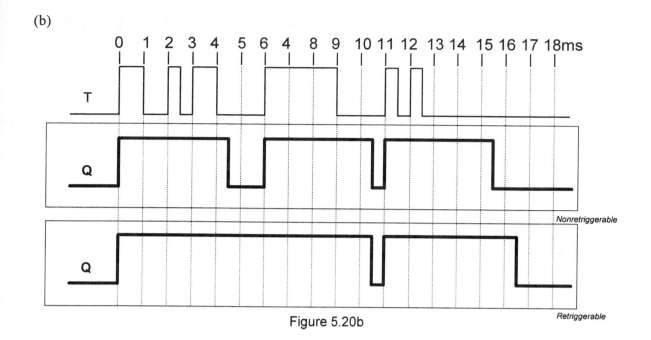

Figure 5.20b

SECTION 5.25 *Troubleshooting Flip-Flop Circuits*

5.21 (a) The data present at inputs A_3-A_0 (1001) will be transferred to outputs B_0-B_3 after SW1 is depressed. Thus, after the transfer outputs B_3=1, B_2=0, B_1=0, and B_0=1.

     (b) The INVERTERS are used between the J and the K inputs to insure that each J-K flip-flop will never operate in the toggle mode. Thus, upon clocking the flip-flops, they can only get Set or Clear.

5.22 By careful analysis of the table of Figure P5.22, it can be determined that outputs B_0 - B_2 always reflect inputs A_0 - A_2 after SW1 is activated. The problem is with output B_3, which appears to be faulty at times (*). It should also be noted that, when SW1 is pressed for a second time after a faulty transfer has occurred, the resulted output is correct. Thus, the question is, what particular fault with flip-flop B_3 could cause the observed results?

A_3	A_2	A_1	A_0	B_3	B_2	B_1	B_0	
1	0	0	1	0	0	0	0	after SW2 is depressed.
1	0	0	1	1	0	0	1	after SW1 is depressed.
1	1	0	0	1	0	0	1	after # A_0 - A_3 is changed.
*1	1	0	0	*0	1	0	0	after SW1 is depressed.
1	1	0	0	1	1	0	0	after SW1 is depressed again.
1	1	1	1	1	1	0	0	after # A_0 - A_3 changed.
*1	1	1	1	*0	1	1	1	after SW1 is depressed.
1	1	1	1	1	1	1	1	after SW1 is depressed again.
1	1	1	1	0	0	0	0	after SW2 is depressed.

Figure P5.22

If the K input to flip-flop B_3 is permanently HIGH, then flip-flop B_3 may occasionally get in the toggle mode (when J=K=1), and consequently changes states with each clock transition. Without the usage of some troubleshooting equipment, we can only guess about possible causes:

Some possibilities:

(a) Either the K input of flip-flop B_3 or the output of INVERTER Z3-A is internally or externa connected to Vcc.

(b) An open connection between the output of INVERTER Z3-A and the K input of flip-flop B would also cause the same results.

5.23 The following lists the sequence of events necessary for a transfer of data to occur:

1. Binary data must be present and stable at inputs A_3 - A_0.
2. A 10 Hz squarewave must be present at the input of Z2-A-1.
3. SW1 must be actuated momentarily, and then the Q output of the One-Shot goes from its normal state to its Quasi-Stable state for 10ms.
4. The 10ms logic HIGH at the input of the AND gate Z2-A-2 allows a NGT of the 10Hz squarewave to occur at output of AND gate Z2-A-3.
5. The NGT at the output of AND gate Z2-A-3 will clock the data from inputs A_3-A_0 to outpu B_3-B_0.

(a) The problem is with step 4. The designer of this circuit did not make any provisions for synchronization between output Q of the One-Shot and the NGT of the 10Hz squarewa Thus, the pulse from the One-Shot can occur at any time during the 10Hz squarewave. Her there is a good chance that the pulse from the One-Shot will occur during the off time of 10Hz squarewave; one possible scenario is shown in Figure P5.23a. At such times, flip-f B_0-B_3 won't be clocked and no transfer of data will take place. As a matter of fact, it may t a few actuations of switch SW1 for data to be successfully transferred to the output.

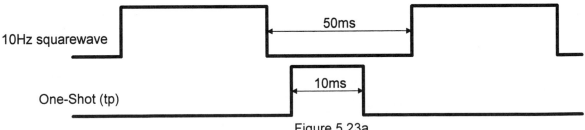

Figure 5.23a

(b) There are several ways of fixing this synchronization problem:

1. Increase the squarewave frequency so that its period is much smaller than the pulse w t_P of the One-Shot.
2. Increase t_P of the One-Shot to a value greater than the period of the squarewave.
3. A more complex, but much more elegant way of fixing the problem is to use an extra type flip-flop and place between the One-Shot and the AND gate Z2-A. Figure P5. shows the logic circuit that will synchronize the clocking of flip-flops B_0-B_3 and the 1 squarewave.

6.6

6.4

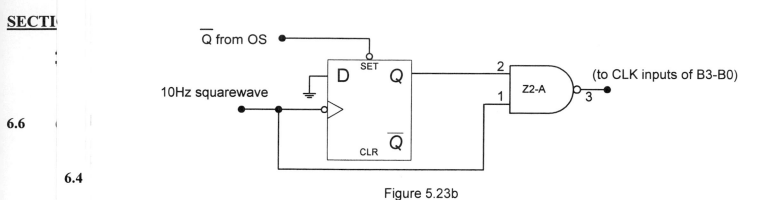

Figure 5.23b

5.24   Flip-flops B_0-B_3 are clocked when Z2-A-3 goes LOW. Z2-A-3 goes LOW when either Z2-A-2 or Z2-A-1 goes LOW. If the output of the OS goes LOW while Z2-A-1 is HIGH, a race condition will occur between the synchronous inputs of the flip-flops and the clock signal. In other words, the flip-flops are clocked at the same time that the logic levels at the J and K inputs are changing. This will result in random data being loaded in register B_0 - B_3.

This problem can be eliminated by using J-K flip-flops with zero hold time requirements (t_H=0).

SECTION 5.26 *Applications Using Programmable Logic Devices*

5.25 (a) The preprocessor command **$define** allows a constant numeric value to be assigned a name at the top of the source file.
     (b) The word **sequence** tells the compiler that we are using the state transition mode of hardware description.

5.26 (a)

```
Q = !QBAR # !SBAR;        QBAR = !Q # !CBAR;
```

(b)   Refer to Figure P5.26b.

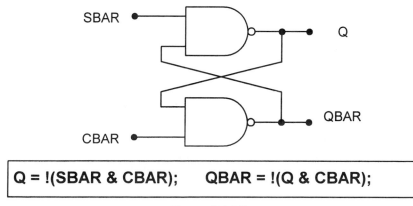

```
Q = !(SBAR & CBAR);     QBAR = !(Q & CBAR);
```

Figure P5.26b

6.7   (a) $[75F_{16} + 32D_{16}]$

<u>One way</u>: $75F_{16}$ = $0111\ 0101\ 1111_2$
            $32D_{16}$ = $0011\ 0010\ 1101_2$
                        +
                        _____
                          $1010\ 1000\ 1100_2 = A8C_{16}$

<u>Another way</u>:   7   5 F_{16}
                          3   2 D_{16}

                     +
                     _____

                     ↓ ↓ ↓ _____ $(15+13)=28;\ 28-16 = 12_{10}$ + Carry = C_{16}
                       ↓ ↓ _____ $(5+2+\text{Carry}) = 8_{10} = 8_{16}$
                         ↓ _____ $(7+3)=10_{10} = A_{16}$

Therefore, $[75F_{16} + 32D_{16}] = A8C_{16}$

☞ *When the addition of two hexadecimal digits results in a number equal or greater than 16,
then 16 must be subtracted from that number in order to obtain the proper result, in additio
a CARRY is generated into the next hex digit position.*

(b) $[12A_{16} - FF_{16}]$

        FF_{16} = $0000\ 1111\ 1111_2$ subtrahend
                  $1111\ 0000\ 0000_2$ 1's Complement
                  $1111\ 0000\ 0001_2$ 2's Complement of the subtrahend.

        $12A_{16}$ = $0001\ 0010\ 1010_2$ minuend
              + $1111\ 0000\ 0001_2$ 2's Complement of the subtrahend.
                  _____
                  ± $0000\ 0010\ 1011_2 = 2B_{16}$

              ↑ Overflow is disregarded in the subtraction.

<u>Another way</u>:

              1 2 A_{16} (minuend)
          -   0 F F $_{16}$ (subtrahend)
          _____

          ↓ ↓ ↓ _____ $((10+16)-15) = {}^*11_{10} = B_{16}$
            ↓ ↓ _____ $((1+16)-15) = 2_{10} = 2_{16}$
              ↓ _____ $(1-1) = 0_{10} = 0_{16}$

Therefore, $[12A_{16} - 0FF_{16}] = 02B_{16}$

When a hexadecimal number is being subtracted from a smaller number (A_{16}-F_{16} as in the above example), then a 1_{16} must be borrowed from the next digit (2_{16}) of the minuend and added to the previous digit of the minuend (A_{16}). This process is repeated with the next digit position. Note that the hexadecimal 1_{16} that is borrowed weights 16_{10} due to its relative position to the digit that is borrowing.

(c)   [7834_{16} + $ABCD_{16}$]

$$7834_{16} \quad = \quad 0111\ 1000\ 0011\ 0100_2$$
$$ABCD_{16} \quad = \quad 1010\ 1011\ 1100\ 1101_2$$
$$+ \quad \overline{}$$
$$\overline{1\ 0010\ 0100\ 0000\ 0001} = \mathit{12401}_{16}$$
$$\uparrow \textbf{\textit{NOT}} \text{ disregarded in the addition.}$$

<u>Another way</u>:

$$7\ 8\ 3\ \ 4_{16}$$
$$A\ B\ C\ D_{16}$$
$$+ \quad \overline{}$$

$\downarrow\downarrow\downarrow\downarrow$ _____(4+13)=17; 17-16 = $\mathit{1}_{16}$ + Carry

$\downarrow\downarrow\downarrow$ _____(3+12+Carry)=16; 16-16 = $\mathit{0}_{16}$ + Carry

$\downarrow\downarrow$ _____(8+11+Carry)=20; 20-16 = $\mathit{4}_{16}$ + Carry

$\downarrow$ _____(7+10+Carry)=18: 18-16 = $\mathit{2}_{16}$ + Carry

Therefore, [7834_{16}+$ABCD_{16}$] = $\mathit{12401}_{16}$

SECTIONS 6.9-6.15   *Arithmetic Circuits/Parallel Binary Adder/Complete parallel Adder with Registers/ Integrated-Circuit Parallel Adder/2's Complement System*

6.8

Sum	[A]	[B]	[S]	
#1 →	1101	0110	10011	Correct result
#2 →	1000	0111	10111	Incorrect result
#3 →	0100	0101	01001	Correct result
#4 →	0011	0100	01111	Incorrect result

We must try to find a common pattern of the incorrect binary results from the additions #2 and #4. Additions #2 and #4 should have yielded 01111_2 and 00111_2 respectively. By careful analysis of all four additions, it can be concluded that additions #2 and #4 are the only ones where Carry C_3 is generated into the input C_{in} of the MSB's Full-Adder.

Since this is a TTL logic circuit, if the C_3 connection between the full-adders became open, a logic 1 would always be added to the B_3 and A_3 bits. Thus, an incorrect sum occurs whenever the addition of B_2 and A_2 generates a logic LOW at C_3. This of course, would not affect additions where C_3 results in a logic HIGH.

6.9

$[A_0-A_7]$	$[B_0-B_7]$	SW1	Outputs (C_{out}, S_7-S_0)
01100111	10001011	0 (add)	011110010
11000001	10100010	1 (sub.)	000011111
10100101	11000010	0 (add)	101100111
11100110	11000110	1 (sub.)	000100000

SECTION 6.16 *BCD Adder*

6.10

A_3	A_2	A_1	A_0	B_3	B_2	B_1	B_0	S_3	S_2	S_1	S_0	X	Σ_3	Σ_2	Σ_1	Σ_0
1	0	0	1	1	0	0	1	0	0	1	0	1	1	0	0	0
1	0	0	0	0	0	1	1	1	0	1	1	1	0	0	0	1
0	1	1	1	0	1	0	1	1	1	0	0	1	0	0	1	0
0	1	1	0	0	0	1	1	1	0	0	1	0	1	0	0	1

6.11   A logic '1' would always be added to the final BCD sum ($\Sigma_3-\Sigma_0$). Thus, the sum would always be greater by a factor of '1' and, in some cases the final BCD sum would be an illegal BCD code.

6.12   Whenever output X from the 'correction logic' is HIGH, a correction factor of 0110_2 has to be added to the results of the 4-bit parallel adder 74HC283 (see Figure 6.3). Figure P6.12 shows how two Half-Adders and a Full-Adder can be connected to implement the 'correction adder'.

6.13   By looking at the table, we can see that whenever X=1, the BCD sum is correct. When X=0, the result exceeds the correct answer by four, and in one case causes an illegal BCD code. Thus, we can conclude that the 'Correction Adder' circuit adds four to the answer when X=0, and in cases when X=1, it adds six. The following are the possible problems that could have caused the malfunction:

1)   Output X is connected to only A_1 of the 'Correction Adder'; while A_2 is externally open (always HIGH).
2)   Input A_2 of the 'Correction Adder' is internally open or shorted to Vcc.

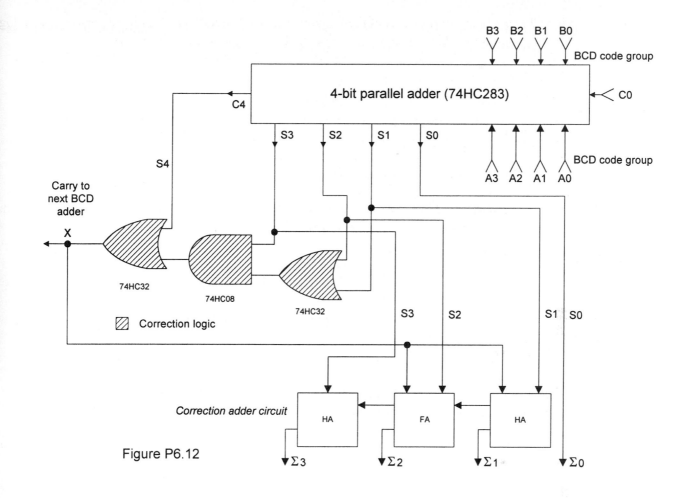

Figure P6.12

SECTION 6.17 *ALU Integrated Circuits*

6.14 (a) When $S_2S_1S_0 = 010$ the ALU will perform the *A minus B* operation on the data. These data are: $A_3A_2A_1A_0 = 1100$ and $B_3B_2B_1B_0 = 0101$. Since the ALU is performing a subtraction, the ALU will take the 2s complement of data B and then add it to data A.

$$
\begin{array}{lcl}
A_3A_2A_1A_0 & = & \mathit{1100} \\
B_3B_2B_1B_0 & = & 0101 \\
\text{1s Comp.} & = & 1010 \\
\text{2s Comp.} & = & \mathit{1011} \\
\hline
& & 1\ \mathit{0111}
\end{array}
$$

Therefore, outputs $F_3F_2F_1F_0 = 0111$ and C_{N+4} output will 1 since there was a carry out of the MSB position.

(b)   When $S_2S_1S_0 = 101$ the ALU will perform the *A OR B* logic operation on the data. These data are: $A_3A_2A_1A_0 = 1100$ and $B_3B_2B_1B_0 = 0101$.

$$
\begin{array}{rcl}
A_3A_2A_1A_0 & = & 1100 \\
B_3B_2B_1B_0 & = & 0101 \\
\hline
& & 1101
\end{array}
$$

Therefore, outputs $F_3F_2F_1F_0 = 1101$.

(c)   When $S_2S_1S_0 = 100$ the ALU will perform the *A $\oplus$ B* logic operation on the data. These da are: $A_3A_2A_1A_0 = 1100$ and $B_3B_2B_1B_0 = 0101$.

$$
\begin{array}{rcl}
A_3A_2A_1A_0 & = & 1100 \\
B_3B_2B_1B_0 & = & 0101 \\
\hline
& & 1001
\end{array}
$$

Therefore, outputs $F_3F_2F_1F_0 = 1001$.

6.15   First, we must make the select inputs $S_2S_1S_0 = 011$ in order for the operation *A plus B* to be performed. Second, according to the function table of Figure 6.4 (b), for the *A plus B* operation be performed input $C_N = 0$.

6.16   See Figure P6.16

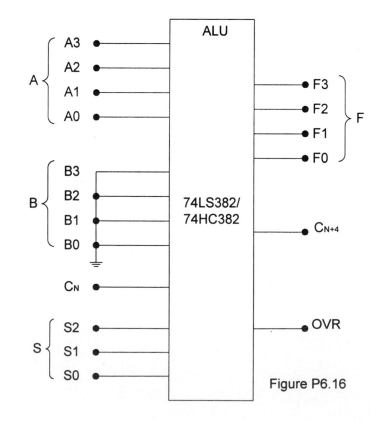

Figure P6.16

6.17   See Figure P6.17

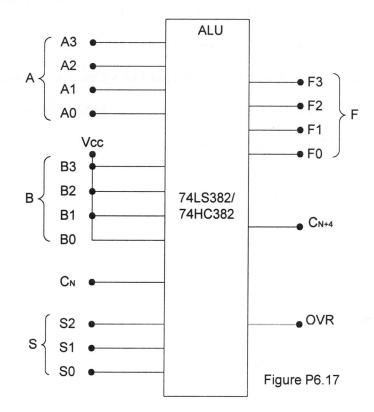

Figure P6.17

SECTION 6.18 *IEEE-ANSI Symbols*

6.18   This is the IEEE/ANSI symbol for a 4-bit parallel adder IC.

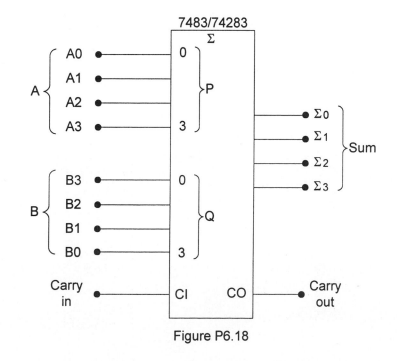

Figure P6.18

SECTION 6.20 *A PLD full adder*

6.19   (a)   In CUPL notation a **SET** can be ,made up of several individual variable bits.

(b)   The notation *pin [1..3] = [X0..2]* assigns pin 1 to **X0** pin 2 to **X1** and pin 3 to **X2**

(c)   In a CUPL source file, the $ symbol represents the **XOR** operation.

(d)   *A3, A2, A1, A0* is an example of a group of **INDEXED** variables in CUPL notation.

6.20   (a)   **Z = Anum $ Bnum**: *(Anum EXORed with Bnum)*

$$[A] = \quad 1100$$
$$[B] = \quad 0011$$

$$\overline{}$$
$$[Z] = \quad 1111$$

(b)   **Z = Anum & Bnum**: *(Anum ANDed with Bnum)*

$$[A] = \quad 1100$$
$$[B] = \quad 0011$$

$$\overline{}$$
$$[Z] = \quad 0000$$

(c)   **Z = Anum # Bnum**: *(Anum ORed with Bnum)*

$$[A] = \quad 1100$$
$$[B] = \quad 0011$$

$$\overline{}$$
$$[Z] = \quad 1111$$

7   COUNTERS AND REGISTERS

PART I

SECTION 7.1 *Asynchronous (Ripple) Counters*

2^6

64

7.1

	MOD-#	Clock Frequency	Output Frequency	# of JK flip-flops
(a)	**64**	256 KHz	4 KHz	**6**
(b)	32	350 KHz	***10.93 KHz***	**5**
(c)	**8**	***800 KHz***	100 KHz	3
(d)	**128**	500 KHz	***3.9 KHz***	7

(a) $\text{MOD\#} = \dfrac{\text{Input Frequency}}{\text{Output Frequency}} = \dfrac{256\text{KHz}}{4\text{KHz}} = 64$

       # of Flip-Flops = N
       $2^N = 64$
       $N = 6$

(b) $\text{Output Frequency} = \dfrac{\text{Input Frequency}}{\text{MOD\#}} = \dfrac{350\text{KHz}}{32} = 10.93\text{KHz}$

       # of Flip-Flops = N
       $2^N = 32$
       $N = 5$

(c) $\text{MOD\#} = 2^N$
                $= 2^3 = 8$
    Input Frequency = (Output Frequency) x (MOD-#)
                        = 100KHz x 8
                        = 800KHz

(d)   MOD-# $= 2^7$
                 $= 128$

      $\text{Output Frequency} = \dfrac{500\text{KHz}}{128} = 3.9\text{KHz}$

<u>**SECTIONS 7.2, 7.3, 7.24**</u> *Counters With MOD Numbers <2^N/IC Asynchronous Counters/ Troubleshooting.*

7.2   (a) If the inputs to the 3-input NAND gate of Figure 7.2 are A, B and C, then its output will be LOW when the counter reaches the count of seven (0111_2). Therefore, the counter will cou~~nt~~ from binary 0000_2 to 0110_2 and then clear at the count of 0111_2. Since this counter go~~es~~ through seven different states before recycling, it is called a MOD-7 counter.

        (b) For this combination of inputs, the counter will be cleared at the binary count of thirte~~en~~ (1101_2). This counter will go through thirteen different states (0000_2-1100_2), and therefore~~ it~~ is called a MOD-13 counter.

        (c) Since one of the inputs to the NAND gate is always a logic 1 (+Vcc), its output will be LO~~W~~ when inputs A and B are HIGH. Thus, this counter will count from binary 0000_2 to 0010_2 a~~nd~~ then clear on the next count, binary 0011_2. Therefore, this is a MOD-3 counter.

7.3   When the circuit of Figure 7.3 is working properly, and it reaches the binary count 110_2, the Set/Cle~~ar~~ flip-flop Q will be Set and counter A B C will clear. Thus, any condition that may prevent t~~he~~ Set/Clear flip-flop from clearing the counter will cause the counter to count from binary 000_2 to 11~~1~~ repeatedly, or operate as a MOD-8 counter. The following are some of the possible causes for t~~his~~ malfunction:

        1.   The connection from the output of the decoding 2-input NAND gate to the SET input of the Set/Clear flip-flop is open.

        2.   The connection between the Q of the Set/Clear flip-flop and the CLR inputs of the J-K flip-flops is open.

        3.   The connection from the CLK input to the INVERTER is open.

        4.   The connection between the output of the INVERTER and the CLEAR input of the Set/Clea~~r~~ flip-flop is shorted to ground.

7.4   Under normal conditions flip-flops Q_1-Q_3 of counter Z1 form a MOD-8 counter. Thus, the frequen~~cy~~ at output Q_3 of Z1 is 8.64KHz/8 = 1.08KHz. Counter Z2 is wired as a MOD-9 counter and thus its ~~Q~~ output should be 1.08KHz/9 = 120Hz. This signal is connected to CP_0 of Z1, which divides t~~his~~ frequency in half to produce a 60Hz squarewave. If counter Z2 is wired as a MOD-10 counter, then Q_3 output is 1.08KHz/10 = 108Hz. This signal is then halved by counter Z1 and a 54Hz squarewa~~ve~~ will be present at point X. Thus, in order for counter Z2 to be wired as a MOD-10, its MR1 inp~~ut~~ would have to be connected to its Q_1 output instead of Q_0.

SECTIONS 7.5,7.24 *Propagation Delay in Ripple Counters/Troubleshooting*

7.5   The ripple counter of Figure 7.5 is incremented from count 7 (111_2) to count zero (000_2). Therefore, all three J-K flip-flops change from a logic HIGH to a logic LOW (t_{pHL}). According to the TTL Data Manual the 74LS112 has a value of 24ns for t_{pHL}. Thus, it will take 72ns (3x24ns) before FF C changes states.

7.6   By analyzing the counting sequence, it should be clear that the logic states for outputs A and B are correct. Therefore, it can be deduced that the problem is with output C. Output C should be LOW for four counts and HIGH for four counts. When the counter sequences through its states properly, output C changes after output B goes through a negative going transition. Unfortunately, output C is doing just the opposite; it changes when output B goes through a positive going transition. Thus, the most probable cause for this malfunction is a mistake in the wiring of the circuit. If output $\overline{B}$ instead of B is connected to the CLK of flip-flop C, then the counting sequence would be as recorded.

SECTIONS 7.6-7.9,7.24   *Synchronous (Parallel) Counters/Synchronous Down and Up/Down Counters Presettable Counters/The 74ALS193/HC193 Counter/Troubleshooting.*

7.7   ***Asynchronous Counter****:*

Advantage - Since it requires the fewest amount of components to build, simplicity of construction is the major advantage of this type of counter.

Disadvantage - The speed at which it operates is dependent on the number of flip-flops in the counter. As the number of flip-flops increase, the maximum allowable input clock frequency decreases. This is because of the inherent propagation time delay of each flip-flop. Thus, for example, in a serial counter the $N^{\underline{th}}$ flip-flop (MSB) can change only *after* all of the other flip-flops in the counter have changed.

Synchronous Counter:

Advantage - The speed at which it operates is independent of the number of flip-flops in the counter. The flip-flops, which make this type of counter, are all clocked simultaneously (in parallel) by the input clock signal. Therefore, no flip-flop in the counter has to wait for the previous flip-flop in the chain to change in order for it to change.

Disadvantage - This type of counter requires more logic circuitry and a greater number of connections than the asynchronous counter.

7.8

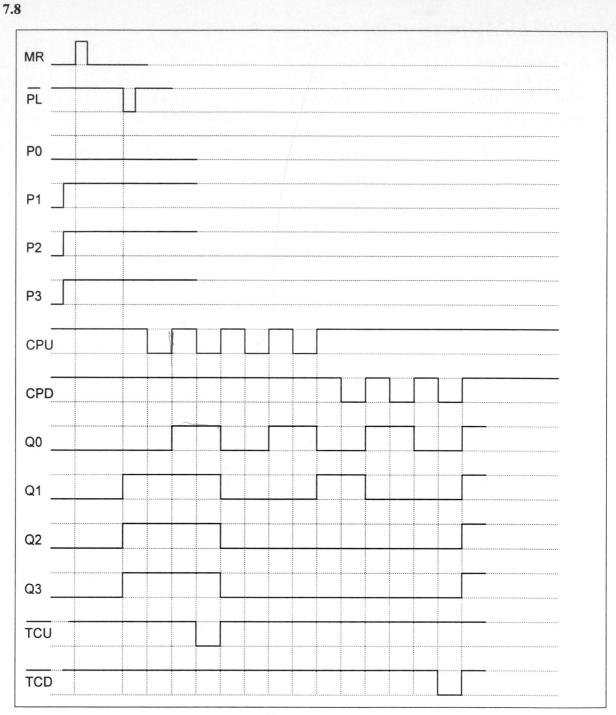

Figure P7.8

7.9

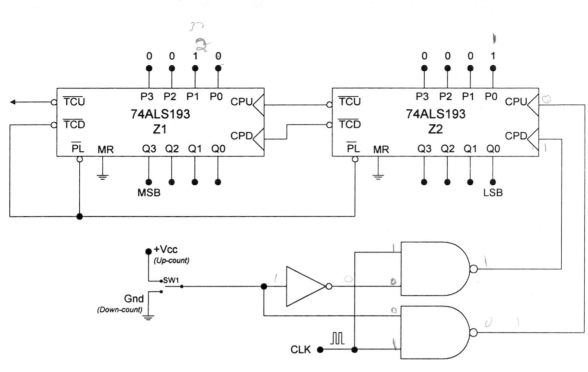

Figure P7.9

7.10 This counter should be dividing the input frequency by 256 when SW1 is in the *Count-Up* position. Since the technician measured 39Hz at the MSB (output Q_3 of Z1 in Figure P7.9) when the counter was counting up, we can conclude that the counter works properly in this mode, since 10KHz/256 is equal to about 39Hz. When switch SW1 is in the *Down-Count* position, the frequency at the MSB (output Q_3 of Z1 of Figure P7.9) should be 294.1Hz (10KHz/34).

Since the measured frequency is about 39Hz regardless of the position of switch SW1, it can be concluded that the counter always divides the 10KHz input frequency by 256. In order for the circuit of Figure P7.9 to operate as a MOD-256 counter when SW1 is in the Down-Count position, each of the 74ALS193 counters must be working as a MOD-16 counter. Thus, it can be concluded that counters Z1 and Z2, of Figure P7.9 never get loaded with the binary number 00100001_2 $(33_{10})^*$, but rather are allowed to count down from binary 11111111_2 to 00000000_2 repeatedly.

For the counter (Z1 and Z2) to be a MOD-34 down counter, it must be loaded with binary 00100001_2 (33_{10}) and be allowed to count down to 00000000_2 (0_{10}). In other words, go through 34 different states.

The following are a few of the possible causes for the malfunction:

1. Connection between the $\overline{\text{PL}}$ inputs and the output $\overline{\text{TCD}}$ of Z1 is open.
2. Parallel inputs to Z1 and Z2 are all floating, or HIGH.
3. The ground connection from switch SW1 is open.

SECTION 7.10   *More on the IEEE-ANSI Dependency Notation*

7.11 (a) This MOD-256 counter (CTRDIV 256) can count from 0-255.

(b) MS1 and MS2 are inputs to an Exclusive-OR gate. Whenever these two inputs are equal, the counter is loaded with the count 150_{10} (CT=150).

(c) MR1 is an active HIGH input to a two-input OR gate. When MR1 is HIGH the counters clears.

(d) Label '3D' establishes the dependency of flip-flops A through H on the common input C3.

(e) At count 255 ($\bar{1}$ CT=255), output $\overline{CO}$ will go LOW, provided input 'Down' is LOW.

(f) When either MR1 or MR2 are HIGH, this counter will be cleared (CT=0).

(g) When output $\overline{BO}$=0, it means that the counter is cleared or is at binary count 00000000_2, and that input 'Up' is LOW.

(h) The symbol inside of the box whose inputs are MR1 and MR2, would have to be changed to (&).

(i) The '+' symbol at the input UP, indicates that the counter will increment as pulses are applied to this input.

SECTIONS 7.11-7.13, 7.24   *Decoding a Counter/Decoding Glitches*
                                Cascading BCD Counters/Troubleshooting

7.12 (a) When the output of a ripple (serial) counter is being decoded, temporary states caused by the propagation delays of the individual counter flip-flops are also decoded. Figure P7.12 shows the counting sequence of the ripple counter, including the temporary states. The temporary states are marked with an asterisk. The states in dotted boxes are decoded (000_2) the AND gate Z1-A. Flip-flop Z2 is cleared when the counter reaches the count of 011_2, and set when the temporary state 000_2 occurs.

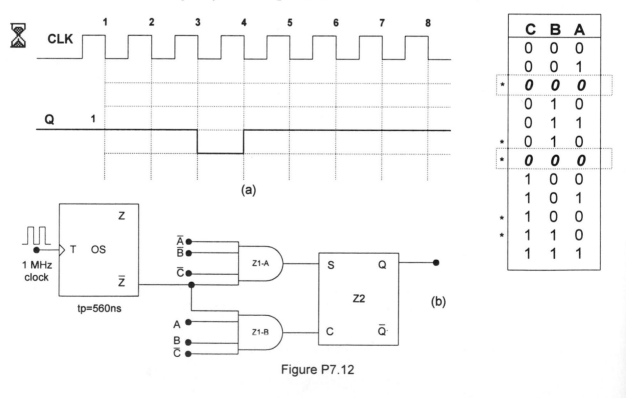

Figure P7.12

(b)   The unused inputs of AND gates Z1-A and Z1-B can be utilized for a strobe input. After determining the maximum propagation delay for the flip-flops used by the ripple counter, a one-shot with the proper t_p value, could be used to eliminate the decoding of the temporary state (000_2) by flip-flop Z2.

Figure P7.12 (b) shows the circuit modification. It is assumed that the ripple counter has an input clock of 1MHz (T=1μs) and that the propagation delay of each of its flip-flops is 20ns maximum.

Circuit Operation:

When a NGT of the 1MHz clock occurs, the ripple counter is incremented. The transitional states of the counter occur shortly after this NGT. The worst case is when the counter is cycling from 111_2 to 000_2 and all three flip-flops are changing from a set to a clear condition. This will cause transitional states to be present at the counter outputs ABC for approximately 60ns maximum (3x20ns).

When a PGT of the 1MHz clock occurs, the One-shot triggers for 560ns and consequently its $\bar{Z}$ output goes LOW for 560ns. This LOW will keep the outputs of AND gates Z1-A and Z1-B LOW, thereby preventing any of the transitional states from being decoded during the 560ns interval. Note that the transitional states will be present for 60ns (worst case) after a NGT of the clock occurs, which is 560ns after the One-shot gets triggered by a PGT. After the One-shot goes back to its normal state, the transitional states are no longer present and therefore no transitional state will ever be decoded by the AND gates Z1-A and Z1-B.

7.13   The Decoder/displays show the correct number of input pulses up to 79. When one more input pulse is counted the displays show 180. What has to be determined is why did the "Hundreds" BCD counter incremented at this particular time?

From count 79 to 80, the outputs of the "Tens" BCD counter went from 0111_2 to 1000_2. Since it is at this time that the "Hundreds" BCD counter is incremented, we can probably guess that output C of the "Tens" BCD counter, which just went through its first negative going transition, clocked the "Hundreds" BCD counter. This would have occurred if the technician made a mistake in wiring the circuit. He most likely connected output C from the "Tens" BCD counter to the "Hundreds" BCD counter instead of output D, as the circuit diagram calls for.

This would have caused the recorded display readings and consequently, anytime the "Tens" BCD counter goes from count seven to eight (0111_2-->1000_2), the "Hundreds" BCD counter is incremented.

SECTION 7.14 *Synchronous Counter Design*

7.14   The following six step procedure can be used in the design of any synchronous counter, although the reader may choose to use less than six and still obtain the proper counter design.

(a) **Step 1:** *Determine the desired number of bits (FFs) and the desired counting sequence.*

In this case the number of bits are three. Let's assume that they are 'ABC' where A is the LS and D is the MSB.

Step 1   *Step 2*

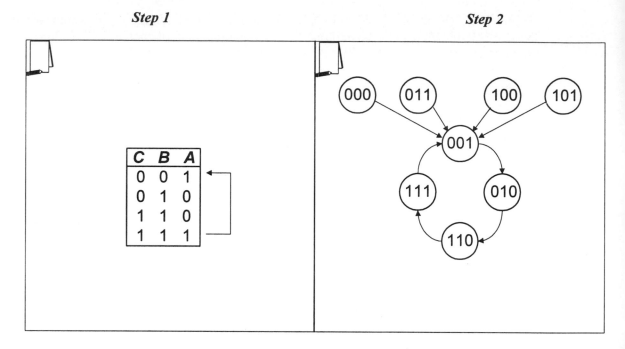

Step 2: *Draw the state transition diagram showing all possible states, including those that are not part of the desired counting sequence.*

Step 3: *Use the state transition diagram to set up a table that lists all present states and their next states.*

Present State			*Next State*		
C	**B**	**A**	**C**	**B**	**A**
0	0	0	0	0	1
0	0	1	0	1	0
0	1	0	1	1	0
0	1	1	0	0	1
1	0	0	0	0	1
1	0	1	0	0	1
1	1	0	1	1	1
1	1	1	0	0	1

Step 4: Add a column to this table for each J and K input. For each present state, indicate the levels required at each J and K input in order to produce the transition to the next state.

Present State			Next State			Jc	Kc	Jb	Kb	Ja	Ka
C	B	A	C	B	A						
0	0	0	0	0	1	0	x	0	x	1	x
0	0	1	0	1	0	0	x	1	x	x	1
0	1	0	1	1	0	1	x	x	0	0	x
0	1	1	0	0	1	0	x	x	1	x	0
1	0	0	0	0	1	x	1	0	x	1	x
1	0	1	0	0	1	x	1	0	x	x	0
1	1	0	1	1	1	x	0	x	0	1	x
1	1	1	0	0	1	x	1	x	1	x	0

The table below shows the levels required at each J and K input in order to produce the transition from the present state (Q) to the NEXT state (Q+1).

Q	Q+1	J	K
0	0	0	x
0	1	1	x
1	0	x	1
1	1	x	0

Step 5: Design the logic circuits to generate the levels required at each J and K input.

Simplify the Sum-of-Products expressions for Ja, Ka, Jb, Kb, Jc, and Kc by using the Karnaugh map method:

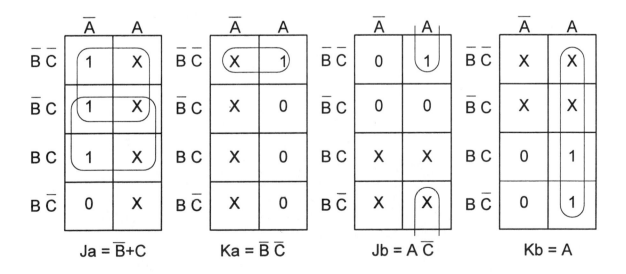

$$Ja = \overline{B} + C \qquad Ka = \overline{B}\,\overline{C} \qquad Jb = A\,\overline{C} \qquad Kb = A$$

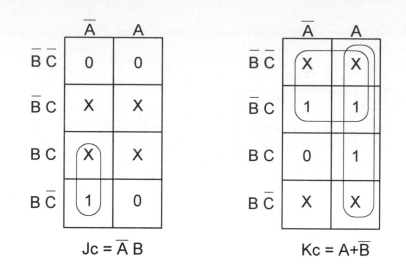

$$Jc = \overline{A}\,B \qquad\qquad Kc = A + \overline{B}$$

Step 6: *The last and final step is to draw the synchronous counter circuit of Figure P7.14(a*

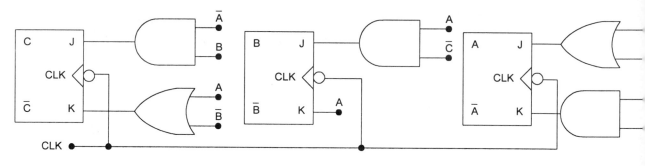

Figure P7.14 (a)

(b) **Use the same step-by-step procedure established in problem 7.14(a).**

Step 1: *Determine the desired number of bits (FFs) and the desired counting sequence. (Same number of bits and counting sequence as the previous problem.)*

Step 2: *Draw the state transition diagram showing all possible states.*

Step 1   **Step 2**

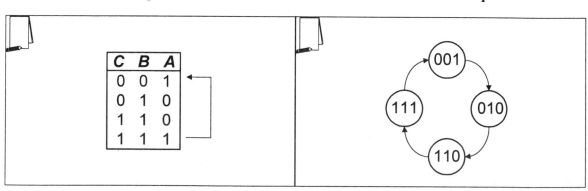

Step 3: Use the state transition diagram to set up a table that lists all present states and their next states.

Present State			Next State		
C	**B**	**A**	**C**	**B**	**A**
0	0	0	x	x	x
0	0	1	0	1	0
0	1	0	1	1	0
0	1	1	x	x	x
1	0	0	x	x	x
1	0	1	x	x	x
1	1	0	1	1	1
1	1	1	0	0	1

Step 4: Add a column to this table for each J and K input. For each present state, indicate the levels required at each J and K input in order to produce the transition to the next state.

Present State			Next State			Jc	Kc	Jb	Kb	Ja	Ka
C	**B**	**A**	**C**	**B**	**A**						
0	0	0	x	x	x	x	x	x	x	x	x
0	0	1	0	1	0	0	x	1	x	x	1
0	1	0	1	1	0	1	x	x	0	0	x
0	1	1	x	x	x	x	x	x	x	x	x
1	0	0	x	x	x	x	x	x	x	x	x
1	0	1	x	x	x	x	x	x	x	x	x
1	1	0	1	1	1	x	0	x	0	1	x
1	1	1	0	0	1	x	1	x	1	x	0

Step 5: Design the logic circuits to generate the levels required at each J and K input.

Simplify the S-of-P expressions for Ja, Ka, Jb, Kb, Jc, and Kc by using the Karnaugh map method:

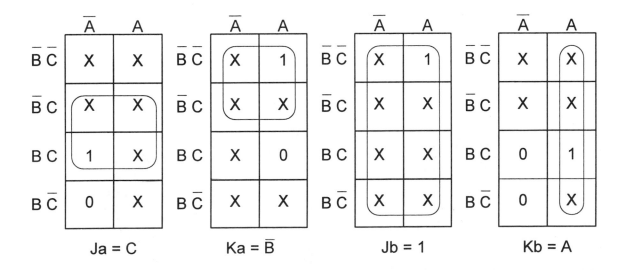

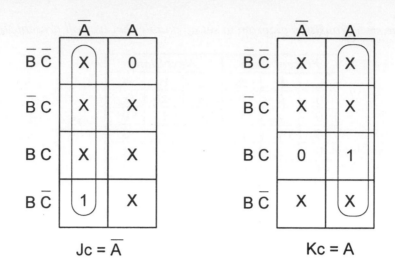

$J_C = \overline{A}$ $K_C = A$

Step 6:   *The last and final step is to draw the synchronous counter circuit of Figure P7.14(b)*

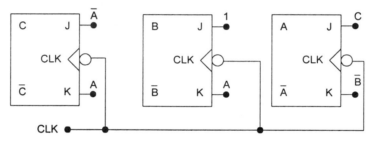

Figure P7.14 (b)

PART II

SECTIONS 7.15 *Shift-Register Counters*

7.15   Waveform Q_0 of Figure 7.9 repeats itself every six clock pulses. Since Q_0 is one of the outputs of 1 Ring counter, there must be six flip-flops in the counter. Note that each flip-flop output waveform this counter has a frequency equal to one-sixth of the clock frequency, since this is a MOD-6 coun

7.16   (a)   To build a MOD-*23* Ring Counter, it requires 23 flip-flops.

(b)   To decode any state of a MOD-14 Johnson Counter, it requires a *two* input AND gate.

(c)   If the frequency of the input clock of a 6-bit Johnson Counter is *60* kHz, then the output sig at any of the flip-flops in the counter is equal to 5 kHz, *50%* Duty Cycle.

SECTIONS 7.16, 7.17, 7.24 *Counter Applications: Frequency Counter and Digital Clock/Troubleshooting*

7.17   The counter is incremented by the "Unknown frequency" pulses only when signals "SAMPLE pulses" and "X" are HIGH (see Figure 7.10). Note that signal "X" stays HIGH for two "SAMPLE pulses" (FF X is a MOD-2 counter). Therefore, if the counter was incremented during the time interval which signal "X" is HIGH, the resulting reading on the Decoder/Display would be a value that is larger by a factor of two. Thus, a broken connection between the "SAMPLE pulses" signal and the input of the AND gate could cause the circuit to behave as it does. Note that this essentially creates a constant HIGH at that input of the AND gate.

7.18   In the circuit of Figure 7.11, the output of the NAND gate is active only when flip-flop X is set and the BCD counter reaches the count of three (0011_2). When these conditions are present, flip-flop X is cleared and the BCD counter is parallel loaded with binary 0001_2, thereby causing this section of the digital clock to cycle from <u>12</u>:59 to <u>01</u>:00. If flip-flop X fails to be cleared at this time, then the BCD counter is parallel loaded with binary 0001_2 every time it reaches the binary count of 0011_2. This of course causes the "Hours" section of the digital clock to oscillate between the hours of 11:00 and 12:00. Therefore, a possible cause for the malfunction is a nonexistent or broken connection between the CLR input of the X flip-flop and the output of the 3-input NAND gate.

SECTIONS 7.20, 7.21, 7.24   *Serial In/Serial Out - The 4731B*
   Parallel In/Serial Out - The 74ALS165/74HC165
   Troubleshooting.

7.19   Figure P7.19 shows the four 64-bit shift registers on the 4731B chip and an external inverter wired together as a MOD-512 Johnson counter or twisted-ring counter.

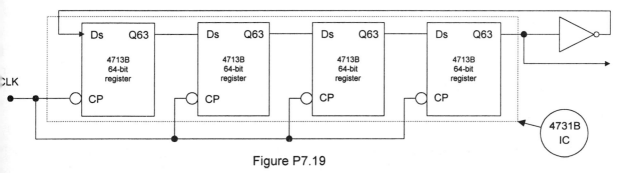

Figure P7.19

7.20   Since input Ds changes while data is being clocked into the register, it helps to visualize the flow
data within the 74LS165 IC, Figure P7.20 (a), before we draw the waveforms of Figure P7.20 (b

Ds	Q0	Q1	Q2	Q3	Q4	Q5	Q6	Q7	
0	1	0	1	1	1	0	0	*1*	*After loading*
0	0	1	0	1	1	1	0	*0*	*After 1st shift pulse*
1	1	0	1	0	1	1	1	*0*	*After 2nd shift pulse*
0	0	1	0	1	0	1	1	*1*	*After 3rd shift pulse*
0	0	0	1	0	1	0	1	*1*	*After 4th shift pulse*
0	0	0	0	1	0	1	0	*1*	*After 5th shift pulse*
0	0	0	0	0	1	0	1	*0*	*After 6th shift pulse*
0	0	0	0	0	0	1	0	*1*	*After 7th shift pulse*
0	0	0	0	0	0	0	1	*0*	*After 8th shift pulse*
0	0	0	0	0	0	0	0	*1*	*After 9th shift pulse*
0	0	0	0	0	0	0	0	*0*	*After 10th shift pulse*
0	0	0	0	0	0	0	0	*0*	*After 11th shift pulse*

Figure P7.20 (a)

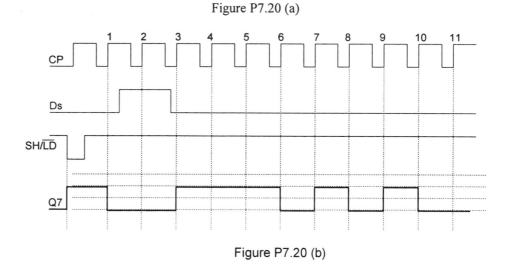

Figure P7.20 (b)

SECTION 7.23   *IEEE-ANSI Register Symbols.*

7.21   The best way of determining the function of this, or any other, dependency notation diagram, is to
decipher and understand each bit of information given within the IEEE/ANSI diagram.

1.   When the CLR input signal is HIGH the outputs are cleared (LOW).
2.   Outputs are enabled when inputs M and N are both LOW.
3.   When both gated data enable inputs $\overline{G1}$ and $\overline{G2}$ are LOW, data at the D inputs are loaded in
their respective flip-flops on the next PGT of the clock.
4.   Data inputs (1D) in the control block, show dependency on the circuit C1 (shaded block 3).
5.   Four registers with tri-state outputs.

SECTION 7.25 *Programming PLDs as Counters Using Boolean Equations*

7.22 (a)   **Step 1:** *Draw the Present State, Next State table*

Present State			Next State		
Q2	Q1	Q0	Q2	Q1	Q0
0	0	0	0	1	1
0	0	1	0	0	0
0	1	0	0	0	1
0	1	1	1	1	0
1	0	0	0	1	0
1	0	1	1	0	0
1	1	0	1	1	1
1	1	1	1	0	1

Step 2: *Write the unsimplified SOP expressions for each D input in terms of the Present States of the flip-flops:*

Q2.D = !Q2&Q1&Q0 # Q2&!Q1&Q0 # Q2&Q1&!Q0 # Q2&Q1&Q0

Q1.D = !Q2&!Q1&!Q0 # !Q2&Q1&Q0 # Q2&!Q1&!Q0 # Q2&Q1&!Q0

Q0.D = !Q2&!Q1&!Q0 # !Q2&Q1&!Q0 # Q2&Q1&!Q0 # Q2&Q1&Q0

(b)   Field count = [Q2, Q1, Q0]

/* Hardware Description */

```
count.D  =  'b'011 & count:0;
   #        'b'000 & count:1;
   #        'b'001 & count:2;
   #        'b'110 & count:3;
   #        'b'010 & count:4;
   #        'b'100 & count:5;
   #        'b'111 & count:6;
   #        'b'101 & count:7;
```

Note that, for example *'b'011 & count:0;* will make count.D = 011 whenever the Present State of count is 000_2 (0_{10}).

8 INTEGRATED-CIRCUIT LOGIC FAMILIES

SECTIONS 8.1-8.3 *Digital IC Terminology/The TTL Logic Family/Standard TTL Data Sheets.*

8.1 (a) V_{OL}, stands the voltage level at the output of a TTL logic circuit in the LOW state.

(b) I_{IL}, stands the current that flows ***into*** a TTL input when a specified low-level voltage is applied to that input.

(c) t_{pLH}, is the delay time from a logic 0 to a logic 1.

(d) ***Fan out***, stands for the maximum number of logic inputs that an output can reliably drive.

(e) PGA stands for ***Pin Grid Array.***

(f) BGA stands for ***Ball Grid Array.***

(g) Transistor Q4 on the output of a standard TTL gate is often referred to as the current - ***sink*** transistor.

(h) Transistor Q3 on the output of a standard TTL gate is often referred to as the current - ***sourcing*** transistor.

(i) The NOR TTL circuit does not use a ***multiple-emitter*** transistor.

8.2 (a) $V_{NL} = V_{IL(max)} - V_{OL(max)}$
$V_{NL} = 0.8V - 0.5\ V$
$V_{NL} = 0.3$ volts

$V_{NH} = V_{OH(min)} - V_{IH(min)}$
$V_{NH} = 2.5V - 2.0\ V$
$V_{NH} = 0.5$ volts

Thus, the guaranteed worst-case dc noise margin for the 74AS series is ***300mV***.

(b) The maximum average propagation delay of a TTL circuit is $t_{p(max.)} = \dfrac{t_{PLH} + t_{PHL}}{2}$
From Table 8.1 and for the 74AS series, we obtain t_{PLH}=4.5ns and t_{PHL}=4ns. Therefore, the maximum average propagation delay of one 74AS circuit is ***4.25ns***.

(c) The maximum average current of a TTL IC is equal to: $I_{CC(max.)} = \dfrac{I_{CCH} + I_{CCL}}{2}$.
From Table 8.1 and for the 74AS series, we obtain I_{CCH}=3.2mA and I_{CCL}=17.4mA. The average $I_{CC(max.)}$ for the circuit is 10.3mA
The maximum average power dissipation is equal to: $P_D = I_{CC(max.)} \times V_{CC(max.)}$.
Thus, the maximum average power dissipation is equal to 10.3mA x 5.5V or ***56.65mW***.

SECTIONS 8.4-8.6   *TTL series Characteristics/TTL Loading and Fan-Out/Other TTL Characteristics.*

8.3   (a)   Since the input to IC1 is tied to Vcc, its output is a constant logic LOW. When a TTL's Totem-Pole output is LOW, it *sinks* current from the driving inputs. In this situation, IC1 has to sink the cumulative I_{IL} currents from the inputs of IC2, IC3, and IC4. The following table shows how much I_{IL} flows *out* of each input:

IC	I_{IL}
7404	-1.6mA
7420	-1.6mA*
7432	-1.6mA

* *When the inputs of a TTL NAND gate are tied together, and they are at a logic LOW, the total current that flows out of the inputs is equal to I_{IL} in the LOW state. Furthermore, current I_{IL} is leaving that input and therefore it is preceded by a negative sign.*

Thus, the output of IC1 must sink current I_X, which is 4.8mA (1.6mA x 3).

(b)   If the input of IC1 is LOW, then its output is HIGH. When a Totem-Pole output is HIGH, that output *sources* current to the inputs that are being driven.

In this situation, the output of IC1 has to *supply* the needed cumulative I_{IH} currents to the inputs of IC2, IC3, and IC4. The following table shows how much current I_{IH} flows into each input:

IC	I_{IH}
7404	40μA
7420	160μA*
7432	40μA

* *When the inputs of a TTL NAND gate are tied together, the total current that flows into the inputs is equal to (I_{IH} x number of inputs tied together). Thus, current Ix is 240μA (40μA x 6 inputs), and flows from the output of IC1 into the inputs of ICs 2, 3 and 4.*

(c)   If IC1 is changed to a 74HCT04 and its input is HIGH, the current Ix will not change and the output of IC1 still has to sink 4.8mA. Consequently, a problem arises because the $I_{OL(max.)}$ for the 74HCT04 is exceeded. For question (a), IC1 (7400) could sink as much as 16mA ($I_{OL(max.)}$). Since it had to sink an Ix current of 4.8mA, its rating for the maximum sinking current was far from being exceeded. However, this is not the case if IC1 is a 74HCT04.. From the Table 8.2 for a 74HCT04, we obtain an I_{OL} rating of 4mA, which would clearly be exceeded by Ix. This will cause the voltage at point Z (V_{OL}) to be greater than what is normally expected, and perhaps even exceed the maximum allowable value for an input TTL voltage ($V_{IL(max)}$). Furthermore, it will reduce the dc noise margins of the logic circuits being driven by IC1, thereby making them more susceptible to noise.

8.4   When the output of IC1 is LOW, it must sink 0.1mA from IC2, 0.1mA from IC3, and 0.1mA from IC4. Thus, IC1 must sink a total of *0.3mA* (3 inputs x 0.1mA).
When the output of IC1 is HIGH, it must supply 20μA to IC2, 80μA to IC3, and 20μA to IC4. Thus, in the HIGH state, IC1 must supply a total of *120μA* (6 inputs x 20μA).

8.5   LOW-state dc noise margin for any TTL logic family: $V_{NL} = V_{IL(max)} - V_{OL(max)}$
HIGH-state dc noise margin for any TTL logic family: $V_{NH} = V_{OH(min)} - V_{IH(min)}$

Refer to Table 8.1 of this Study Guide

For the 74F series: V_{NL}=0.8V-0.5V; V_{NL}=*300mV* ; V_{NH}=2.5V-2.0V; V_{NH}=*500mV*

For the 74LS series: V_{NL}=0.8V-0.5V; V_{NL}=*300mV* ; V_{NH}=2.7V-2.0V; V_{NH}=*700mV*

The 74LS series has the same LOW-state dc noise margin (300mV) as the 74F series. However, its HIGH-state dc noise margin (700mV) is a little bit better than that of the 74F04 IC (500mV).

8.6   *Refer to Table 8.2 of this Study Guide.*

(a)   When the output of a 74 series device is in the HIGH state, it can supply 400μA (I_{OH}). The input of a 74F series draws 20μA (I_{IH}). Thus, in the HIGH state, the output of a 74 device can drive a maximum of *20* (400μA/20μA) 74F inputs.

(b)   When the output of a 74S series device is in the LOW state, it can sink 20mA (I_{OL}) from input. The input of a 74ALS series device will sink 0.1mA (I_{IL}). Thus, in the LOW state, the output of a 74S device can drive a maximum of *200* (20mA/0.1mA) 74ALS inputs.

(c)   When the output of a 74F series device is in the LOW state, it can sink 20mA (I_{OL}) from input. The input of a 74LS series device will sink 0.4mA (I_{IL}). Thus, in the LOW state, the output of a 74F device can drive a maximum of *50* (20mA/0.4mA) 74LS inputs.

(d)   When the output of a 74AS series device is in the HIGH state, it can supply 2mA (I_{OH}). The input of a 74ALS series draws 20μA (I_{IH}). Thus, in the HIGH state, the output of a 74AS device can drive a maximum of *100* (2mA/20μA) 74ALS inputs.

When the output of a 74AS series device is in the LOW state, it can sink 20mA (I_{OL}) from an input. The input of a 74ALS series device will sink 0.1mA (I_{IL}). Thus, in the LOW state, the output of a 74AS device can drive a maximum of *200* (20mA/0.1mA) 74ALS inputs.

Therefore, the output of a 74AS device can drive *100* (most restrictive of the two values) 74ALS inputs without exceeding its fan out.

(e)   When the output of a 74ALS series device is in the LOW state, it can sink 8mA (I_{OL}) from an input. The input of a 74 series device will sink 1.6mA (I_{IL}). Thus, in the LOW state, the output of a 74ALS device can drive a maximum of *5* (8mA/1.6mA) 74ALS inputs.

(f)   When the output of a 74ALS series device is in the LOW state, it can sink 8mA (I_{OL}) from an input. The input of a 74S series device will sink 2mA (I_{IL}). Thus, in the LOW state, the output of a 74ALS device can drive a maximum of **4** (8mA/2mA) 74ALS inputs.

(g)   When the output of a 74ALS series device is in the HIGH state, it can supply 0.4mA (I_{OH}). The input of a 74HC series draws 1μA (I_{IH}). Thus, in the HIGH state, the output of a 74ALS device can drive a maximum of **400** (0.4mA/1μA) 74HC inputs.

When the output of a 74ALS series device is in the LOW state, it can sink 8mA (I_{OL}) from an input. The input of a 74HC series device will sink 1μA (I_{IL}). Thus, in the LOW state, the output of a 74ALS device can drive a maximum of **8000** (8mA/1μA) 74HC inputs.

Therefore, the output of a 74ALS device can drive **400** (most restrictive of the two values) 74HC inputs without exceeding its fan out.

(h)   When the output of a 74HC series device is in the HIGH state, it can supply 4mA (I_{OH}). The input of a 74ALS series draws 20μA (I_{IH}). Thus, in the HIGH state, the output of a 74HC device can drive a maximum of **200** (4mA/20μA) 74ALS inputs.

When the output of a 74HC series device is in the LOW state, it can sink 4mA (I_{OL}) from an input. The input of a 74ALS series device will sink 0.1mA (I_{IL}). Thus, in the LOW state, the output of a 74HC device can drive a maximum of **40** (4mA/0.1mA) 74ALS inputs.

Therefore, the output of a 74HC device can drive **40** (most restrictive of the two values) 74ALS inputs without exceeding its fan out.

SECTIONS 8.7-8.10   *MOS Technology/Digital MOSFET Circuits/Complementary MOS Logic/ CMOS Series Characteristics*

8.7   (a) **TTL** logic uses Bipolar transistors, while CMOS uses **Field Effect** transistors.

     (b) In a circuit that utilizes **CMOS** logic, the power dissipation is directly proportional to the frequency at which it operates.

     (c) CMOS should be chosen over **TTL**, if the main consideration is packing density.

     (d) Among all the MOSFET circuits, **N-MOS** has the lowest packing density.

     (e) The usage of negative voltages is a disadvantage of **P-channel** MOSFETs.

     (f) Current spikes are drawn from the biasing power supply, each time a CMOS output switches from **LOW** to **HIGH**.

     (g) In both the HIGH and LOW states, the **dc noise margin** of **CMOS** logic can be determined by multiplying V_{DD} by 30%.

     (h) Damage can occur to a **CMOS** circuit, if its inputs are left floating.

     (i) **High-Speed CMOS** is an improved version of the 74C series, which has a tenfold increase in switching speed.

     (j) **BiCMOS** logic combines the best of features of bipolar and CMOS logic.

     (k) Because of parasitic PNP and NPN transistors embedded in the substrate of CMOS ICs **latch-up** can occur under certain circumstances.

8.8   In the HIGH state, the 74HCT and 74ACT series have the best dc noise margin (2.9 volts). In the LOW state, the 4000B has the best dc noise margin (1.45 volts).

8.9   In the HIGH state, the 74 series have the worst dc noise margin (0.4 volts). In the LOW state, the 74LS and 74AS series have the worst dc noise margin (0.3 volts).

SECTIONS 8.11-8.14 *Low-Voltage Technology/Open-Collector/Open-Drain Outputs/ Tristate (Three-State) Logic Outputs/High Speed Interface Logic*

Refer to Tables 8.2 and 8.4 of this Study Guide

8.10   (a) The *ALVC* Low-Voltage logic family offers the best performance.

(b) The *LVC* Low-Voltage logic family offers the widest range of operating voltages.

(c) The output levels of the *LVT* Low-Voltage logic family are equivalent to TTL levels.

8.11   When the output of a 74LVT series device is in the HIGH state, it can supply 32mA (I_{OH}). The input of a 74 series draws 40µA (I_{IH}). Thus, in the HIGH state, the output of a 74LVT device can drive a maximum of *800* (32mA/40µA) 74 inputs.

When the output of a 74LVT series device is in the LOW state, it can sink 64mA (I_{OL}) from an input. The input of a 74 series device will sink 1.6mA (I_{IL}). Thus, in the LOW state, the output of a 74LVT device can drive a maximum of *40* (64mA/1.6mA) 74 inputs.

8.12   (a) Totem-pole outputs cannot be tied together or wire-ANDed. Only open-collector or open-drain outputs can be wire-ANDed connected.

(b) One possibility:

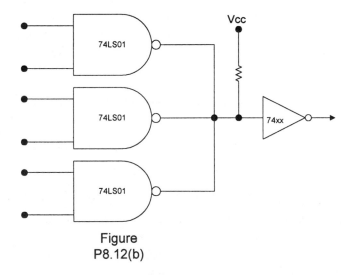

Figure
P8.12(b)

8.13   By careful analysis of the tabulated results of Table 8.5, it can be observed that whenever inputs A and B are different, an indeterminate logic level results at points C and D respectively. Furthermore, if inputs A and B are different, and either or both of the IC2 buffers are enabled, indeterminate logic levels will be present at outputs X and/or Y. The most probable cause for the malfunction is a short between points C and D in the circuit of Figure 8.3. This would cause the voltage levels at points C and D to be about 2.5V (1/2 Vcc). This situation occurs only when CMOS outputs are tied together and each of the outputs is forced to go to different logic levels.

8.14   When output X from the Ring counter is HIGH the outputs of counter Z3 are placed on data bus ABC, via the tristate buffers Z7. Likewise, the outputs of counters Z2 and Z1 are placed on the data bus when the outputs of the Ring counter Y or W are HIGH respectively. We can see from the table below, that the data underlined in "**Bold**-type" are placed on the data bus at the right time and without getting changed.

Ring Counter			Z_1			Z_2			Z_3			Data Bus		
W	Y	X	A_1	B_1	C_1	A_2	B_2	C_2	A_3	B_3	C_3	A	B	C
0	0	1	1	1	0	0	1	0	**0**	**1**	**1**	**0**	**1**	**1**
0	1	0	1	1	1	**0**	**0**	**1**	1	0	0	**0**	**0**	**1**
1	0	0	**1**	**1**	**0**	1	1	0	0	1	0	**1**	**1**	**0**
0	0	1	1	1	0	0	0	0	*1*	*0*	*1*	*1*	*1*	*1*
0	0	1	0	1	1	1	1	1	*0*	*0*	*0*	*0*	*1*	*0*

A problem exists however with the data from counter Z3 expressed in the table in underlined "*Italic*-type". As stated before, when output X from the Ring counter is HIGH, the outputs of counter Z3 should be allowed to be placed on the data bus. This does not always happen, particularly when B3 is LOW. It appears that whenever counter Z3 is selected by the Ring counter, output B3 always ends up as a logic HIGH on the data bus. The circuit will behave according to the table, if the connection from output B3 to the input of the tristate buffer Z7-b was open or shorted to Vcc.

8.15   Tristate buffers Z5 are enabled when output W from the Ring counter is HIGH. Since the circuit of Figure 8.4 is a TTL circuit, if the connection from output W was open buffers Z5-a through Z5-c would always be enabled, thereby allowing the outputs from counter Z1 to always be present on the data bus. This open line would make it possible for two MOD-8 counters to place their data on the data bus at the same time. This particular situation is often referred to as "Bus contention."

8.16   (a) If the physical distance between components in a system is more than about *4* inches, the bus wires between them need to be viewed as *transmission lines.*

   (b) *GTL* series is more suitable for high-speed busses within a single circuit board or between boards in small enclosures like a personal computer case.

   (c) *BTL* series is specially designed to drive the relatively long busses that connect modules in the back of an industry standard 19-inch rack mounting system.

<u>SECTIONS 8.15-8.20</u> *The ECL Digital IC family/CMOS Transmission Gate (Bilateral Switch)/IC Interfacing TTL Driving CMOS/CMOS Driving TTL/ Analog Voltage Comparators*

8.17 (a) The latest ECL series by Motorola is called *ECLin PS.*

(b) The transistors in the ECL logic circuit never *saturate,* and so switching speed is very high.

(c) The worst case ECL noise margins are approximately *150mV.*

(d) In ECL logic the typical voltage for a logic LOW is *-1.7* V, and *-0.8* V for a logic HIGH.

(e) There is no need for Inverters in the ECL logic family because an ECL logic block produces a output and its *complement.*

(f) A special type of CMOS gate that passes signals digital as well as analog in both directions is called a *bilateral switch.*

8.18 The problem with the circuit of Figure 8.5 is that different logic families were interfaced with any special design consideration. First, the 7404 TTL Inverter *cannot* drive the 4001B CMOS N gate directly. A 10KΩ pull-up resistor should be used between the output of IC1 and the input IC2. This allows the TTL output voltages to be comparable with the CMOS input voltages. Anot way of achieving the same results is to use either a 74HCT04 IC or a 74ACT04 IC inverter inst of the CMOS 4001B NOR gate (The 4001B is being used as an inverter).

The next problem that should be addressed is that of the output of the 4001B CMOS NOR g driving the inputs of a 74 TTL gate directly. When the output of a 4001B NOR gate is LOW it only sink 0.4mA. In the LOW state, the three inputs tied together of the TTL 7410 NAND gate s a total of 1.6mA (I_{IL}) through the output of the 4001B Inverter. Clearly the NOR gate CMOS out cannot sink the 1.6mA current coming from the inputs of the 7410 NAND gate. Since a 400 output can reliably drive one 74LS input, the replacement of the 7410 IC with a 74LS10 would t care of the problem.

8.19 The problem with this circuit is the different biasing voltages between the 4001B NOR gate and 7404 Inverter. The voltage level at the output of the 4001B NOR gate will be either 0V or 1 Understandably, the 10V level is too high as a logic HIGH input for the TTL 7404 Inverter Voltage-Level translator circuit that converts the High-Voltage +10V input to a +5V output ha be interfaced between the output of IC1 and the input of IC2. A 4050B non-inverting buffer is possible voltage-level translator that could be used to solve the problem.

8.20 The output of the LM339 Voltage Comparator will go HIGH when the voltage on the (+) inpu greater than the voltage on the (-) input. Since the (-) input is permanently referenced at +2V, output of the Pressure Sensor has to exceed +2V in order for the output of the Voltage Comparat LM339 to go HIGH, and cause the alarm to go ON.

Consequently, we have to determine the pressure at which the output of the Pressure Sensor reac +2V. The output voltage of the Pressure Sensor increases by 20µV for each increase of 1 P.S. pressure. Therefore, when the output voltage of the Pressure Sensor is +2V, it represents a press of 100,000 P.S.I. (2V x 1 P.S.I.)/20µV).

Therefore, any pressure exceeding 100,000 P.S.I. will cause the alarm to turn ON.

SECTION 8.21 *Troubleshooting.*

8.21   *One way to isolate the problem*:

While monitoring point C with the logic probe, inject pulses with the logic pulser into input A. The logic probe should indicate the presence of pulses by blinking its indicator light. Move the logic probe to point D and inject pulses again with the logic pulser into input A. Again, the logic probe should indicate the presence of pulses. We can than conclude that from the results obtained with the logic probe, a short must exist between points C and D.

8.22   *One way to isolate the short:*

Place the logic pulser at the output of tristate buffer Z5-b. Then place the current tracer just to the right of the logic pulser. While actuating the logic pulser, move the current tracer slowly away from the logic pulser towards node K on the data bus. The current tracer should cease indicating the presence of current pulses just after crossing node K, which is where the short to ground exists.

8.23   The following are the most probable circuit faults that could make output Z to be always HIGH.

1.   Input to IC1 is shorted to ground.
2.   The output of IC1 is shorted to Vcc or the node at the input of IC2 is shorted to Vcc.
3.   The output of IC2 is shorted to ground.
4.   The node at the input of IC3 is shorted to ground.
5.   Output Z is shorted to Vcc.

Procedure to determine faults [1] or [2]:

Inject a pulse into the input of IC1 using the logic pulser, while monitoring the output of IC1 with a logic probe. If the logic probe indicates the presence of a pulse, then faults [1] or [2] do not exist. If the logic probe doesn't detect the pulse, then the current tracer along with the logic pulser may be used to determine where the input of IC1 is grounded or the input of IC2 is shorted to Vcc.

Procedure to determine faults [3] or [4]:

Inject a pulse into the input of IC2 using the logic pulser, while checking the output of IC2 with a logic probe. If the logic probe indicates the presence of a pulse at the output, then we can eliminate faults [3] and [4]. However, if the logic probe does not detect a pulse between the output of IC2 and inputs of IC3, then the current tracer along with the logic pulser may be used to determine where the short to Vcc exists.

If the previous procedures do not reveal the fault, than the most probable fault is [5]. This can be verified by pulsing the node at the input of IC3 with the logic pulser, while monitoring its output with the logic probe. If output Z is indeed shorted to Vcc, then the logic probe indicator will remain lit, thereby indicating a permanent logic HIGH at the output.

9   MSI LOGIC CIRCUITS

SECTIONS 9.1-9.2 *Decoders/BCD-to-7-Segment Decoder-Drivers.*

9.1   (a)   A 1-of-16 decoder is a circuit that accepts *four* binary inputs and has *16* outputs.

       (b)   A BCD-to-Decimal decoder can also be called a *1-of-10* decoder.

9.2   For output $\overline{O}13$ of Figure 9.1 to be active, the 74LS138 with outputs $\overline{O}8$ - $\overline{O}15$ must be selected. order to select this decoder, signal A_3 must be HIGH and signal A_4 must be LOW. Once t decoder is selected, the binary combination at its inputs A_2, A_1, and A_0 must be such that out $\overline{O}13$ is active. Thus, for output $\overline{O}13$ to be LOW, inputs A_0-A_4 must be at the following lo levels: A_0=1, A_1=0, A_2=1, A_3=1, and A_44=0.

9.3   The selection of the first and last decoders ($\overline{O}0$ - $\overline{O}7$, $\overline{O}24$ - $\overline{O}31$) are not affected by the wir mistake, since both logic levels at inputs A_3 and A_4 are equal when these particular decoders active. However, a problem arises when signals A_3 and A_4 are at different logic levels. Whene the logic conditions at inputs A_0-A_4 dictate the selection of the decoder with outputs $\overline{O}8$ - $\overline{O}15$, decoder with outputs $\overline{O}16$ - $\overline{O}23$ is selected instead, and vice-versa.

SECTIONS 9.3-9.4 *Liquid Crystal Displays/Encoders.*

9.4   (a)   LCDs and LEDs have different operational requirements and therefore cannot be u interchangeably. For example, to light up a LCD segment, requires an AC signal appl between the segment and the backplane. LEDs don't have backplanes at all. LEDs requ much more power to operate than LCDs. For that reason LCDs are generally found in desi which utilize CMOS devices.

       (b)   Reflective LCDs use *ambient* light, while back-lit LCDs use a *light source*.

       (c)   Some LCD modules allow the user to create a graphical display by controlling individual d on the screen called *pixels*.

       (d)   The newer LCD displays are called active matrix *TFT* (thin film transistor) LCDs.

       (e)   The older LCD screens are called *Super Twisted Nematic* (STN) and are referred to passive LCDs.

9.5   The following are some of the reasons as to why segment 'a' of Figure 9.2 would be lit intermittentl

     1.   Output 'a' of the 74HC4511 is open or floating.

     2.   Input 'a' to the LCD is open or floating.

     3.   The 40-Hz connection to the input of the exclusive OR gate, which controls segment 'a', is open or floating.

9.6   (a)   When switch SW8 is depressed, the outputs $\overline{O}_3$ - $\overline{O}_0$ of the 74LS147 encoder are 0111_2 respectively.

(b)   Since the 74LS147 encoder is a priority encoder, whenever two of its inputs are active simultaneously, the output will respond to the highest-numbered input. Therefore, if switches SW3 and SW8 are depressed at the same time, the output will be 0111_2 (SW8).

9.7   The major difference between priority and non-priority encoders is that a non-priority encoder may have an ambiguous output when two of its inputs are active at the same time, while a priority encoder will not. When two or more inputs are activated simultaneously, the priority encoder will respond to the highest-numbered input.

SECTION 9.5 *Troubleshooting*

9.8   It can be concluded from the sequence of events that, as the switches are actuated, the corresponding BCD code is entered into the registers and displayed on the displays. However, some entries get displayed in the wrong LED display. By careful analysis of the recorded results, we can conclude that displays K3 and K2 always have the wrong data. These results would be observed if the connections from flip-flops Y and Z to modules K2 and K3 were reversed.

SECTIONS 9.6-9.9 *Multiplexers/Multiplexer Applications/Demultiplexers/More Troubleshooting.*

9.9   (a)   When inputs I_3 and I_4 are multiplexed, output Z stays at a voltage level which is halfway between a logic LOW and a logic HIGH. Two CMOS outputs will behave this way when they are tied together and each is trying to be at different logic levels at the same time. Thus, it can be concluded that multiplexer inputs I_3 and I_4 are shorted.

(b)   The contents of the Storage register can be determined by looking at waveform Z, with the exception of bits X_3 and X_4. Since it was determined in the previous problem that these two inputs were shorted together and were simultaneously trying to be at different logic levels the storage registers X_3 and X_4 may have either combination of bits shown in the dotted box in Figure P9.9.

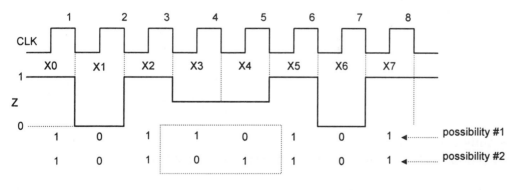

Figure P9.9

9.10 Let's set up the truth table since the expression $Z = \overline{C}\overline{B}A + C\overline{B}\overline{A} + CBA$ cannot be simplified any further either algebraically or by Karnaugh mapping:

C	B	A	Z	
0	0	0	0	
0	0	1	1	$\overline{C}\overline{B}A = 001_2 = 1_{10}$
0	1	0	0	
0	1	1	0	
1	0	0	1	$C\overline{B}\overline{A} = 101_2 = 4_{10}$
1	0	1	0	
1	1	0	0	
1	1	1	1	$CBA = 111_2 = 7_{10}$

Now, let's connect input variables ABC to S_0, S_1, and S_2 respectively. The levels on the inputs S_0, S_2 will determine which data at the input of the Multiplexer will be present at output Z. Clear output Z will be a logic HIGH only when inputs CBA are 001_2, 101_2, or 111_2. Any other combinati of CBA will result in a logic LOW at output Z. Thus, the circuit of Figure P9.10 will implement Boolean expression $Z = C\overline{B}A + C\overline{B}\overline{A} + CBA$.

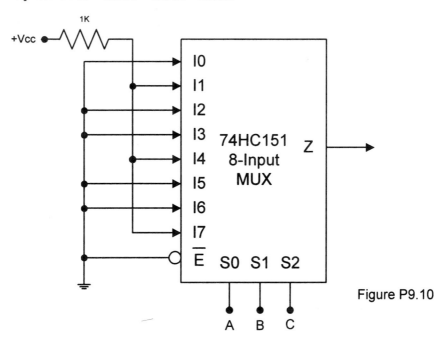

Figure P9.10

9.11 It can be readily seen that the wrong LED flashes when doors 1, 2, 5, or 6 are open. What has to be determined is if there is any commonality among these four situations.

Upon closer examination of the circuit, it can be concluded that during these four situations MOD-8 counter has its outputs Q_0 and Q_1 with logic levels that are different from each oth Furthermore, any of these four conditions causes LED 1 to flash when LED 2 should, and vi versa. Similar behavior is observed for LEDs 5 and 6.

On the other hand, whenever logic levels of Q_0 and Q_1 are equal, the proper LED flashes. These facts take us to the conclusion that either of the following faults may exist:

(1) Q_0 is connected to S_1, and Q_1 is connected to S_0.
(2) Q_0 is connected to A_1, and Q_1 is connected to A_0.

SECTIONS 9.10-9.14   *Magnitude Comparator/Code Converters/Data Busing/ The 74173-ALS173-HC173 Tristate Register/Data Bus Operation*

9.12   The Truth Table of the 74HC85 comparator in your textbook (or TTL CD ROM) shows that, when inputs A and B are $11001101_2 (205_{10})$, and 11001110_2 (206_{10}) respectively then the outputs are: $I_{A>B}=0$, $I_{A<B}=1$, $I_{A=B}=0$.

9.13   The circuit of P9.13 shows three 4-bit magnitude comparators arranged to compare two 9-bit binary numbers.

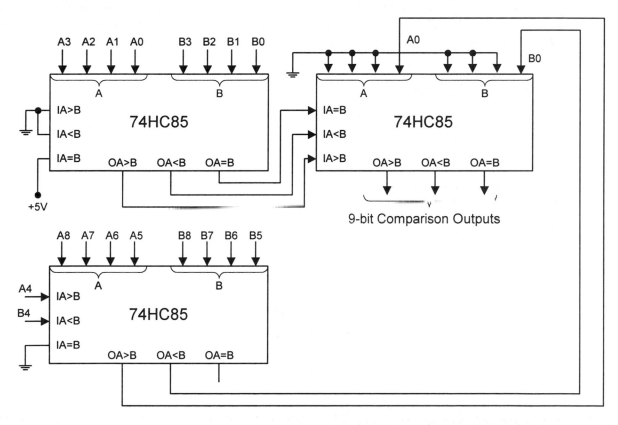

Figure P9.13

9.14   (a)   After close examination of the equivalent 4-bit regular binary and the 4-bit gray code
               tables, it can be concluded that:

1.   Gray bit G_0 is LOW only when binary bits B_0 and B_1 are equal.
2.   Gray bit G_1 is LOW only when binary bits B_1 and B_2 are equal.
3.   Gray bit G_2 is LOW only when binary bits B_2 and B_3 are equal.
4.   Gray bit G_3 is is always equal to B_3.

Thus, a 4-bit Binary-to-Gray code converter can be implemented by using three XOR gates (Figur
P9.14(a)).

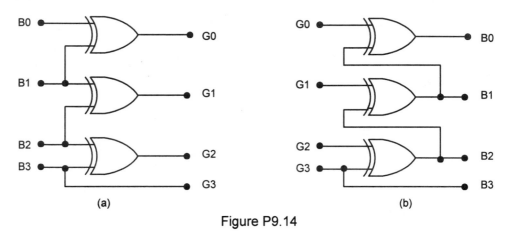

(a)   (b)

Figure P9.14

(b)   Again, after close examination of the equivalent 4-bit regular binary and the 4-bit gray code
       tables, it can be concluded that:

1.   Binary bit B_0 is LOW only when gray bit G_0 and binary bit B_1 are equal.
2.   Binary bit B_1 is LOW only when gray bit G_1 and binary bit B_2 are equal.
3.   Binary bit B_2 is LOW only when gray bit G_2 and binary bit B_3 are equal.
4.   Binary bit B_3 is always equal to G_3.

Thus, a 4-bit Gray-to-Binary code converter can be implemented by using three XOR gates (Figur
P9.14(b)).

9.15   (a)   If input $\overline{IE}_B$ is always LOW, then any time a positive going transition occurs on the clock, th
               data present on the data bus will be loaded into tristate register B.

(b)   If input $\overline{OE}_B$ is always LOW, then tristate register B is always placing its contents on the da
       bus. If either of the tristate registers A or C have their outputs enabled, then 'bus contentio
       will occur. ***Bus contention*** occurs any time two different devices place data on the same da
       bus simultaneously.

9.16

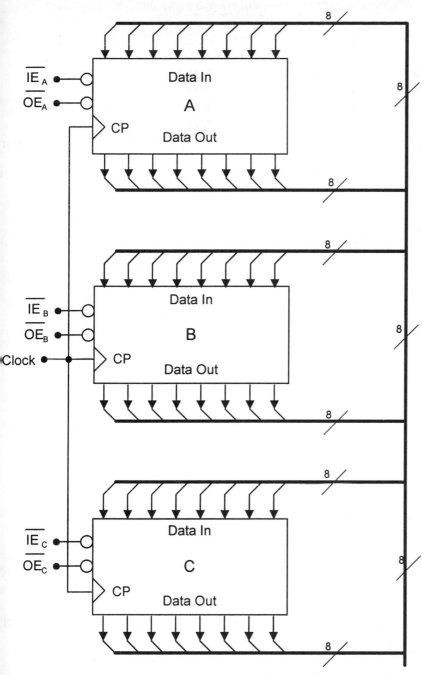

Figure P9.16

9.17   *Set Format*   *Binary Set Values*

Table	[A,B]	⇒	X		Table	[A,B]	⇒	X
{	[0,0]	⇒	0;		{	'b'00	⇒	0;
	[0,1]	⇒	0;			'b'01	⇒	0;
	[1,0]	⇒	0;			'b'10	⇒	0;
	[1,1]	⇒	1;}			'b'11	⇒	1;}

Decimal Set Values

Table	[A,B]	⇒	X
{	'd'00	⇒	0;
	'd'01	⇒	0;
	'd'10	⇒	0;
	'd'11	⇒	1;}

9.18

```
/*1-of-4 Decoder*/

/* Inputs */

pin1  =   Eone;
pin2  =   Aone;
pin3  =   Bone;

   /* Outputs* /

pin[15..12]   =    ![Y3..Y0]

   /* Set Definitions */

field inputs    = [Eone, Aone, Bone];
field outputs  = [Y3..Y0];

   /* Hardware Description */
```

Table	Inputs	⇒	Outputs
{	'b'000	⇒	'b'1110;
	'b'001	⇒	'b'1101;
	'b'010	⇒	'b'1011;
	'b'011	⇒	'b'0111;}

10 INTERFACING WITH THE ANALOG WORLD

SECTIONS 10.1-10.2 *Interfacing With the Analog World/Digital-to-Analog Conversion.*

10.1 With 10 bits, there will be 1023 steps (2^{10} - 1). Since the full-scale value is 15V, the step-size is 14.66mV (15V/1023). Therefore, when the binary input is 1010110111_2 the output is 10.19V (695x14.66mV).

10.2 There are two different ways of determining the % Resolution of a D/A converter:

Method #1: % Resolution $= \dfrac{\text{Step - Size}}{\text{Full - Scale}} \times 100\% = \dfrac{14.66\text{mV}}{15\text{V}} \times 100\% = 0.097\%$

Method #2[*]: % Resolution $= \dfrac{1}{2^n - 1} \times 100\% = \dfrac{1}{2^{10} - 1} \times 100\% = 0.097\%$

[*] *Note that % Resolution is only dependent on the number of bits of the Digital-to-Analog Converter.*

10.3 (a) The problem with the DAC's output staircase waveform is that it is missing a step. The missing step is the one corresponding to the input binary code 0110_2.

   (b) The effect of this missing binary code is that the motor will not be able to be controlled over a certain range of RPMs. The full-scale value of the DAC is 2mA, and its step size is (2mA/15) = 133.3µA. Therefore, when the input binary code is 101_2 the motor will be rotating at (133.3µA x 5 x 1000 RPM)/2mA = 333.3 RPMs. The next time the DAC's output increments, it will be at (133.3µA x 7) = 933.1µA and the motor will be rotating at (133.3µA x 7 x 1000 RPM)/2mA = 466.6 RPMs. Thus, the computer is not able to set the motor to any RPM value between 333.3 and 466.6 RPMs.

10.4 (a) If the input D_1 (MSB) weight is 2.24V, then the LSB weight is (2.24V/80) = 28mV, which represents the resolution of the DAC.

   (b) The output of this DAC can have a maximum of 99 steps. Thus, the full-scale value is (99 x 28mV) = 2.772V.

   The % Resolution of the BCD Digital-to Analog converter is $\left(\dfrac{28 \text{ mV}}{2.772\text{V}} \times 100\% \right) = 1.01\%$.

(c)   If the output is 2.156V, then the DAC input must be $\dfrac{2.156 \text{ V}}{28 \text{ mV}} = 77_{10}$.

Thus, the BCD input is $0111\ 0111_{BCD}$.

SECTIONS 10.3,10.4,10.6 *D/A-Converter Circuitry/DAC Specifications/DAC Applications*

10.5   In order for this DAC to have a step-size equal to -78.13mV, its R_f resistor must be equal to $(78.13\text{mV x } 8K\Omega)/5V = 125\Omega$.

10.6   The step-size for this DAC is $(1.590V) / (2^{10}-1) = 1.554\text{mV}$. The binary input 1100110110_2 equivalent to 822_{10}. Therefore, in this situation, the ideal output voltage is $(822 \times 1.554\text{mV})$ 1.278V. The error that can exist on any conversion performed by this DAC is $\pm(0.25\% \times 1.59V)$ $\pm3.975\text{mV}$.   Thus, for this particular binary input the output voltage of 1.283V *does not* fall with the acceptable accuracy range of 1.274V - 1.282V.

10.7   The settling time is the time that takes the output of a DAC to settle within $\pm1/2$ of its step siz From the graph of Figure 10.4 it can be determined that it takes *approximately* 70ns before th output oscillations stay within 1/2 the step-size (1/2 LSB).

SECTIONS 10.7-10.9 *Troubleshooting DACs/Analog-to-Digital Conversion/Digital-Ramp ADC*

10.8   Since this is a digital-ramp ADC, its conversion time is directly proportional to the size of th analog signal being converted. The *maximum* conversion time for this ADC will be when th counter has to increment to its maximum count of (2^8-1) clock cycles.

The *minimum* conversion time is the time that takes for the counter to increment from zero to th first step. Thus, for an 8-bit digital-ramp DAC with a clock frequency of 1MHz the time that tak to increment the DAC by one-step is $(1/1\text{MHz}) = 1\mu s$

Thus, $t_{C(max)} = 255\mu s$, $t_{C(min)} = 1\mu s$ and $t_{C(avg)} = 128\mu s$.

10.9   The step-size for the Digital-to-Analog converter is $(12.35V/255) = 48.43\text{mV}$. Since binary 10110001_2 is equivalent to decimal 177_{10}, output $V_{A'}$ will be $(48.43\text{mV} \times 177) = 8.572V$.

10.10   From the previous problem it can be seen that when the counter output is binary 10110001_2, V_A 8.572V. If $V_A = 8.572V$, then the comparator will not switch since $V_{A'}$ has not exceeded V_A by (0.1mV). Therefore, signal $\overline{EOC}$ (End of Conversion) will remain HIGH. This will allow o more clock pulse to increment the counter, thereby causing the final binary count to be 10110010

10.11   Several circuit conditions could cause the counter to continuously count. The following are the most probable causes:

(a) V_A is greater than the DAC's full-scale value.
(b)   The output of comparator IC1 is open or shorted to Vcc.
(c)   The output of the DAC ($V_{A'}$) is open.

10.12 (a) Yes, but only up to a certain point. First, there is a maximum allowable operating frequency for the counter as well as the AND gate being used. However, it is highly probable that before the counter is affected by the high input frequency, the op-amps' slew-rate within this ADC circuit will be exceeded and the ADC will start behaving erratically or stop working altogether.

(b) No. This will result in a more accurate conversion but it will take longer to perform it.
(c) See answer (a).
(d) Yes, but at the cost of lower accuracy.

10.13 A system will produce a signal alias when the system is sampling an incoming signal at a rate less then the minimum rate identified by Nyquist (twice the highest incoming frequency). The alias frequency is always the difference between any integer multiple of the sample frequency Fs (25 kHz in this problem) and the incoming frequency. In this particular situation, for no alias signal to occur, the input frequency has to be 12.5 kHz or less.

(a) Output frequency = 5 kHz
(b) Output frequency = 10.1 kHz
(c) Output frequency = 12.3 kHz
(d) Output frequency = 6.3 kHz (25 kHz-18.7 kHz)
(e) Output frequency = 3 kHz (25 kHz-22 kHz)
(f) Output frequency = 400 Hz (25 kHz-24.6 kHz)

SECTIONS 10.10-10.12 *Data Acquisition/Successive-Approximation ADC//Flash ADCs.*

10.14 (a) The step-size of the ADC is about 48.4mV (see problem 10.9). Another way which the step-size can be expressed for this ADC is 4.8mV/100μs. The digitized waveform is obtained by joining points *a* through *l* of Figure P10.14(a).

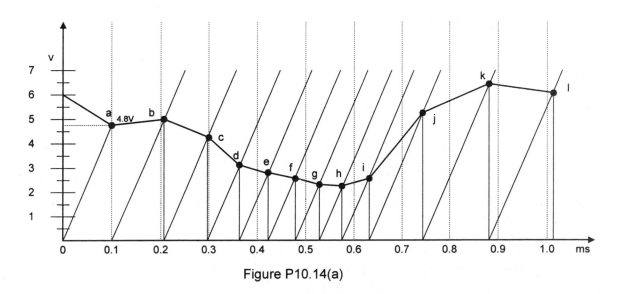

Figure P10.14(a)

(b) If a highly accurate reproduction of the analog signal of Figure 10.6 is desired, a much short
conversion time has to be obtained. One possible way is to use an 8-bit successiv
approximation ADC instead of the 8-bit digital-ramp ADC used in the circuit of Figure 10.
Note that the average conversion for the 8-bit digital-ramp ADC of Figure 10.5 was 128μ
(see problem 10.8). If we used the same frequency of 1MHz and an 8-bit successiv
approximation ADC, the conversion time would be (1μs x 8 bits) = 8μs. A flash ADC
another possibility, since it is among the fastest ADCs available.

10.15 The dots shown on the *Input Triangle Waveform* of Figure P10.15 represent the points where the
Flash ADC took samples at intervals of 75μs

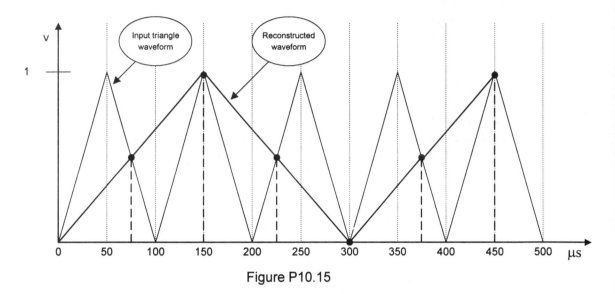

Figure P10.15

(a) The graph of Figure P10.15 shows a *sample* frequency of 13.33 kHz (1/75 μs) and a *triangle*
input frequency of 10 kHz (1/100 μs).

(b) The *difference* between the sample frequency and the triangle input frequency is 3.33 kHz
(13.33 kHz -10 kHz).

(c) Finally, Figure P10.15 shows the *reconstructed* triangle waveform with a frequency of 3.33
kHz (1/300 μs).

10.16 *Sample calculation for VA':* The step size is equal to 10mV.
Therefore, when D_7 is HIGH (128_{10}) VA' is equal to (10mV x 128_{10}) = 1.28V. (See Figures
P10.16a and P10.16b)

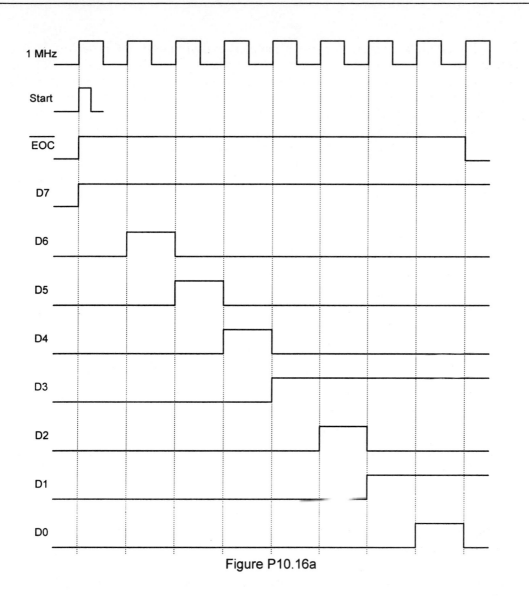

Figure P10.16a

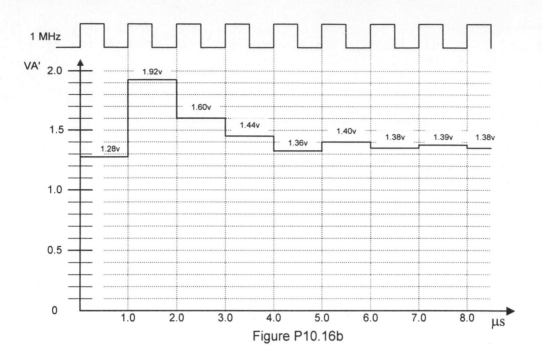

Figure P10.16b

10.17 (a) Since the $V_{ref}/2$ input is left open, the analog input range is 0 - 5V and the resolution of the ADC is 19.61mV (see table in the textbook). Therefore, when the temperature reaches 60° $(V_{in}(+) = 5V)$, the output of the ADC0804 will be at full-scale or *11111111₂*.

(b) At a temperature of 60°C the ADC output is at its full-scale value of 5V. Consequently, one incremental step of the ADC is equivalent to a temperature change of +0.235°C (60°C/25! Therefore, the resolution in °C is *0.235°C/step*.

(c) The resolution of an ADC is determined by dividing the full-scale value of the ADC (5V) by th maximum number of steps (255) that the ADC can take. Hence, the resolution is *19.61mV/step*

(d) If the $V_{ref}/2$ input is held at +1.5V the analog input range becomes 0 - 3V and the resolution o the ADC0804 is 11.76mV (3.0V/255). Thus, when the ambient temperature is at 30°C the binary output will be at its maximum, or *11111111₂*.

SECTIONS 10.13-10.18   *Other A/D Conversion Methods/Digital Voltmeter/Sample-and-Hold Circuits/ Multiplexing/Digital Storage Oscilloscope/Digital Signal Processing*

10.18 (a) Dual-slope ADC   (b) Voltage-to-frequency ADC   (c) Tracking ADC
        (d) Dual-slope ADC   (e) Sigma/Delta ADC

10.19 From the recorded results it can be determined that for input signals which are less than 90mV th display shows 000₂. This means that the counters are not being incremented for these particul analog values. If COMP signal is LOW, then the counters will be prevented from counting. Thus, can be concluded that $V_{A'}$ somehow is always greater than 90mV, thereby keeping the output of t op-amp comparator LOW. The next step is to determine the reason why $V_{A'}$ is always greater th 90mV and how that could cause the rest of the recorded data to appear the way it does.

It can be concluded from the recorded results that the connection from the LSB of the second MSD counter to the BCD-to-Analog Converter is permanently HIGH. This would cause the display to show a count that, at certain times, would exceed the actual value by 100mV. The false readings on the display become evident whenever V_A values are such that will cause the LSB of the second MSD to be LOW (i.e. 1.0V, 8.0V, 9.0V, 9.2V). V_A values that make the LSB of the MSD of the counter to be HIGH would display as good readings (i.e. 1.1V, 8.5V, 9.5V).

10.20 First the computer must make signals S1, S2, and S3 LOW, thereby placing the outputs of the transmission gates (IC1) in their HI-Z state. Next, the binary data that controls the positioning controller *A* has to be sent into the DAC from the computer. After allowing sufficient time for the conversion to take place, the computer will enable transmission gate IC1-A by making S1 HIGH. IC1-A must be enabled long enough for capacitor C1 to charge up to the analog voltage present at the output of the DAC. Next the computer must make S1 LOW, and then output the proper data for *positioning controller B*.

After allowing sufficient time for the conversion to occur, signal S2 is made HIGH, thereby allowing C2 to charge up to the voltage at the output of the DAC. The same procedure is finally used for the last set of data, that correspond to *positioning controller C*. The timing for the sequence described above will be achieved via a computer program (software).

10.21 The maximum rate at which data can be sent to each positioning controller is limited by the conversion time of the DAC, and the time required for the capacitors of the Sample-and-Hold circuits to charge.

10.22 An increase in operational speed would be the major advantage of using three DACs instead of the multiplexing scheme of Figure 10.11. The disadvantage however, would be a substantial increase in the cost of the circuit.

10.23 The following are the basic sequence of operations performed by a DSO: Data acquisition / Digitizing / Storage / Data outputting.

10.24 Filtering and conditioning of analog signals.

10.25

Sample calculations: $Out[n] = \dfrac{In[n-4] + In[n-3] + In[n-2] + In[n-1] + In[n]}{5}$

Calculation: $Out[5] = \dfrac{In[1] + In[2] + In[3] + In[4] + In[5]}{5} = \dfrac{0+0+0+0+4}{5} = \dfrac{4}{5} = 0.8$

Calculation: $Out[6] = \dfrac{In[2] + In[3] + In[4] + In[5] + In[6]}{5} = \dfrac{0+0+0+4+6}{5} = \dfrac{10}{5} = 2.0$

Calculation: $Out[7] = \dfrac{In[3] + In[4] + In[5] + In[6] + In[7]}{5} = \dfrac{0+0+4+6+8}{5} = \dfrac{18}{5} = 3.6$

Calculation: $Out[8] = \dfrac{In[4] + In[5] + In[6] + In[7] + In[8]}{5} = \dfrac{0+4+6+8+10}{5} = \dfrac{28}{5} = 5.6$

Calculation: $\mathrm{Out}[9] = \dfrac{\mathrm{In}[5] + \mathrm{In}[6] + \mathrm{In}[7] + \mathrm{In}[8] + \mathrm{In}[9]}{5} = \dfrac{4 + 6 + 8 + 10 + 12}{5} = \dfrac{40}{5} = \boldsymbol{8.0}$

Calculation: $\mathrm{Out}[10] = \dfrac{\mathrm{In}[6] + \mathrm{In}[7] + \mathrm{In}[8] + \mathrm{In}[9] + \mathrm{In}[10]}{5} = \dfrac{6 + 8 + 10 + 12 + 14}{5} = \dfrac{50}{5} = \boldsymbol{10}$

Calculation: $\mathrm{Out}[11] = \dfrac{\mathrm{In}[7] + \mathrm{In}[8] + \mathrm{In}[9] + \mathrm{In}[10] + \mathrm{In}[11]}{5} = \dfrac{8 + 10 + 12 + 14 + 14}{5} = \dfrac{58}{5} = \boldsymbol{11.6}$

Calculation: $\mathrm{Out}[12] = \dfrac{\mathrm{In}[8] + \mathrm{In}[9] + \mathrm{In}[10] + \mathrm{In}[11] + \mathrm{In}[12]}{5} = \dfrac{10 + 12 + 14 + 14 + 14}{5} = \dfrac{64}{5} = \boldsymbol{12.8}$

Sample n	*1*	*2*	*3*	*4*	*5*	*6*	*7*	*8*	*9*	*10*	*11*	*12*
In[n] (v)	*0*	*0*	*0*	*0*	*4*	*6*	*8*	*10*	*12*	*14*	*14*	*14*
Out[n] (v)	*0*	*0*	*0*	*0*	*.8*	*2*	*3.6*	*5.6*	*8*	*10*	*11.6*	*12.8*

10.26

Sample calculations: $\mathrm{Out}[n] = \dfrac{\mathrm{In}[n-3] + \mathrm{In}[n-2] + \mathrm{In}[n-1] + \mathrm{In}[n]}{4}$

Calculation: $\mathrm{Out}[5] = \dfrac{\mathrm{In}[2] + \mathrm{In}[3] + \mathrm{In}[4] + \mathrm{In}[5]}{4} = \dfrac{0 + 0 + 0 + 4}{4} = \dfrac{4}{4} = \boldsymbol{1.0}$

Calculation: $\mathrm{Out}[6] = \dfrac{\mathrm{In}[3] + \mathrm{In}[4] + \mathrm{In}[5] + \mathrm{In}[6]}{4} = \dfrac{0 + 0 + 4 + 6}{4} = \dfrac{10}{4} = \boldsymbol{2.5}$

Calculation: $\mathrm{Out}[7] = \dfrac{\mathrm{In}[4] + \mathrm{In}[5] + \mathrm{In}[6] + \mathrm{In}[7]}{4} = \dfrac{0 + 4 + 6 + 8}{4} = \dfrac{18}{4} = \boldsymbol{4.5}$

Calculation: $\mathrm{Out}[8] = \dfrac{\mathrm{In}[5] + \mathrm{In}[6] + \mathrm{In}[7] + \mathrm{In}[8]}{4} = \dfrac{4 + 6 + 8 + 10}{4} = \dfrac{28}{4} = \boldsymbol{7.0}$

Calculation: $\mathrm{Out}[9] = \dfrac{\mathrm{In}[6] + \mathrm{In}[7] + \mathrm{In}[8] + \mathrm{In}[9]}{4} = \dfrac{6 + 8 + 10 + 12}{4} = \dfrac{36}{4} = \boldsymbol{9.0}$

Calculation: $\mathrm{Out}[10] = \dfrac{\mathrm{In}[7] + \mathrm{In}[8] + \mathrm{In}[9] + \mathrm{In}[10]}{4} = \dfrac{8 + 10 + 12 + 14}{4} = \dfrac{44}{4} = \boldsymbol{11.0}$

Calculation: $\mathrm{Out}[11] = \dfrac{\mathrm{In}[8] + \mathrm{In}[9] + \mathrm{In}[10] + \mathrm{In}[11]}{4} = \dfrac{10 + 12 + 14 + 14}{4} = \dfrac{50}{4} = \boldsymbol{12.5}$

Calculation: $\mathrm{Out}[12] = \dfrac{\mathrm{In}[9] + \mathrm{In}[10] + \mathrm{In}[11] + \mathrm{In}[12]}{4} = \dfrac{12 + 14 + 14 + 14}{4} = \dfrac{54}{4} = \boldsymbol{13.5}$

Sample n	*1*	*2*	*3*	*4*	*5*	*6*	*7*	*8*	*9*	*10*	*11*	*12*
In[n] (v)	*0*	*0*	*0*	*0*	*4*	*6*	*8*	*10*	*12*	*14*	*14*	*14*
Out[n] (v)	*0*	*0*	*0*	*0*	*1*	*2.5*	*4.5*	*7*	*9*	*11*	*12.5*	*13.5*

11 MEMORY DEVICES

SECTIONS 11.1-11.2   *Memory Terminology/General Memory Operation.*

11.1   a) The *capacity* of a certain memory device is 1Kx8.

b) The term used to describe an 8-bit word is a *byte*.

c) Any device that is capable of storing a single bit can be called a *memory cell*.

d) A *volatile* memory is a memory that requires the application of electrical power in order to store information.

e) The amount of time required to perform a read operation is called the *access* time.

f) A *static* memory is a semiconductor memory in which the stored data will remain permanently stored as long as power is applied. Data stored in a *dynamic* memory, on the other hand, does not remain stored even with power applied, unless it is periodically refreshed.

g) *Main* memory stores instructions and data the CPU is currently working on.

h) In a *RAM* the access time is the same for any address in memory.

i) Any memory that can be read from or written into with equal ease is called a *RWM*.

11.2   The following is the procedure used to read the contents of memory location 11001_2 of Figure 11.1:

(a) First apply address 11001_2 to the Address inputs (A_4-A_0) of the 32x4 memory.
(b) Next, make the Memory Enable input HIGH.
(c) Finally, make the R/$\overline{W}$ input HIGH.
(d) Data will now be ready at the Data Outputs.

11.3 $2^{10} = 1024$ memory locations.

SECTION 11.3 *CPU-Memory Connections*

11.4   a) The bus that carries data between the CPU and the memory ICs is *Bidirectional*.

b) During a *READ* operation data may flow from a memory IC into the CPU via the data bus.

c) During a *WRITE* operation data flows out of the CPU via the data bus.

SECTIONS 11.4-11.6   *Read-Only Memories/ROM Architecture/ROM Timing.*

11.5   When $A_0=1$, $A_1=1$, $A_2=1$, and $A_3=0$, Row 3 and Column 1 are active. This combination of Column and Row will enable Register 7 to send its contents to the Output buffers D_7-D_0.

11.6   For Register 14 to be selected, its Enable inputs must be HIGH simultaneously. Thus, any anomaly that would cause an open on either enable input would prevent register 14 from being accessed.

11.7   a)   Since there are ten address lines (A_0-A_9) going into the address inputs of the memory, it can be determined that there are 2^{10} memory locations or 1024 locations. This memory has four output lines, therefore it can be concluded that each memory location can store any combination of four 1s and 0s. Thus, the capacity of this memory is 1024x4 or 1Kx4.

b)   Since this memory has four data inputs, four data outputs and a $R/\overline{W}$ input, we can conclude that it is a RAM. Remember that, data can be stored (written) only once into ROMs. Thus, there is no need for either data or $R/\overline{W}$ input lines in a ROM.

11.8   The data that is loaded into Register A, cannot be determined. This unpredictability stands from the fact that the Enable input of the memory must be LOW for a minimum of 150ns (t_{OE}) in order for stable data to be present at the output of the memory. Since we are allowing the Enable pulse to be LOW for only 100ns, ambiguous and unpredictable data will be loaded into Register A.

SECTIONS 11.7-11.9   *Types of ROMs/Flash Memory/ROM Applications*

11.9   a)   False. EPROMs do not need power applied to them in order for them to keep data stored.
b)   True.
c)   False. MROMs are very expensive to build and therefore should only be used in circuit designs where large quantities are needed.
d)   True.
e)   True.
f)   True.

11.10   (a)   The code 00_{16} must be loaded into the 28F256A's command register in order to perform a READ operation.

(b)   The code 20_{16} is loaded twice into the 28F256A's command register in order to erase the entire contents of the memory.

(c)   To verify that all memory cells have been erased, code $A0_{16}$ is loaded into the 28F256A's command register followed by a READ operation on the address to be verified.

(d)   Data can be written into a desired address by writing code 40_{16} into the 28F256A's command register.

(e)   Code $C0_{16}$ is loaded into the 28F256A's command register whenever the **Program Verify** operation is to be executed.

11.11   (a)   This two-step sequence erases all cells in the 28F256A CMOS array.

(b)   After all memory cells have been erased, all bytes $= 11111111_2 = FF_{16}$, including memory location 0300_{16}.

11.12   Let us consider the logic state of the SID signal during each positive-going transition   of   the SCK. As Figure P11.12 shows, the 16-bit data will be 0000 1111 1000 1110, assuming that the LSB is shifted out first. Therefore, the value $0F8E_{16}$ will be loaded into the 16-bit Latch of the ML2035 Programmable Sine Wave Generator.

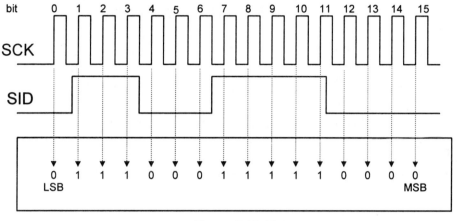

Figure P11.12

11.13   Figure P11.13 is the waveform that should appear at the output X of the 16x1 PROM.

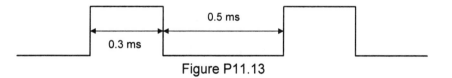

Figure P11.13

The MOD-16 counter is incremented once every 100µs (ClK=10KHz). This means that each memory location of the 16x1 PROM is being accessed every 100µs. Consequently, the content of each memory location is present at the output of the PROM for only 100µs. The following is the data that must be stored in the PROM in order for the waveform of Figure P11.13 to be present at output X:

Address	Data	
0000	1	}
0001	1	} ON for 3-bits (300μs)
0010	1	}
0011	0	]
0100	0	]
0101	0	] *OFF for 5-bits (500μs)*
0110	0	]
0111	0	]
1000	1	}
1001	1	} ON for 3-bits (300μs)
1010	1	}
1011	0	]
1100	0	]
1101	0	] *OFF for 5-bits (500μs)*
1110	0	]
1111	0	]

SECTIONS 11.12-11.16   *Static RAM (SRAM)/Dynamic RAM (DRAM)/Dynamic RAM Structure and Operation/DRAM Read/Write Cycles/DRAM Refreshing*

11.14   a)   SRAM memory cells are essentially *flip-flops* that will stay in a given state indefinitely, provided that power to the circuit is not interrupted.

b)   If the t_{RC} of a SRAM is 50ns, the CPU can read *20* million words per second.

c)   Dynamic RAMs require periodic recharging of the memory cells; this is called *refreshi.* the memory.

d)   In order to reduce the number of pins on high-capacity DRAM chips, manufacturers util. address *multiplexing*.

e)   During a read cycle the $\overline{RAS}$ signal is activated *before* the $\overline{CAS}$ signal.

f) $\overline{RAS}$-only refresh method is performed by strobing in a row address with $\overline{RAS}$ while $\overline{C}$ and $R/\overline{W}$ remain HIGH.

g)   In the TMS44100 4Mx1 DRAM, *16 ms* is the longest time that the memory can be witho. being refreshed before it loses its contents.

h)   A *DRAM Controller* is a chip that may be used to perform address multiplexing and refre. count sequence generation.

i)   The term *latency* is often used to describe the time required to perform certain DRAM tim. operations.

SECTION 11.17 *DRAM Technology*

11.15 a) A *SIMM* is a memory card with 72 functionally equivalent contacts on both sides of the card.

b) In a *SDRAM* the data is clocked out by the bus system clock in bursts of memory locations within the same page.

c) A *DIMM* is a memory card with 84 functionally unique contacts on each side of the card.

d) A *SODIMM* is a memory card used for compact applications, such as lap-top computers.

e) RIMM stands for *Rambus In-line Memory Module.*

f) In a *EDO DRAM,* the data on a given page and at a current memory location is sensed and latched onto the output pins.

g) *FPM DRAM* allows quicker access to random memory locations within the current page.

h) *DDRSDRAM* technology allows for transfers of data on the rising and falling edges of the system clock, effectively doubling the potential rate of data transfer.

i) *SLDRAM* can operate at bus speeds up to 200 MHz and clocks of data synchronously on the rising and falling edges of the system clock.

SECTIONS 11.18-11.19 *Expanding Word Size and Capacity/Special Memory Functions*

11.16 Figure P11.16 shows a 4Kx8 memory. Note that, the area within the dotted lines is a 1Kx8 arrangement and that we need three more identical arrangements to have a total of 4Kx8. All eight R/W lines are common as well as the eight $\overline{\text{CS}}$ lines.

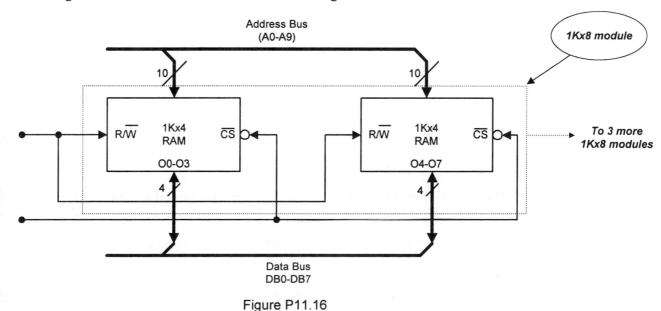

Figure P11.16

11.17   The 2125A RAM is a 1Kx1 memory and therefore it requires 8 ICs to build a 1Kx8 memory b[...]
Thus, it will take 32 of the 2125A RAM ICs (1Kx8s) in order to build a 4Kx8 memory module[...]

11.18   Since it's stated that regardless of the address on the Address bus the data on the Data bus is al[...]
in the Hi-Z state, we can conclude that outputs 0 through 3 from the decoder are always H[...]
Thus, there are only two possible causes for this malfunction. One is an inoperative 3-to-8[...]
decoder. The other possibility, and most probable, is input C to the decoder has become open.[...]
would allow only outputs 4 through 7 from the decoder to be active, which of course woul[...]
enable any of the PROMs in the circuit.

11.19   One method of preventing the loss of memory data during a system power failure is to sto[...]
RAM critical data during a normal system operation. The RAM is powered from backup batt[...]
whenever power is lost. There are special types of CMOS RAMs that have a small lithium ba[...]
built right on the chip for this very purpose.

A second method of preventing the loss of memory data during a system power failure is to sto[...]
critical system data in nonvolatile flash memory. This method has the advantage of not requirin[...]
any backup battery power. However, it is more difficult to change the data stored in a flash mer[...]
than in a static RAM.

A third method of preventing the loss of memory data during a system power failure is to hav[...]
CPU store all data in high-speed, volatile RAM during normal system operation. During a p[...]
interruption the CPU executes a short power-down program that resides in ROM which tran[...]
critical data from the system RAM into either battery-backup CMOS RAM or flash memory. [...]
resumption of power, the CPU executes a power-up program from ROM that transfers the cri[...]
data from the backup storage memory to the system RAM.

11.20   The numbers 7-2-2-2 means that it will require 7 clock cycles to obtain that memory the first 6[...]
word and each of the next three 64-bit words would require 2 clock cycles each. A total of 13 c[...]
cycles are necessary to get the four words out of memory.

SECTIONS 11.20-11.21   *Troubleshooting RAM Systems/Testing ROM.*

11.21

Module	A_{15}	A_{14}	A_{13}	A_{12}	A_{11}	A_{10}	A_9	A_8	A_7	A_6	A_5	A_4	A_3	A_2	A_1	A_0
0	1	0	0	0	0	0	x	x	x	x	x	x	x	x	x	x
1	1	0	0	0	0	1	x	x	x	x	x	x	x	x	x	x
2	1	0	0	0	1	0	x	x	x	x	x	x	x	x	x	x
3	1	0	0	0	1	1	x	x	x	x	x	x	x	x	x	x

Module 0: 8000_{16}-$83FF_{16}$ *Module 1:* 8400_{16}-$87FF_{16}$
Module 2: 8800_{16}-$8BFF_{16}$ *Module 3:* $8C00_{16}$-$8FFF_{16}$

11.22   If the decoder is enabled during the time when the Address bus is still changing, then it is possible that erroneous data are written into random memory locations. The decoder is enable only when the E-clock is in the HIGH state. Note that when the Address bus is changing from the old to the new address the data bus is in the HI-Z state (floating). If at this time, memory is enabled (allowed to be written into), then whatever is floating on the data bus will be stored in memory. Thus, one can deduce that probably the RAM is enabled during the time when the address bus is changing. One of the functions of the E-clock is not allowing the decoder outputs to change during the time when the address bus is changing.

Thus, if during this critical time, input $\overline{EI}$ of the decoder is LOW, the results would be as the technician witnessed. This suspicion can be verified by using a dual trace oscilloscope.

The oscilloscope should be triggered on the positive slope of the E-clock signal. The outputs of the decoder should then be monitored one-by-one on the other channel of the oscilloscope. Decoder outputs 0 through 3 should go LOW only during the time when the E-clock is HIGH.

11.23

Address	Binary Data	Hex Data
0 0 0 0	0 0 1 1 0 1 1 0	36
0 0 0 1	1 1 0 0 1 1 0 0	CC
0 0 1 0	1 1 0 0 0 0 0 1	C1
0 0 1 1	0 0 1 1 1 0 0 1	39
0 1 0 0	1 1 1 1 1 1 1 1	FF
0 1 0 1	0 0 0 0 0 0 0 0	00
0 1 1 0	0 1 1 1 0 0 1 1	73
0 1 1 1	1 0 0 1 1 0 0 1	99
1 0 0 0	0 0 0 1 0 0 0 1	11
1 0 0 1	0 1 0 1 1 1 1 1	5F
1 0 1 0	1 1 0 0 0 0 1 1	C3
1 0 1 1	1 0 0 1 0 0 1 0	92
1 1 0 0	0 0 1 1 1 1 0 1	3D
1 1 0 1	1 1 1 0 0 0 0 0	E0
1 1 1 0	1 0 0 0 0 0 0 0	80
1 1 1 1	*0 1 1 0 1 0 0 1*	*69*

The checksum is obtained by adding the fifteen hex data numbers ignoring carries from the MSD. Adding the fifteen 8-bit data words ignoring the carries from the MSB can accomplish the same thing. The following is the procedure that was used to arrive at the checksum of 69_{16}:

$36+CC=02 \rightarrow 02+C1=C3 \rightarrow C3+39=FC \rightarrow FC+FF=FB \rightarrow FB+00=FB \rightarrow FB+73=6E \rightarrow$
$6E+99=07 \rightarrow 07+11=18 \rightarrow 18+5F=77 \rightarrow 77+C3=3A \rightarrow 3A+92=CC \rightarrow CC+3D=09 \rightarrow$
$09+E0=E9 \rightarrow E9+80=[69_{16}] \ or \ [01101000_2]$

12 PROGRAMMABLE LOGIC DEVICES: HARDWARE AND APPLICATIONS

SECTIONS 12.1-12.2   *Fundamentals of PLD Circuitry/PLD Architecture*

12.1   The circuit of Figure P12.1 shows the conditions of the fuses needed to implement the desired SOP outputs. *(Note: A blown OR input acts as a logic 0)*

$O1 = 1; O2 = 0; O3 = AB; O4 = \overline{A}\,\overline{B} + \overline{A}\,B$

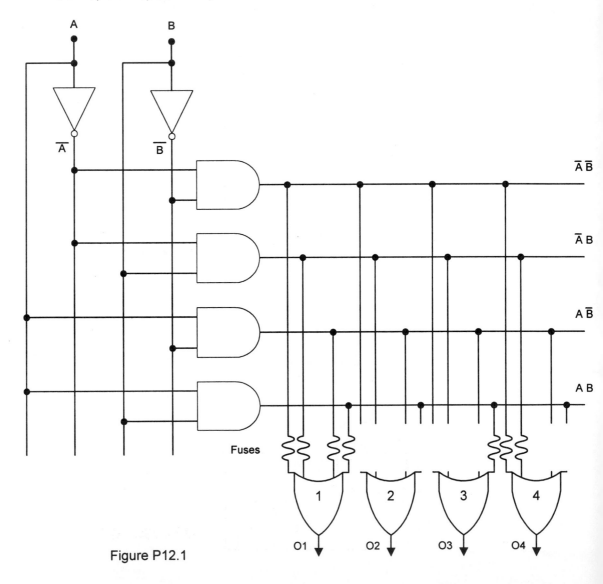

Figure P12.1

12.2

$O0 = \overline{A}\,\overline{B}\,\overline{C}\,\overline{D} + \overline{A}\,B\,\overline{C}\,\overline{D} + A\,B\,\overline{C}\,\overline{D} + A\,\overline{B}\,\overline{C}\,\overline{D} + \overline{A}\,B\,C\,\overline{D} + A\,B\,C\,\overline{D} + A\,\overline{B}\,C\,\overline{D} + \overline{A}\,\overline{B}\,C\,\overline{D} + A\,\overline{B}\,\overline{C}\,D + \overline{A}\,B\,\overline{C}\,D +$
$\quad \overline{A}\,\overline{B}\,C\,D + A\,B\,C\,D$

$O1 = \overline{A}\,B\,\overline{C}\,\overline{D} + A\,B\,\overline{C}\,\overline{D} + \overline{A}\,\overline{B}\,C\,\overline{D} + A\,\overline{B}\,C\,\overline{D} + \overline{A}\,B\,\overline{C}\,D + A\,B\,\overline{C}\,D + \overline{A}\,\overline{B}\,C\,D + A\,\overline{B}\,C\,D$

$O2 = \overline{A}\,\overline{B}\,C\,\overline{D} + \overline{A}\,B\,C\,\overline{D} + \overline{A}\,B\,C\,D + A\,B\,C\,\overline{D} + \overline{A}\,B\,\overline{C}\,D + A\,\overline{B}\,\overline{C}\,D + \overline{A}\,B\,C\,D + A\,B\,C\,D$

$O3 = \overline{A}\,B\,\overline{C}\,D + A\,B\,\overline{C}\,D + \overline{A}\,B\,C\,D + A\,B\,C\,D$

Let's use Karnaugh maps to simplify the sum-of-products expressions for $O0$-$O3$.

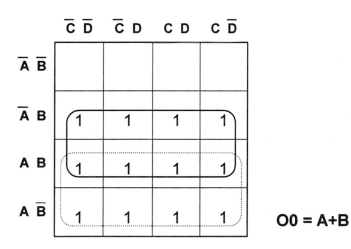

O0 = A+B

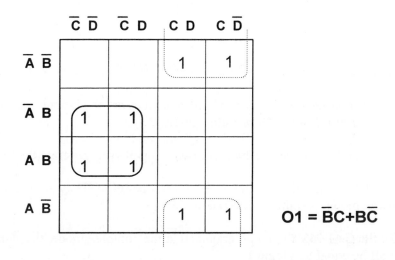

O1 = $\overline{B}C + B\overline{C}$

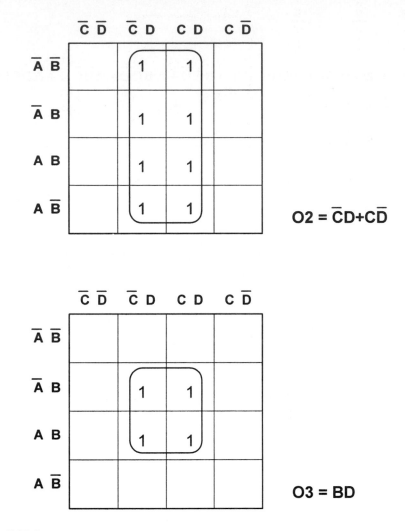

$O2 = \overline{C}D + C\overline{D}$

$O3 = BD$

12.3   See Figure P12.3

12.4   (a)   O3 would be the Ored result of the functions present at the outputs of AND gates 1, 2, and

      (b)   O3 would always be at a logic 1.

SECTIONS 12.3-12.4   *The GAL16V8/Relating CUPL Fuse Plots to GAL16V8 Architecture*

12.5   (a)   The major components of the GAL16V8 devices are the input term *matrix*, the *AND* gates and the *Output Logic Macro Cells (OLMC)*.

      (b)   Within each OLMC the products are *ORed* together to generate the SOP.

      (c)   The GAL16V8 has three different modes of operation. They are the *Simple* mode, the *Complex* mode, and the *Registered* mode.

12.6   In order for the GAL16V8 to be programmed in the complex mode, the signals *SYN, AC0,* and *AC1* must all be equal to a logic 1.

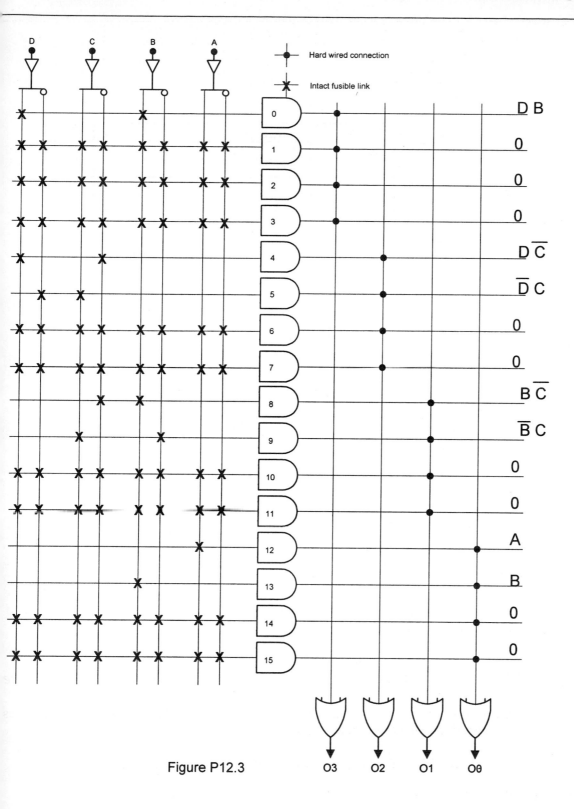

Figure P12.3

12.7 $Z = A\,BC + \overline{A}\,\overline{B}C + A\,\overline{B}\,\overline{C}$

12.8

Mode	Configuration	SYN	AC0	AC1
Simple mode	IN	1	0	1
	OUT	1	0	0
Complex mode		1	1	1
Registered mode	Registered	0	1	0
	Combinational	0	1	1

SECTION 12.5   *Design Problems*

12.9   X = !A # !C & D # A $ B # !B & D

$X = \overline{A} + \overline{C}\cdot D + A\cdot\overline{B} + \overline{A}\cdot B + \overline{B}\cdot D = \overline{A} + \overline{C}\cdot D + (A \oplus B) + \overline{B}\cdot D$

12.10   Truth Table

B	A	O₀	O₁	O₂	O₃
0	0	0	1	1	1
0	1	1	0	1	1
1	0	1	1	0	1
1	1	1	1	1	0

Write equations for LOW outputs:

!O0 =   !B & !A
!O1 =   !B & A
!O2 =   B & !A
!O3 =   B & A

Source File

```
Name            ;
Partno          ;
Date            ;
Revision        ;
Designer        ;
Company         ;
Assembly        ;
Location    Problem 12.10;
Device              G16V8;
/********************************************************************************/
/*                        7442 (1-OF-10 DECODER)                           */
/********************************************************************************/
/*                        Target Device GAL 16V8A                          */
/********************************************************************************/
/*          Inputs   */
pin 1       = A                         ;       /* LSB select input        */
pin 2       = B                         ;       /* MSB select input        */

/*          Outputs  */
pin 19      = !O0                       ;       /* Goes LOW for BA = 00     */
pin 18      = !O1                       ;       /* Goes LOW for BA = 01     */
pin 17      = !O2                       ;       /* Goes LOW for BA = 10     */
pin 16      = !O3                       ;       /* Goes LOW for BA = 11     */
/********************************************************************************/
/*          Equations                                                      */
/********************************************************************************/
O0.OE    = 'b'1;
O1.OE    = 'b'1;
O2.OE    = 'b'1;
O3.OE    = 'b'1;
O0 = !B & !A;
O1 = !B &  A;
O2 = B & !A;
O3 = B &  A;
```

💡 **12.11**

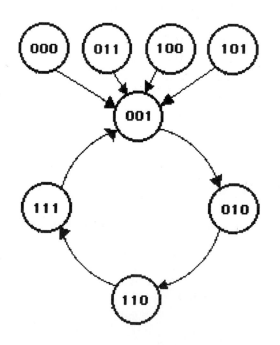

Present			Next		
QC	QB	QA	QC	QB	QA
0	0	0	0	0	1
0	0	1	0	1	0
0	1	0	1	1	0
0	1	1	0	0	1
1	0	0	0	0	1
1	0	1	0	0	1
1	1	0	1	1	1
1	1	1	0	0	1

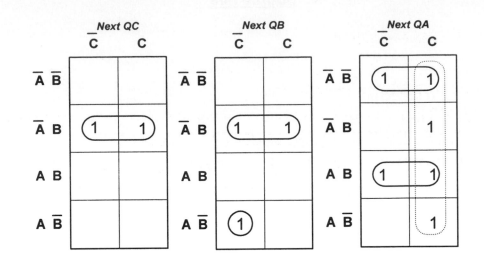

$$QA = C + \overline{A} \cdot \overline{B} + A \cdot B$$

$$QB = \overline{A} \cdot B + A \cdot \overline{B} \cdot \overline{C}$$

$$QC = \overline{A} \cdot B$$

Source File

Name	;
Partno	;
Date	;
Revision	;
Designer	;
Company	;
Assembly	;
Location	CHAP.12 problem 12.11;
Device	G16V8;

```
/******************************************************************************/
/*          SYNCHRONOUS COUNTER DESCRIBED ON PROBLEM 7.14(a) OF STUDY GUIDE        */
/******************************************************************************/
/*          Target Device GAL 16V8                                              */
/******************************************************************************/
/*          Inputs          */
pin 1          = CLOCK                        ;      /* COUNTER CLOCK                    */

/*          Outputs         */
pin 11         = OE                           ;      /* OUTPUT ENABLE (ACTIVE LOW)       */
pin 12         = QA                           ;      /* OUTPUT QA                        */
pin 13         = QB                           ;      /* OUTPUT QB                        */
pin 14         = QC                           ;      /* OUTPUT QC                        */


/******************************************************************************/
/*          Equations                                                           */
/******************************************************************************/
QA.D     =     C # !A & !B # A & B;
QB.D     =     !A & B # A & !B & !C;
QC.D     =     !A & B;
```

SECTION 12.6   *The GAL22V10*

12.12

(a)   The GAL 22V10 has *10* output pins.

(b)   Each OR gate in the GAL 22V10 does not combine the same number of *product terms.*

(c)   In the GAL 22V10, the AR input stands for *Asynchronous Reset.*

(d)   In the GAL 22V10, the SP input stands for *Synchronous Preset.*

(e)   In the GAL 22V10, the number of product terms range from *8* to *16*

SECTION 12.8   *Advanced PLD Development*

12.13   (a)   ISP stands for *in-system programmable*. Hence, the ISPGAL22V10 does not require a "programmer" device. The ISPGAL22V10 is programmed by connecting a cable from the PC directly to a special set of pins on the ISPGAL22V10.

(b)   These types of devices are available only in PLCC packages.

12.14

(a)   *CPLDs* are devices that combine an array of PAL-type devices on the same chip.

(b)   *FPGAs* offer a number of configurable logic blocks that contain programmable combinational logic and registers for sequential circuits.

(c)   *Gate Arrays* are ULSI circuits that offer hundreds of thousands of gates.

(d)   VHDL stands for *VHSIC Hardware Description Language.*

(e)   A one-time programmable connection that is originally an open circuit until it is programmed to cause a short is often referred to as an *anti-fuse.*

TEST 1

1....... (d)
2....... (c)
3....... (d)
4....... (c)
5....... (d)
6....... (b)
7....... (a)
8....... (b)
9....... (c)
10   (d)

TEST 2

1....... (b)
2....... (c)
3....... (b)
4....... (b)
5....... (d)
6....... (d)
7....... (b)
8....... (d)
9....... (a)
10..... (a)

TEST 3

1....... (b)
2....... (b)
3....... (d)
4....... (b)
5....... (c)
6....... (d)
7....... (c)
8....... (b)
9....... (a)
10..... (b)

TEST 4

1....... (a)
2....... (a)
3....... (c)
4....... (b)
5....... (b)
6....... (a)
7....... (d)
8....... (c)
9....... (c)
10..... (a)

TEST 5

1 ....(e)
2 ....(d)
3 ....(b)
4 ....(c)
5 ....(e)
6 ....(d)
7 ....(d)
8 ....(e)
9 ....(c)
10 .....(b)

TEST 6

1 ....(b)
2 ....(d)
3 ....(d)
4 ....(c)
5 ....(a)
6 ....(b)
7 ....(c)
8 ....(b)
9 ....(a)
10 .....(b)

TEST 7

1 ....(c)
2 ....(a)
3 ....(d)
4 ....(b)
5 ....(a)
6 ....(c)
7 ....(d)
8 ....(b)
9 ....(a)
10 .....(b)

TEST 8

1 ....(b)
2 ....(d)
3 ....(c)
4 ....(d)
5 ....(b)
6 ....(b)
7 ....(d)
8 ....(b)
9 ....(a)
10 .....(a)

TEST 9

1....... (d)
2....... (c)
3....... (b)
4....... (c)
5....... (a)
6....... (a)
7....... (b)
8....... (d)
9....... (b)
10..... (a)

TEST 10

1....... (a)
2....... (b)
3....... (a)
4....... (a)
5....... (a)
6....... (a)
7....... (b)
8....... (a)
9....... (a)
10..... (b)

TEST 11

1....... (c)
2....... (d)
3....... (a)
4....... (c)
5....... (b)
6....... (d)
7....... (a)
8....... (b)
9....... (b)
10..... (b)

TEST 12

1....... (b)
2....... (d)
3....... (c)
4....... (b)
5....... (d)
6....... (b)
7....... (a)
8....... (d)
9....... (b)
10..... (a)